THOMAS YOUNG
NATURAL PHILOSOPHER
1773-1829

Thomas Young M.D.
Sec. R.S.

THOMAS YOUNG
NATURAL PHILOSOPHER
1773-1829

BY THE LATE

ALEXANDER WOOD
M.A., D.Sc.

Fellow of Emmanuel College, Cambridge, and
University Lecturer in Experimental Physics

COMPLETED BY

FRANK OLDHAM
M.A., B.Sc., F.Inst.P.

St John's College, Cambridge
Headmaster, Hinckley Grammar School

WITH A MEMOIR OF ALEXANDER WOOD BY

CHARLES E. RAVEN

Formerly Master of Christ's College, and
Regius Professor Emeritus of Divinity in
the University of Cambridge

CAMBRIDGE
AT THE UNIVERSITY PRESS
1954

PUBLISHED BY

THE SYNDICS OF THE CAMBRIDGE UNIVERSITY PRESS

London Office: Bentley House, N.W.1
American Branch: New York

Agents for Canada, India, and Pakistan: Macmillan

Printed in Great Britain by The Carlyle Press, Birmingham 6

CONTENTS

LIST OF PLATES

LIST OF ILLUSTRATIONS IN THE TEXT

ALEX WOOD—A MEMOIR

It is appropriate that as a prelude to this book which he did not live to finish, some account should be given of its author—appropriate but not on that account easy. My only qualifications for the task are long acquaintance, close co-operation in some at least of his activities, and an admiration which amounted, in my case as in that of many others, to reverence. To explain this it is permissible to quote words spoken to me of him by one of his senior colleagues, John Oman the philosopher, who was for many years Principal of Westminster College—words which sum up his distinction. Oman had met me in Petty Cury: we stopped; he talked and I tried to understand. Suddenly lifting his head and with an unusual clearness of utterance he said, 'When I speak of a Christian, I mean a man for whom to see is to act. . . . I've known three such men . . . only one of them is still alive, Alex Wood.' That is a just tribute by one great man to another; and it accounts for the difficulty of my task.

Alex was a son of the kirk though not of the manse. Born on 3 May 1879 and the son of Sir Alexander Wood of Partick, he was educated at the Partick High School and at Glasgow University, where he graduated B.Sc. in 1901 and gained his doctorate in 1907. As a pupil of Lord Kelvin he absorbed much from both aspects of his teacher's character: the prayer with which Kelvin opened his lectures; the sense of high vocation which he impressed upon his classes; the combination in him of profound theoretical knowledge with a shrewd insight into the practical applications of his researches—these became for Wood a memory that conditioned his own development. In 1902 he came up to Emmanuel College as an Advanced Student; took his B.A. in 1904, and was elected into a Junior Fellowship in 1907. He was working in the Cavendish Laboratory but took an active part in the life of the College and made a reputation for himself as a speaker at the Union. My first recollection of him as a keen politician with Conservative views, a Scottish accent, a high seriousness, and on occasion a keen though northerly sense of humour. Almost as soon as he graduated he began to teach; and in 1905 was lecturing on the subject with which his researches were always chiefly concerned, the problems of sound. From 1908 till 1910 he was a University demonstrator; and though he gave up this position on becoming the Science Tutor of his College, he continued lecturing and in 1920 was appointed to the University lectureship which he held till 1944. He remained as Tutor at Emmanuel for thirty years; and after his retirement from his offices continued in the active service of the College and of the Cavendish.

He was in the habit of speaking lightly and slightingly of his research-work. 'I have no specialist's contribution to make. My rôle has always been that of interpreter,' so he said to the Acoustics Group of the Physical Society in 1947; and though the work published in his books *The Physical Basis of Music, Sound Waves and their Uses,* and *A Text-book of Acoustics* and carried out in co-operation with Hope Bagenal, the consulting architect, may not have been in the full sense original, it created a new understanding of the subject and had widespread practical importance. It proves that he could have been a great scientist —that he had the qualities of observation and patience, judgment and clearness of mind that make for discoveries: but it proves also that he was a great teacher, capable of lucid and absorbing exposition, of happy and often humorous illustration, and of swift sympathy with the interests and human quality of his audience. He was in fact a quite excellent lecturer, equally good with the senior forms of schools, with the younger classes in mechanics, heat, light and sound, and with senior men training for a start in research. He had much skill in the choice of phrase so as to express his meaning precisely and attractively and in the arrangement of his material so that the subject opened up naturally, and an evident and infectious interest both in the particular details and in their bearing upon wider problems of thought and life. It is impossible to overstate the value of his influence in the laboratory and in his classes, in the

College and in his supervisions. His little book on the history of the Cavendish, and the present volume with its tribute to a predecessor at Emmanuel disclose the strength of his concern for science and for sound learning.

But he was unable to give his whole life to academic duties, and was never in danger of becoming a mere don. From his first arrival in Cambridge he took an active interest in the social problems of the town, and when in 1907 he married Eleanor Mann and settled down in the house in St Barnabas Road which was their home until his death, he made it a centre not only for his pupils, but for work among boys and young people. Through the York Street Mission he founded a Bible-class and Boys' Club; encouraged similar developments throughout the borough; and in a few years was able to set up the Federation of Boys' Clubs which has had so powerful an influence in raising the whole tone of juvenile life in Cambridge, in preventing blind-alley employment, and in drawing the University into closer relations with the town. His convinced advocacy of the temperance movement—one of the several minority causes on which he was not ready to conceal his views, even though its advocacy made success in public life difficult—found expression in his presidency of the Band of Hope.

On the outbreak of the First World War he felt it impossible to compromise on an issue on which his mind had already been much occupied. Along with his friends the Minister of St Columba's, Dr Johnston Ross, and the Vicar of St Paul's Church, Dr Stokes, he had been exploring the problem of the Christian's attitude to war long before most of us realized that an outbreak was likely. In the autumn of 1914 he threw himself into Red Cross work, formed a company of Ambulance workers out of the boys of his clubs, and throughout the war organized and carried out the arrangements for meeting convoys of wounded at the station, conveying them either to the Auxiliary Red Cross Hospital in Wordsworth Grove, of which he was Commandant, or to the First Eastern General Hospital erected on the old King's and Clare ground now occupied by the University Library. He was not present at the meeting of Christian pacifists in Cambridge in December 1914 when the Fellowship of Reconciliation was founded, but joined it shortly afterwards, and remained a member from then onwards. As the years went by, pacifism, as it has come to be called, became increasingly an essential element in his character and a chief outlet for his activity.

His pacifism was in its origin and content the outcome and expression of his religion: his own deeply Christian experience, his family life, his genius for friendship, and his concern for the underprivileged combined to convince him that warfare in its modern form was not only evil but in the long run futile: and as a physicist he foresaw at a very early stage the peril of the misuse of the catastrophic power which atomic energy, if ever its release were achieved, would make available for mankind. As early as 1925 he was publishing warnings that our moral and spiritual development had not yet reached a stage at which we could be sure to use our new resources for human welfare; and as he saw the tragedy developing he dedicated himself increasingly to the effort to avert it. No man did so with purer motives or more transparent honesty: no man was more obviously free from self-righteousness or fear or contempt of others. When at the end of his life he summed up his message in his broadcast on the Church and the Atom, there can have been few who heard or read it without being impressed both by the strength of his case and by the quality of his character. He showed in it not only the intellectual power which had made him so great a teacher but the fairness of mind, the generosity of temper and the consistency of outlook which gained him the affection and respect of all who knew him. These same qualities had been signally shown when, as Chairman of the Peace Pledge Union, he was involved in legal actions against the Union and its Secretary at a time when public feeling ran high against him.

But his pacifism was never of the doctrinaire and 'absolutist' kind. He knew that short of exile on a desert island or indeed of suicide no one can in these days contract out of his social relationships; that complete consistency is impossible if we are to live in the modern world; and that he must combine loyalty to his principles with the uttermost readiness to co-operate with those who did not share them. He must live 'in the world' if not 'of it'. He must recognize in others the liberty which his conscience compelled him to claim for himself. He must work with them wherever possible 'in all things lawful and honest', as a citizen and a politician.

In the course of the war he found himself drawn into contact with the Labour party and increasingly convinced that only the programme which they advocated was adequate to the situation then developing both internally and internationally. Like many others he saw in it the expansion of the political idealism of his youth; for the individualism of the 'nonconformist conscience' was no longer adequate to a world of which collective action and social solidarity were now chief characteristics. Socialism in the form advocated by the doctrinaire was not indeed a position which he was prepared to accept as a creed: he was always concerned with people rather than with economics, with human situations and needs and with the best means for removing injustices and enlarging opportunities. He became a member of the Borough Council for St Matthew's Ward in 1926 and remained on it till he was made an alderman in 1945. In 1927 he became Chairman of the University Labour Party. In 1929 he stood as a Labour candidate for Parliament in the University and in 1931, 1934 and 1935 stood for the Borough. That he was not successful was hardly surprising: his refusal to conceal or accommodate his opinions, though it won the respect and affection of a great number of supporters and opponents did not secure the sort of blind loyalty which is given to a figurehead or a slogan. But his complete integrity, though restricting his opportunities, gave him an unrivalled influence where his quality was understood. By the outbreak of the Second World War he had won a position of authority in Cambridge which no one else in the political life of the town or the University has held in recent years. As Chairman of the Regional Planning Committee since 1930, and of the Joint Planning Committee from 1945 till 1948, and as Chairman of the Housing Committee from 1940 till the time of his death he affected the life and development of the area more intimately than any of his fellow-citizens.

It was in the matter of housing after the war that he found his fullest opportunity. He was tireless in giving close personal attention to the crowds of applicants who sought his advice, listening to their pleas, sympathizing with their hardships, striving to find some means to relieve their difficulties if he was unable to fulfil all their hopes. Even those who had inevitably to be refused came away from their talk with him conscious that he had done his uttermost to understand and to help, aware that he was deeply and genuinely concerned with their position, and confident that his own verdict was forced upon him by circumstances and did not depend upon any personal preference or prejudice. During these years he became to a unique degree the confidant of Cambridge folk as he enlisted their support in the attempt to see that the available resources were distributed to those whose need was greatest. That his own sensitiveness was deeply involved, that he found it almost intolerable to be able to do so little, and that the strain and distress of certain cases hastened his own death was plain to all who knew him. It is to be hoped that he also realized how much his efforts were appreciated, and how widespread were the gratitude and affection of his fellow-citizens.

To recount the 'plain tale' of his services to College and University and to town and country is to miss the centre and source of his inspiration. When he first came from Scotland, he joined the membership of St Columba's Church and was an elder there for very many years. Working with a succession of Ministers of outstanding ability and in close contact with Westminster College, he played a great part not only in the life of Presbyterianism but in the whole Christian activity of Cambridge. In days when co-operation between the denominations hardly existed and the work of bodies like the Y.M.C.A. and the Student Christian Movement had hardly begun to influence the sedate Anglicanism of the University, Alex Wood was a pioneer. After the First World War when an interdenominational Council was established in the University and a United Council of Christian Witness in the town, he was a prime mover in both spheres. At Swanwick and in the Colleges he was constantly in demand as a speaker both on the problems of religion and science and on those of the social and political application of Christianity. But as in his teaching and public work so in his religious activities, though he was an excellent speaker and leader, it was in his personal dealings with individuals that he gave his most characteristic service. To his colleagues in academic work, to the committees in civic or pacifist or religious service, to the young, whether his own pupils or the newly married or the boys and girls of his Bible Classes, he was (though he probably never realized it) a last court of appeal. We took to him only such questions as really mattered: we found him in his study with a large pipe (until at the outbreak of the Second World War he gave up his lifelong habit); he listened grave and alert while we set out our trouble; he asked a question or two to make sure that he had all the facts; and then he lifted the whole issue on to a higher level by the lucidity of his understanding and the integrity of his outlook. If he was austere he was never inhuman; if he made big demands upon us, we knew that he was living up to them himself; if he spoke with detachment it was never with a sense of superiority and never without humour and a smile. We knew that he was not thinking about himself, was not concerned to create an impression or to maintain traditional or partisan standards, was not anxious to impose his own outlook or proselytize or convert. So even those of us who seldom sought human advice or sympathy brought to him the worries which no one else knew and the perplexities that we could not by ourselves resolve. When the long and ascetic face of our friend came suddenly alight with purpose and affection we knew that all was well.

It was certainly true of him that like most Scots he did not wear his heart on his sleeve or his sense of humour on the surface. But though there was in him a streak of the Puritan, and, on occasion, of what his friends called firmness and his critics obstinacy, no man who knew him intimately or in his home could suppose that he had anything in him of the prig or the fanatic. His holidays were always the same—a boatful of young people, his daughters and his pupils, on the Broads with an edge on the wind and a lop on the water, gave him complete satisfaction; and for years he took his relaxation that way. Scattered over the world in universities and schools, in parishes and mission-stations, in laboratories and engineering-shops, indeed wherever Cambridge men are at work, are a number of them who look back to their days of sailing and swimming with Alex as the high spot of their education. His astonishing ability to carry through an incessant programme of varied and exacting work without getting irritable or exhausted was due in large part to the long days and nights that he spent in the narrow waterways and wide horizons of East Anglia.

Of the deepest springs of his life it is not possible for anyone except perhaps his wife to speak with knowledge. Certainly he had somehow won release from self-concern, not merely from the ambitions and fears of the careerist but from the self-pity and self-censure which so easily masquerade as penitence and discipline. Certainly he had reached a spontaneous and immediate consciousness of other people's qualities and needs, an ability to respond at once to them without any shade of exploitation or of sentimentality. Certainly he saw more clearly than the rest of us what his Christian discipleship involved, and having seen could not but act in accordance with the vision and without aggressiveness or evasion. But of the means by which such capabilities were produced and sustained we outsiders can only form guesses: he was incapable of the pietism or the poses which so often advertise religion; and though he would joyfully discuss questions affecting the circumference of Christian thought or action, the central realities were perhaps too real to him for argument. Plainly he lived apart—'in the heavenlies' as St Paul would put it: but such detachment merely quickened his sensitiveness and increased his vitality for the affairs of this world.

CHARLES E. RAVEN

PREFACE

THERE are good reasons for bringing before the public a new life of Dr Thomas Young. By the range and nature of his original investigations in Natural Philosophy, Mathematics, the Mechanical Arts, Languages and Medicine, Dr Young belongs to the eighteenth century; by the discoveries he made in the first three decades of the nineteenth century he is a link between the great men of science of his own age and those of today.

Apart from a short memoir by Hudson Gurney published in 1831, two years after Young's death, the world had to wait twenty years before George Peacock, Dean of Ely, Lowndean Professor of Astronomy in Cambridge, completed the task of editing Young's scientific papers, together with an account of his life. Coming to the present century, Professor C. H. Lees wrote the admirable account to be found in the *Dictionary of National Biography*, to which is appended a full list of references. A short life was written by me in 1933, the object being to bring to the notice of Sixth Form scholars the debt science owed to Young. Independently, over the last forty years, the late Dr Alex Wood had been accumulating new matter concerning Young's life, which made it possible to reassess his claims to fame. Many new sources were found, and the material used for reference by Lees, Peacock and Gurney verified. The labour occupied much of Dr Wood's leisure till the early part of 1950; at the time of his death he had written the first ten chapters of this book in the form in which they now appear, and had left notes on the next two chapters. Through the kind invitation of the Syndics of the Cambridge University Press, I was asked to complete the work—a task which I readily undertook in view of the admiration for Dr Young which I shared with Dr Wood.

The late Sir Joseph Larmor advanced Young's claims as one of those great pioneers who created the science of mathematical physics. In a review of the life of Young in the February 1934 number of *Nature* he says,

In those early days scientific people did not write numerous treatises, and, as a result, into their work as intended for permanence they put their most sustained thought. . . . The greatest and most original of all general lecture courses was Young's 'Lectures of Natural Philosophy and the Mechanical Arts', over which there was no delay, as the two massive and very complete yet concise quarto volumes were published (1807) at the age of thirty-four years, a few years after the course was delivered.

The rival claims of Champollion and Young in the priority of deciphering the hieroglyphics were considered by Peacock, who assigned the credit to Young, although the general balance of opinion abroad was against the decision. New facts have been brought to light by Dr Wood which certainly present Young's claims in a far more favourable light.

Of Young's work for the 6th edition and Supplement of the *Encyclopaedia Britannica* Larmor states,

Even more remarkable surely by one of the workings of fortune which the Greeks named Nemesis, in compensation for his supreme classical contributions to it, the name of Young occurs only in a secondary way in the general index to the new volumes; yet one of his most notable works is the long series of scientific biographies which he contributed with much research to the supplement of the early publication.

The present volume brings out clearly how much the editor of the *Encyclopaedia* valued Young's scholarship and how much he depended on him in the production of the original work.

Another field of inquiry to which Young applied all his powers was the mechanism of the eye and the nature of light, as in the theory of interference and the mysteries of double refraction. This brought him into friendly rivalry with the contemporary French school of scientists, in particular Arago, Fresnel and Laplace, all of whom were familiar with the new mathematical analyses developed by Lagrange. Young was equally at home with the moderns as with the British school who closely followed Newton. Here again, Larmor's comments are germane; 'Young's instincts were Newtonian, aiming at a general view of the order of Nature.'

The early part of the nineteenth century saw the formation of the Royal Astronomical Society and the decease of the Board of Longitude. These years were a stormy period for Young as secretary of the Board of Longitude and editor of the *Nautical Almanac*. Young, who was essentially a liberal of the Adam Smith school, was anxious to preserve freedom of science from Government control and at the same time he defended the Royal Society from any infringements on what he considered its preserves. A further interesting development to be found in this work is Young's relations with the Admiralty. As a pioneer in 'Life Assurance' Young's claims are not strong, but he was sufficiently familiar with the subject for his observations to merit attention, and for his appointment as adviser and medical referee to one of the newly formed Insurance Societies.

One chapter has been devoted to Young's work in medical science. From it we realize the obligations he considered necessary to warrant the public's faith in a medical man, and the necessity for the cloak of anonymity which concealed his authorship of the majority of his publications.

Young forms a fascinating subject in the field of biography, not only from his amazing scientific record and his wide classical learning combined with his remarkable depth of knowledge in philosophy, but also as a humanist working disinterestedly in the cause of truth.

January 1953   F. OLDHAM

ACKNOWLEDGMENTS

THANKS are due to the following for help at various stages in the preparation of the MS: Mr Phillip Young; Professor C. H. Lees; Mr Q. E. Gurney, T.D.; Mr Oliver R. Barclay; Mr H. St George Gray, O.B.E., F.S.A.; the Chief Librarian, Public Libraries, Worthing; Professor H. W. Bailey; Mr C. P. T. Winkworth; D. M. Turner (Mrs D. Feyer); Professor H. Robinson, D.Sc., F.R.S.; Mr W. J. Green; Mr Stanley A. Manning; Harveian Librarian (1948), Royal College of Physicians; the Director, British Museum Library; Dr W. F. Emmons; Professor S. R. K. Glanville; Dr D. Diringer; the Secretary of the Admiralty; the Secretary, the Public Record Office; the Council of the Royal Society; Mr H. S. Bennett; Mr M. E. Ogborn, F.I.A.; Dr G. E. R. Deacon, F.R.S.; Professor J. Proudman, F.R.S.; Professor D. H. Sadler; Mr W. P. Preston; Mr E. C. Witcombe; Mr L. W. Rice; Miss M. A. Beardsmore; Miss E. M. Wood; Mr R. J. L. Kingsford; Mr J. A. Ratcliffe; Mr J. Waller; Edmund Dews.

EARLY YEARS, 1733–92

*'The principles which I imbibed, and the habits which I formed under
the guidance of these dear and excellent relatives, have more or less
determined my character in future life, whatever it may be.'*

YOUNG

ABOUT eight miles out of Taunton on the Barnstaple Road
lies the little village of Milverton. The red sandstone houses
cluster round the church, which stands out as a landmark. It
was in this village that Thomas Young was born. The Old
Bank House, the home of his birth, still stands near the top of
North Street, a street running past a row of substantially built
houses opening on to a raised cobbled pavement. The house is
double-fronted, with bow windows on each side of the door,
and served as both residence and place of business for Thomas
Young, Senior, who combined the activities of mercer (cloth
merchant) and banker. Cloth-making had long been an important industry of Somerset from the breeding of the sheep to
the finishing of the web. It was now past its peak and it may
very well have happened that Thomas Young, Senior, added
the business of banker to that of mercer for this reason. He
had the recommendation for finance that he was a Quaker,
and the Quakers were by now widely respected for their
integrity as men of business. The association of the Barclays,
the Gurneys and other Quaker families with the growth of
Joint Stock Banks is well known.

From the point of view of our interest in Thomas Young,
Junior, the fact that his father was a Quaker is much more
important than the fact that he was a mercer and banker. His
mother, Sarah Davis, was also a Quaker, and both parents
came of Quaker stock. The Quakers, or Religious Society of
Friends, to give their modern official title, originated in the

seventeenth century. In a sense the movement was a reaction against the formalism and artificialities of the prevailing religious observances and against the moral laxity of current habits and customs; but it took the form of a positive belief in the 'inner light', an experience in which truth was directly apprehended by the individual and expressed itself in a new kind of life from day to day. In the earlier days of the sect they not only shared the disabilities of other Nonconformists, but were singled out for particularly brutal persecution. When they spoke in the open air, as they frequently did, they were often beaten and stoned by angry crowds. They maintained simplicity in dress in contrast to the luxurious styles then current, refused to take an oath, and used the 'thee' and 'thou' in all speech instead of making a distinction between superiors and inferiors as was then common.

In the time of Thomas Young, Senior, the missionary zeal of the Quakers had somewhat abated, and the dress and language were tending to become a ritual; but the fire still burned in the Young family. In the journal of Thomas Pole, M.D.,[1] a cousin of Thomas Young, Senior, we find the following entries:

22.9.75. In the evening we had a meeting at Thomas Young's which was a favour'd Time, and I believe strengthening and encouraging to us all in the Way of Well-doing.
(12.6.77). In the evening we had a meeting in our Meeting House. . . . Aunt Young appeared in testimony.

Or again:

1798, 10th mo. 3rd. After an early dish of tea, I walked to Wiveliscombe with cousin Thomas Young. T. Davis and D. Zachary followed us. We had a pretty full meeting. . . . At the conclusion, the Preacher of this house expressed to me his wish that the important truths delivered might sink deeply into the hearts of those present and offered me the use of the house at any time. I told him I was glad to find an increasing liberality in different societies of Christians towards each other. The Parson of the parish attended this meeting, which has been the case in several places where I have

---

[1] In the library of Friends' House, London. I am indebted to Mr John L. Nickalls, the librarian, for much help and advice.

had public meetings. I was kindly invited to stop the night, but concluded to return, having only a short time more with my friends at Milverton, so walked back again by the light of a lanthorn with T. Young and T. Davis.[1]

These contemporary records are of general interest as showing that the opposition of other sects (and particularly of the Church of England) to the Quakers was breaking down, and that the Quakers were still publicly preaching their message in addition to maintaining their own meetings for worship. They are of special interest as showing that Young's father, his grandmother ('Aunt Young') and probably his maternal uncle (T. Davis) were not merely nominal Quakers, but active members of the Society.

The Friends' Meeting House in which the family worshipped is now used as a laundry, but the raised bench and the gallery of the Meeting House are intact. It is approached by a passage which runs past the end of the house then occupied by Young's great-uncle, Thomas Pole, the uncle of the Dr Thomas Pole whose diary has just been quoted. The Poles' house adjoins the Old Bank House, and the end of it can be seen in the illustration.

There can be no question of the lasting influence of the atmosphere in which Young's early days were spent. There is a certain affinity between the Quaker pursuit of truth, with its emphasis on verification in personal experience, and the scientific method. The Quakers were indeed called 'truth-seekers'. Certainly the Society at that time contributed to England far more than its fair proportion of distinguished men in science, natural history and medicine. Among the Fellows of the Royal Society round about Young's time who were Quakers, or came of Quaker families, we find[2] Richard Brocklesby, elected 1746, uncle of Young and a distinguished physician and author; John Fothergill, M.D., elected 1763, founder of Ackworth School, noted physician and one of the earliest members of the American Philosophical Society; Thomas Dimsdale, M.D., elected 1769, noted for the practice of inoculation for smallpox; John

---

[1] *Friends' Historical Society Journal*, Supplement, no. 7.
[2] *Friends' Historical Society Journal*, vol. VII, nos. 1 and 2 (1910).

Coakley Lettsom, M.D., elected 1773, physician and writer; Jeremiah Dixon, elected 1773, astronomer, observed transits of Venus for the Royal Society in 1761 and 1769; Thomas Young, elected 1794; William Allen, elected 1807; Robert Willan, M.D., elected, 1809, physician and dermatologist; John Sims, elected 1814, physician to Princess Charlotte, editor of Curtis's *Botanical Magazine* and original Fellow of the Linnaean Society; Hudson Gurney, elected 1818; Luke Howard, elected 1821, pioneer in meteorology; John Dalton, elected 1822, laid the foundations of the atomic theory. In Young's case, at least, his passion for truth, his insatiable thirst for knowledge (both factual and theoretical), his deep sense of the importance of a right use of time, his sturdy independence and self-reliance, were fostered by his upbringing, and the serious interests of his early years were given greater scope because not merely the frivolities of life, but even art, music, and, to a large extent, literature were banished from Quaker homes.

It was into this background that Thomas Young was born on 16 June 1773. He was the first of ten children and our knowledge of his youth is based on his own accounts. Dr Peacock says:

It may be considered fortunate that the materials for a very minute history of his early studies and occupations exist, in his very ample journals, in his letters to his relatives and others, and in the notes which he has left behind him, upon most of the books which he read for the first twenty years or more of his life.[1]

It is fortunate for us that these records are generously quoted by Peacock, as I have been unable to trace any of this material, if it still exists.

In the literal translation of an autobiographical fragment written in Latin and covering his first fourteen years, we gather something of the precocity of the child and the breadth of his education. Perhaps because of the rapidly increasing size of the family in his own home, the greater part of the first seven years were spent in the home of his maternal grandfather, Robert Davis of Minehead, who took a keen interest in his education.

[1] George Peacock, *Life of Thomas Young* (London, 1855), p. 2.

At two years of age he had learnt to read 'with considerable fluency', and pursued his education in the village school and at home under the guidance of his aunt, Mary Davis. 'Under their instructions I read the Bible twice through, and also Watts's *Hymns*, before I was four years of age.'[1] He was encouraged in the practice of committing poetry to memory, and a quarto edition of Goldsmith's *Deserted Village*, in the possession of the family, bore a memorandum inserted by his grandfather: 'This poem was repeated by Thomas Young to me, with the exception of a word or two, before the age of five.'[2] Latin grammar was begun 'when not quite six years of age', as also was writing, an art in which he excelled. His grandfather encouraged his taste for study in every possible way, and frequently repeated the warning:

> A little learning is a dangerous thing,
> Drink deep, or taste not the Pierian spring.

The principles which I imbibed, and the habits which I formed under the guidance of these dear and excellent relatives have more or less determined my character in future life whatever it may be,

> Quo semel est imbuta recens, servabit odorem
> Testa diu.[3]

In March 1780 he was sent to a 'miserable boarding school' where he 'made very little progress' and he left again in September 1781. He spent the next half-year almost entirely at home, and during this period made his first contact with the sciences. A neighbour of his father's who was a land surveyor gave him the run of his library,

where I found many books relating to science and particularly a Dictionary of Arts and Sciences, in three volumes, folio, which I began to read with the most intense interest and delight; at his house I also found several mathematical and philosophical instruments, the use of many of which I learnt, with the assistance of his daughters and his nephew.[4]

In March 1782, when nearly nine, he was sent to another school at Compton in Dorsetshire, and except for six months spent at home, he remained there until 1786. Of his headmaster he says:

[1] Peacock, *op. cit.* p. 3. [2] *Ibid.* [3] *Ibid.* p. 4. [4] *Ibid.* p. 5.

Mr Thompson was a man of liberal and enlarged mind who possessed a tolerable collection of English and classical books which his pupils were allowed to make use of. It was his custom likewise to allow them a certain degree of discretion in the employment of their time.[1]

As part of the prescribed work of the school he read fairly widely in the classics, including Virgil, Horace, Cicero, Phaedrus, Xenophon and Homer. He committed to memory the greater part of the Westminster Greek Grammar, and read the whole of Beza's Greek and Latin Testament. Nevertheless he felt that he 'was at that time perfectly ignorant of prosody, as well as my master, and possessed no very accurate grammatical knowledge of the Greek and Latin Languages.'[2] This self-criticism indicates the rather exacting standard by which this boy of thirteen was judging his own remarkable achievement. Some mathematics and some book-keeping seem also to have been included in what he 'read with Mr Thompson'.

But it was in the less formal processes of education, for which Mr Thompson's methods allowed great scope, that Young was able to follow the interests which afterwards were to become the sources of his most important contributions to knowledge. 'I was in the habit of rising an hour sooner than my school-fellows in summer, and of going to bed an hour or two later in winter, for the purpose of mastering my lesson for the day; my school business was thus soon finished.'[3] Here we see something of that sense of the value of time and of the importance of industry which he imbibed from his Quaker stock and preserved unimpaired to the end of his life. Writing to his brother in 1793 he says:

Leisure and application are the great requisites for improving the mind; leisure is useless without application; but application with a very little leisure may produce very material benefit. If you are careful of your vacant minutes, you may advance yourselves more than many do who have every convenience afforded them.[4]

---

[1] Peacock, *op. cit.* p. 5.   [2] *Ibid.* p. 7.   [3] *Ibid.*
[4] T. J. Pettigrew, *Medical Portrait Gallery* (London, 1840), vol. IV, 'Thomas Young', p. 13.

Hudson Gurney[1] gives a description of him working on what proved to be his death bed at

the rudiments of an Egyptian Dictionary, which he had brought near to its completion and which he was extremely anxious to be able to finish. It was then in the hands of the lithographers, and he not only continued to give directions concerning it, but laboured at it with a pencil when, confined to his bed, he was unable to hold a pen. To a friend who expostulated with him on the danger of fatiguing himself, he replied that it was no fatigue, but a great amusement to him; that it was a work which if he should live it would be a satisfaction to him to have finished, but that if it were otherwise, which seemed most probable, as he had never witnessed a complaint which appeared to make more rapid progress, it would still be a great satisfaction to him *never to have spent an idle day in his life* (my italics).

Here undoubtedly lies the secret of his remarkable output of work.

The most valuable contact from the point of view of his informal education was that with Josiah Jeffrey, the usher of the school. Jeffrey lent him Benjamin Martin's *Lectures on Natural Philosophy*, and he was 'particularly delighted with the optical part of Martin's book, which contains many detailed rules for the practical construction of optical instruments'. But Jeffrey was also a good mechanic and craftsman, and under his guidance Young learnt the use of the lathe, the making of telescopes, the grinding and preparation of colours, and the binding of books. Jeffrey had a private trade with the scholars 'in paper, copper plates, copy books and colours' to which Young succeeded when Jeffrey left. In 1786 this source of income brought him about 5s., which he added to a gift of 10s. 6d. from his parents, and spent on Greek and Latin books and on a Hebrew Bible 'for which I gave 5s. for I was at that time enamoured of Oriental literature . . . and before I left Compton school, I had succeeded in getting through six chapters of the Hebrew Bible'.[2] To his other languages he

---

[1] Memoir in Young's *Egyptian Dictionary* (London, 1831), p. 41 ff.
[2] Peacock, *op. cit.* p. 6.

added Italian through the kind offices of a schoolfellow, and improved a slight knowledge of French.

The interest which he had acquired, through Jeffrey, in optics and the construction of optical instruments was further developed by a conversation with Morris Birkbeck from which he 'imbibed a wish to study botany'. This led to the procuring of a lathe and the construction of a microscope. On returning home after finally leaving Compton School, he devoted himself almost entirely 'to the study of Hebrew and to the practice of turning and telescope making'. Thus early did he lay the foundations of later work in Oriental languages and optics.

We find Young, then, leaving school at the age of thirteen with some knowledge at least of Greek, Latin, French, Italian and Hebrew; an interest in Natural Philosophy (as Physics was then called), especially in optics, and a competence in the use of the lathe and the construction of optical apparatus. It is a remarkable achievement, and in the department of languages it was pursued further at home. He borrowed Hebrew, Chaldee, Syriac and Samaritan grammars and also the 'Lord's Prayer in more than 100 languages, the examination of which gave me extraordinary pleasure'.

This precocity in languages is enshrined in the following story:

A near relative who brought him up to London a little country lad used to say that as she walked with him through London he was attracted by the booksellers' stalls, and taking up a valuable classic, was soon absorbed in its examination. The owner of the shop seeing this, and thinking that the quaintly dressed little quaker boy was indulging in ignorant curiosity, said 'There, my lad, if you could but translate to me a page of that book (valuable as it is) it should be yours', when, to his astonishment, the really learned prodigy rapidly turned the text into flowing English, and, true to his word, though he winced at the sacrifice, the bookseller made the lad the fortunate possessor of the valuable book.[1]

The next stage of his education continued the opportunities, which the earlier stages had allowed, for the development of his

[1] *Biographical Catalogue* (London Friends' Institute, 1888), p. 751.

particular talents and tastes. Chance (if these things happen by chance) threw him under the general supervision of one of the most outstanding and distinguished Quakers of the older generation of his days, a representative of a remarkable line.

David Barclay of Youngsbury was a descendant of the first David Barclay of Urie in Kincardineshire (1610–86). He had succeeded his father (also David Barclay) in the family house in Cheapside, and like his father was a merchant chiefly engaged in the American trade.[1] He retired from this business at the beginning of the American War; but he was a partner in the banking house afterwards so closely connected with his family, and part owner of Barclay and Perkins' Brewery, from which he derived a large income. When he retired from his merchant's business he lived in a house in Red Lion Square for four months in the winter of each year, and spent the rest of his time at a country house at Youngsbury or Thundridge Bury, near Ware. He was a typical Quaker of his time, interested in the development of education, the promotion of peace and the liberation of the slaves.

It so happened that in 1787 David Barclay was arranging for the education of his grandson, Hudson Gurney, under a private tutor, and was looking for a companion to share Hudson's studies. His niece, Priscilla Gurney, had gone to live for a time with Thomas Young's aunt, who was an intimate friend. Hearing of Young's remarkable achievements she recommended him strongly to David Barclay, and her recommendation was backed by Sir William Watson,[2] who was also a friend of the Young family. The arrangement was made and the two boys went to Youngsbury, Young being then just over fourteen and Hudson Gurney about twelve and a half. The tutor who had been engaged was offered, and accepted, a more attractive post, whereupon Young assumed the direction of his own and Hudson Gurney's studies until the arrival of a Mr John Hodgkin, afterwards a classical scholar of some note. Even then Young continued to direct Gurney's classical studies,

[1] R. Hingston Fox, *Dr John Fothergill and his Friends* (London, 1919).
[2] Sir William Watson (1715–87), physician, naturalist, physicist.

and Hodgkin has left it on record, in a communication made to Peacock, that one reason for taking the post was because it was

a situation which would afford Mr Hodgkin an opportunity of pursuing his own classical studies, and of deriving some advice and assistance in them, from the extraordinary youth, whose stability of conduct and intensity of application seemed to place every desirable object of literary or scientific pursuit within the reach of his astonishing mental powers.[1]

Young's association with Gurney and Hodgkin was a peculiarly happy one. Hudson Gurney (1755–1864) became well known as an antiquary, a writer and a politician. He inherited a large fortune and sat in the House of Commons as member for Newton in the Isle of Wight during six successive parliaments. He had a beautiful estate, Keswick Hall, near Norwich, and was High Sheriff of the County of Norfolk. He was a lifelong friend of Thomas Young, and his letters to Young, which were preserved, were used by Peacock.[2] He was elected a Fellow of the Royal Society in 1818.

Young and Hodgkin were afterwards associated in the publication of a book called *Calligraphia Graeca*, which appeared in 1807 and was dedicated to Young.

At Youngsbury, Young's interest in languages was maintained and extended. 'His journal contains a statement of his having written out specimens of the Bible in thirteen different languages', and Peacock adds in a footnote:

The copy book which contains them is now before me: it contains extracts in English, French, Italian, Latin, Greek, Hebrew, Chaldee, Syriac, Samaritan, Arabic, Persian, Turkish and Aethiopic. The specimens from the Eastern languages are beautifully written.[3]

Young's prowess in languages is crystallized in a story which appears in at least three forms. In the most sober we are told:

Thomas Hodgkin senior has been known to relate how, to his surprise, he became conscious of the lad's linguistic attainment.

---

[1] Peacock, *op. cit.* p. 10.

[2] Through the kindness of the late Mr Gerard Gurney of Keswick Hall I had access to these in 1930, and had them copied. Since Mr Gurney's death I have been unable to trace the originals.   [3] Peacock, *op. cit.* p. 11.

Wishing for some test of how far his education might have advanced, he gave him, on his arrival to be Hudson Gurney's companion, a sentence to write out in a copybook, and wondering why it was so long before being brought to him, found his new pupil, nettled at being set a task so much below his powers, was engaged in writing out the sentence in four or five different languages.[1]

In Pettigrew's *Portrait Gallery* the story is told again, but this time it is David Barclay who sets the task, and the number of languages is *nine*.[2] The authority given is Arago. Finally, in Peacock's *Life* the request was made by a 'friend of Dr Brocklesby', and the number of languages is *fourteen*.[3]

During his five years at Youngsbury he continued to read widely, and his reading list is given by Peacock in full. He read the Classics, and acquired an exact scholarship in Latin and Greek which later enabled him to hold his own in discussion with the foremost scholars of his time. He also read French, Italian and English classics, including works by Fénélon, Corneille, Racine, Shakespeare and Milton. To these he added reading in mathematics, astronomy, natural philosophy and botany. In particular, he eead Newton's *Principia* and his *Opticks*, the botanical works of Linnaeus, works on chemistry by Lavoisier and Black and on medicine by Boerhaave. He made copious notes on all he read, his journals being in Latin, and his criticisms on the French and Italian authors which he read, in French and Italian. His penmanship was remarkable, his formation of Greek letters being beautifully precise and accurate.

In all this he was almost entirely self-taught. He had little confidence in any other method of education. To his brother he wrote:

Although I have readily fallen in with the idea of assisting you in your learning, yet it is in reality very little that a person who is seriously and industriously disposed to improve may not obtain from books with more advantage than from a living instructor; something is wanting for the duration of application in the right

[1] *Biographical Catalogue* (London Friends' Institute, 1888), p. 752. This story presents difficulties. It was John Hodgkin who was tutor to the two boys at Youngsbury, but even so, he arrived after Young and Gurney had been together for some time.

[2] Pettigrew, *op. cit.* p. 2.   [3] Peacock, *op. cit.* p. 12

path, but it must be the strength of the traveller and not of the guide that must conquer the difficulties of the journey. Masters and mistresses are very necessary to compensate for want of inclination and exertion: but whoever would arrive at excellence must be self-taught.[1]

Throughout the five years or so of his residence with David Barclay, he rarely visited his home in Somerset; but about four months of each winter were spent in London at David Barclay's house in Red Lion Square, and then lectures and libraries were available. It was during those visits that he came under the notice of a Quaker uncle, who held a very prominent place in the world of medicine. Richard Brocklesby (1722–97), M.D., F.R.S., was an uncle by marriage on his mother's side. He had been at school in Ireland with Edmund Burke, and had studied medicine at Edinburgh and at Leyden, where he took his M.D. degree in 1745. He was a Fellow of the College of Physicians and of the Royal Society. He had written on the therapeutic value of music, and had produced a standard treatise on military hygiene. He was immensely impressed with the achievements of his brilliant nephew. In 1789, about the middle of his time with the Barclays, Thomas Young had a severe illness in which he was attended by Dr Brocklesby and Baron Dimsdale,[2] and from which, with careful nursing, he completely recovered. This led his uncle to impress upon him the importance of taking more care of his health, and in the same letter to chide him for 'your prudery about abstaining from the use of sugar on account of the Negro Trade'.[3] In this matter, Young was making his protest, like many Quakers and others, against the slave trade, not in the expectation of seriously affecting the import of sugar, but as a challenge and appeal to the conscience of the humane.

In his work on the Greek language he became very interested in the translation of passages from the English classics into Greek verse. He did Wolsey's address to Cromwell from Shakespeare's *Henry VIII*, wrote it out on vellum in his best

---

[1] Pettigrew, *op. cit.* p. 14.

[2] Thomas Dimsdale, created Baron by Catherine of Russia 1768, having successfully vaccinated her and her son and 140 others in Russia without loss.

[3] Peacock, *op. cit.* p. 16.

handwriting, and sent it to Dr Brocklesby. This brought a reply from his uncle which includes the following passages:

Dear Thomas Young, Jun.,

I duly received a pleasing letter from you with a beautiful manuscript on vellum, a paraphrastic translation of Wolsey's fare-well to Cromwell; better judges than I am, give it much praise for the spirit of Euripides, which they say it breathes, but it is much to be lamented that you have not essayed to translate—

> 'Had I but served my God with half the zeal
> I serv'd my king, he would not in mine age
> Have left me naked to mine enemies.'

But Mr Burke[1] has taken the Greek manuscript from me, and means to show it to divers learned men of his acquaintance for their philological criticism. I should be glad to have a copy of the same on vellum, as neatly written, with the addition of your essay to the above: but do it at your leisure, con amore, con studio, a diligenza. Mr Burke wishes you to try what you can make of Lear's horrid imprecations on his barbarous daughters, beginning with this solemn invocation:

> 'Nature, hear! dear goddess, hear a father!'

If you can give the Greek the like compass of energetic expression as my favourite Shakespeare has done in his native tongue, Mr Burke will laud you and judge most favourably of your performance. . . .

Have a care, however, that my frankness towards you may not puff you up with vanity, which has been the rock that many others have split on, and I hope you will steer clear from.[2]

Young's further efforts in the same direction brought him to the notice of several distinguished friends of his uncle. Among them were Dr Charles Burney, organist and composer, and father of Fanny Burney, who was a member of nearly every literary coterie of his day; Dr Thomas Lawrence, medical author and physician to Dr Johnson; and Sir George Baker, M.D., F.R.S., nine times president of the College of Physicians, who was a student of literature as well as of science and a writer of elegant Latin prose.

This singularly wide education, with its bias towards lan-guages, might seem to indicate a special aptitude for a literary

---

[1] Edmund Burke. [2] Peacock, *op. cit.* pp. 19–20.

career. But Young was no great believer in special aptitudes. Pettigrew says of him:

He had little faith in any particular aptitude being implanted by nature for any given pursuits. His favourite maxim was, that whatever one man had done, another might do; that the original difference between human intellects was much less than it was generally supposed to be; that strenuous and persevering attention would accomplish almost anything; and at this season in the confidence of youth and consciousness of his own powers, he considered nothing which had been compassed by others beyond his reach to achieve. Nor was there anything which he thought worthy to be attempted which he was not resolved to master.[1]

In view of this there is nothing surprising in his choice of medicine as a career. After all, a sound classical education was considered at that time to be the essential foundation of medical training. Also, many of the prominent medical men of his day were Quakers, including his uncle. That Dr Brocklesby's persuasions were a strong factor in his decision is made clear in a letter from Young's father to David Barclay.[2]

Milverton. 21st. 1mo. 1791.

Esteemed Friend,

As I find my Son is with the rest of thy family arrived in Town I take the liberty to communicate a few remarks concerning him.

I don't know but the plan for his studdying Phisic is pretty generally approved of by his relations, and I hope not thought very unfavourably of by thyself, altho' I am not more partial to it for him than some other occupation as I am fearfull he will be too intent in his early pursuits, and have to request that thou wilt be so kind to check him in anything that appears inconsistent. I am apprehensive that the connection with his Uncle Brocklesby will add to his natural propensity to study and altho' the Doctor is a man possessed of some valuable quallifications, yet I do not think him altogether fit to have the sole direction of young people therefore were he to make my Son great offers I don't think it would be advisable to accept it, that is to the exclusion of myself and his other kind Friends having the oversight of him, at same time I have no wish to offend him.

[1] Pettigrew, *op. cit.* p. 4.
[2] This letter is in the possession of Mr Robert D. Barclay of Bury Hall, and is published with his kind permission.

I find it is ·proposed for Thomas to attend some Chymical Lectures to which if he is not exposed to improper company, I see no objection, but hope he will continue to reside as much as may be in thy house and endeavor to make himself usefull there.

If anything should occur I shall take it kind if thou wilt communicate thy sentiments to our Uncle Brocklesby as any remark from thee would be received much better than what *I* might say.

We should approve of Thomas spending a little time in an Apothecarys shop as he may thereby gain a better knowledge of Pharmacy, and from his age, he seems to have time enough to spare for it, but this may perhaps be objected to as being out of the regular method.

My Wife desires to unite in gratefull acknowledgements for thine and thy Wifes many favours and with our joint Love to you. . . .

I am thy Assured Friend,

(sgd) THOS. YOUNG

In pursuance of this plan he attended lectures by Dr Higgins in Chemistry during his winter residences at David Barclay's house in Red Lion Square, and made 'some simple experiments of his own on a small scale'.[1] Considering the importance of his subsequent experimental work, it is interesting to find Hudson Gurney writing:

But he was afterwards accustomed to say, that at no period of his life was he particularly fond of repeating experiments, or even of very frequently attempting to originate new ones: considering that, however necessary to the advancement of science, they demanded a great sacrifice of time, and that when the fact was once established, that time was better employed in considering the purposes to which it might be applied, or the principles which it might tend to elucidate.[2]

Here again we see his acute sense of the importance of time. At this point his general education finishes and his professional training begins.

---

[1] Gurney in Young's *Egyptian Dictionary*, p. 12. Bryan Higgins was an Irishman and an M.D. of Leyden, who had opened a school of practical chemistry in Greek Street, Soho, in 1775. He published a good deal of original work and was involved in a dispute with Priestley.   [2] *Ibid.* p. 12.

ADDITIONAL NOTES TO CHAPTER I

David Barclay of Urie (see p. 9).

David Barclay of Urie in Kincardineshire (1610–86) was a very remarkable person. He fought in the Thirty Years' War under Gustavus Adolphus, being promoted first captain and then major. He returned to Scotland to fight with the Covenanters against Charles II, and later his tried and seasoned troopers of Scots Horse played an important part in Cromwell's victory on Marston Moor in 1644. Brought up as a strict Presbyterian and a man of war he did not seem a very likely subject for a Quaker conversion. Nevertheless, during the religious ferment in Scotland, David Barclay heard George Fox preach, and judged 'that the practice and principles of these people were most agreeable to the teaching of Jesus Christ and that if he hath followers, disciples or a visible Church on earth, these must be they.' He 'received the truth' in the Quaker sense in 1666, 'being then in the fifty-sixth year of his age'. He changed his uniform for the Quaker costume, adopted their practices and defied the authorities by attending Quaker meetings and being responsible for one on his own estate. He suffered several terms of imprisonment in his old age, some of them in terrible conditions, and was exposed to public ridicule. He is the subject of Whittier's poem *The Laird of Urie* which begins:

> Up the streets of Aberdeen, by the Kirk and College Green
>   Rode the Laird of Urie,
> Close behind him, close beside, foul of mouth and evil-eyed
>   Pressed the mob in fury.

David's son, Robert (1648–90), had, of course, been brought up a Presbyterian, and had subsequently been to the Scots Theological College at Paris—a Roman Catholic institution of which his uncle was Rector. Nevertheless, he declared himself a Quaker in 1666, the same year as his father. He was a scholar, a master of the Scriptures, of the writings of the early Church Fathers and of Church History. He was mainly responsible for systematizing the theology of the Quakers in his classical treatise *An Apology for the true Christian Divinity as the same is held forth and preached by the people called in scorn Quakers*. He was a friend of William Penn.

His son, David, was born at Urie in 1682, but left the home and country of his fathers and came to London as an apprentice to a glover. He did the judicious thing, although no doubt for quite good Quaker reasons, by marrying the daughter of his employer and going into business with him. He became a very wealthy export merchant, owned one of the finest houses in London (in Cheapside), where on at least two occasions, Quaker as he was, he entertained royalty. He died in 1769.

David Barclay of Youngsbury (see p. 9).

In association with John Fothergill, he founded Ackworth School and, also with Fothergill, played a leading part in the negotiations between the Government of the day and Benjamin Franklin by which it was hoped to avoid the threatened war between Britain and America. The concessions to the Colonies, for which Barclay strove, were mostly granted by the Commons in 1778, but too late to prevent the war and the loss of the Colonies.

'In 1795 he sent out a special emissary to Jamaica, to liberate 30 slaves on a property which had fallen to him as owner;[1] he had them sent on a vessel, chartered for the purpose, to Philadelphia, and there put out by friends as apprentices on equitable terms; the cost to himself was about £3000.'[2] In these matters he was a typical Quaker of his time, interested in the development of education, the promotion of peace and the liberation of the slaves, and with important social and political contacts.

---

[1] Fox, *op. cit.* p. 275.
[2] The *Friends' Historical Register* says £10,000.

II

MEDICAL STUDY IN LONDON AND
EDINBURGH, 1792–4

'His manners, at this period of his life, are described by one who knew him well, as very quiet and pleasing.'　　PEACOCK

THE early years of Young's medical education were spent in London, and owed much to a brilliant group of medical men from Scotland who invaded London about this time and made great contributions to its medical teaching. In the early part of the eighteenth century there was very little organized teaching available. Physicians and surgeons had each their own pupils, but there were no Hospital Medical Schools and very few medical lectures available outside.

In 1740 William Hunter came from Scotland and entered as a surgeon's pupil at St George's Hospital,[1] which was then only seven years old. Of this hospital William Hunter became a Governor, and his brother, John, and later Thomas Young were members of the staff. In William Hunter's days its site at Hyde Park Corner was on the edge of London; Kensington was the country, and Earl's Court a hamlet two miles from London.

William Hunter arrived in London at the beginning of an important era in the development of teaching in anatomy. The barbers had been incorporated by a Royal Charter of Edward IV in 1462 with authority to practise surgery. In 1540 a Gild of Surgeons was united with the Company of Barbers by Act of Parliament, and outside of the Fellows of the College of Physicians no one was allowed to practise the art of surgery except members of the Company of Barber-Surgeons. In 1745 the United Company was dissolved, an embargo against private dissection elsewhere than at the Barbers' Hall was lifted, and in

---

[1] It was one of two hospitals formed from the old Westminster Infirmary.

1752 an Act was passed providing for the dissection of the bodies of *all* persons executed for murder in Great Britain, the disposal of the bodies being at the discretion of the judges.

In 1766 William Hunter purchased a house in Great Windmill Street, and in June 1768 he moved into the property, which he completely rebuilt. It was a residence, a lecture theatre, a suite of dissecting rooms, and a museum.[1] Here Hunter established his great reputation as a teacher of anatomy. It was said of him by Wade that he 'may be considered as the father of the anatomical schools of London, and bequeathed a fame and character to his class which has been supported with un-diminished lustre to the present day' (1827).[2] In the work of building up this school, John Hunter, who followed his brother William to London from Scotland, played no inconspicuous part.[3]

Unfortunately, a dispute separated the brothers in the midst of a successful partnership, and, as far as is known, they never met again. John went his own way to establish a great reputation as a pathologist. William remained at Great Windmill Street; and from all the hospitals in London students came to him for anatomy. He lectured daily at 5.0 p.m. until the counter-attraction of Garrick's acting, against which his most brilliant lecturing was of no avail, compelled him to change his time to 2.0 p.m. In 1779 Matthew Baillie, Hunter's nephew, joined him, and when Hunter died in 1783, Baillie succeeded to the house and lecture theatre.

It was at this 'Hunterian School of Anatomy' that Young, then 19 years of age, began his medical education in the autumn of 1792, and no better introduction to the medical profession was possible. He took rooms in Little Queen Street, Westminster, and in the autumn of 1793 entered St Bartholo-mew's Hospital. William Hunter was now dead; but Baillie and Cruikshank[4] were carrying on the school, and John Hunter

[1] It is now part of the Lyric Theatre, Shaftesbury Avenue.

[2] George C. Peachey, *Memoir of William and John Hunter* (Plymouth, 1924).

[3] It was John who procured the required 'material' and conducted the negotiations with those who supplied it.

[4] Came from Scotland to join Hunter in 1771.

was lecturing in pathology. Young had a distinguished band of teachers. In medicine he had Sir Alexander Crichton (another Scot),[1] one of the leading physicians, and John Latham, subsequently President of the Royal College of Physicians, a very successful practitioner and an authority on *materia medica*. In midwifery his teachers were William Osborne, who claimed to have taught more than 1200 practitioners, and John Clarke, who, after having the largest midwifery practice in London, became a consultant on the diseases of women and children. In botany his lecturer was Sir James Smith, founder and first president of the Linnean Society.[2] Mr Wilson, the eminent anatomist and father of Young's successor on the Staff of St George's Hospital, was the demonstrator in anatomy. Peacock records[3] that Young 'took ample notes of the lectures he attended', in this as in everything else being remarkably conscientious and methodical. The notes were sometimes in Latin with Greek quotations and phrases, and were embellished with mathematical notes and demonstrations with which presumably he occupied himself while waiting for the lectures to begin.

His medical studies, however, did not by any means absorb all his energies. He still devoted some to his literary and linguistic studies, and moved freely in the interesting social circle of which Dr Brocklesby was a member. The circle included his uncle's old schoolfellow, Edmund Burke, whose friendship with Dr Brocklesby was a close one. When the Doctor thought Burke to be in financial difficulties in 1788 he came to the rescue with a gift of £1,000 as a token of 'my veneration of your public conduct for many years past, and my real affection for your private virtues and transcendent worth'. When Burke's favourite son, Richard, was stricken with a fatal illness, it was Dr Brocklesby who was called in.

[1] Crichton was subsequently physician to Alexander I of Russia, and became the head of the whole of the public health services of Russia. He had a remarkable career, and was decorated by the Emperors of Russia and Prussia, and knighted by George IV.

[2] Smith took up the study of botany on the day the elder Linnaeus died. In 1783 on the death of the younger Linnaeus, he purchased the whole of the library, manuscripts, herbarium and natural history collections of the father and son, and housed them in Paradise Row, Chelsea. The Linnean Society was born in his house in Great Marlborough Street on 8 April 1788.   [3] Peacock, *op. cit.* p. 34.

Another close friend was Samuel Johnson. Brocklesby attended Johnson professionally from time to time, and was consultant during his last illness. Sir Joshua Reynolds belonged to the same circle. The great painter did portraits of Johnson and of Burke, and the hospitality of his dinner-table provided a centre for the group. Among other distinguished friends of Dr Brocklesby were William Windham (1750–1810), M.P. for Norwich, Secretary for War under Pitt in 1794; and Frederick North (1766–1827), who became fifth Earl of Guilford in 1817, and was a brilliant linguist and an enthusiast for Greek culture.

This was the circle in which Thomas Young moved during his years of medical study in London. Burke was particularly interested in him, and advised him about his reading and about his career generally. How far Richard Porson was a member of the circle it is hard to say; but he certainly knew Young from 1788 till his own death in 1808. He became Professor of Greek at Cambridge in 1793, and has been described by Young in an article contributed to the *Encyclopaedia Britannica* as 'one of the greatest men, and the very greatest critic of his own or any other age'.

Quoting from 'one who knew him well', Peacock says o Young:

His manners at this period of his life were very quiet and pleasing; like those of the more cultivated members of the Society (of Friends) to which he still outwardly adhered, though he had already abandoned many of the peculiar tenets by which they are distinguished. His conversation, on classical and scientific subjects, showed a confidence and precision which were far beyond his years; whilst his ignorance of popular literature and of the habits of thinking of his equals in age and station, was in striking contrast with the range and accuracy of his other acquirements.[1]

During his two years in London he had one or two notes and articles in the *Gentleman's Magazine*, but his main contribution to knowledge was a paper on the eye, entitled 'Observations on Vision',[2] read to the Royal Society on 30 May 1793, and

[1] Peacock, *op. cit.* p. 32.
[2] *Miscellaneous Works of the late Thomas Young*, edited by George Peacock (London, 1855), vol. I, p. 12.

published in the *Philosophical Transactions* of that year, although based on work done earlier.

The problem which interested Young is set out in the opening words of the paper:

It is well known that the eye, when not acted upon by any exertions of the mind, conveys a distinct impression of those objects only which are situated at a certain distance from itself; that this distance is different in different persons, and that the eye can, by the volition of the mind, be accommodated to view other objects at a much less distance; but how this accommodation is effected, has long been a matter of dispute, and has not been satisfactorily explained.

Two views had been held: (1) that the length of the eyeball could be altered so as to adjust the distance of the retina which receives the image from the lens which forms the image—as is done, of course, in the camera; (2) that the power of the lens was altered, the faces becoming more strongly curved, and the lens therefore more powerful when it was necessary to focus an object at short range. Young's attention seems to have been directed to the subject during the dissection of the eye of an ox. He noticed how flexible and 'muscular' the so-called 'crystalline' lens was. He discusses the work and speculations of earlier inquirers, and gives some cogent reasons for believing that when the eye is relaxed it is focused for distant objects, and that the result of the effort to focus on near objects is that the lens increases the curvature of its faces and so increases its converging power.

The immediate result of the publication of the paper in the *Philosophical Transactions of the Royal Society* was a claim for priority in the discovery by John Hunter, who applied to the President of the Royal Society, Sir Joseph Banks, to be allowed to give the Croonian Lecture the following year upon this subject. Hunter died in the autumn of 1793, but early in 1794 there appeared in the *Philosophical Transactions* a note by his brother-in-law, Sir Everard Home,[1] entitled: 'Some facts relative to the late Mr Hunter's preparation for the Croonian

[1] Surgeon (1756–1832); Professor and first President of the College of Surgeons.

Lecture', in which the fragment he had prepared is given. A more damaging rumour began to circulate that Young's paper had been suggested by Hunter's work, this having been discussed by Sir Charles Blagden, a close friend of Sir Joseph Banks and Secretary of the Royal Society, at a dinner party at the house of Sir Joshua Reynolds in 1791, when Boswell, Brocklesby, Young and others were present. Blagden seems to have given currency to the report, and it caused Young great concern. He wrote to those who had been present, and all, even Blagden, were ready to exonerate him.[1] Indeed, Young's whole attitude to life was inconsistent with any kind of plagiarism. Perhaps the most convincing comment was his election to the Fellowship of the Royal Society in 1794 on the strength of this work.

Mr Thomas Young, of Little Queen Street, Westminster, a gentleman conversant with various branches of literature and science, and author of a paper on Vision, published in the Philosophical Transactions, being desirous of becoming a Fellow of the Royal Society, we recommend him from our personal knowledge as worthy of that honour, and likely to become a useful member of the Society.

Fifteen names are appended to the certificate, which is dated 19 March 1794. Richard Brocklesby risks the charge of nepotism by being one of the signatories. Among the others are three doctors, Matthew Baillie, of the Hunterian School; William Heberden Jr, Physician to St George's Hospital and to George III; and most important of all, John Hunter's brother-in-law, Sir Everard Home. Botany was represented by the signatures of George Shaw, Botanical Lecturer at Oxford, Founder and Vice-President of the Linnean Society, and Sir James E. Smith. The best known among the remaining names are Richard Farmer, Master of Emmanuel College, Cambridge, where Young subsequently became a Fellow Commoner; and William Combe, the eccentric author of 'Dr Syntax'. As Young was elected on 19 June 1794, after Hunter's claim had

[1] Peacock, *op. cit.* p. 39.

been announced, we may dismiss from our minds any suggestion of plagiarism.

His election at the age of twenty-one cannot fail to have given him some satisfaction, and a characteristic letter to his mother refers to the event:[1]

Thy maternal and religious affection towards me appears, as it always has done, in thy kind advice; and I approve thy judgment at the same time that I am obliged by thy care, when, instead of expressing a childish pleasure as many weak parents would do, at what might be esteemed an honourable gratification of their vanity, my dear mother refers this as well as all other circumstances, to the most important consideration, that can engage us for ourselves or for others—the improvement of the heart and fulfilling of the ends of our creation. I hope I am not thoughtless enough to be dazzled with empty titles which are often conferred on weak heads and on corrupted hearts; nor do I agree with those moralists who allow ambition to be laudable as an ultimate object of human conduct. And, considering that I am much more interested in my own welfare than others can be for me, I trust I am equally desirous with thyself, that I may comply with those injunctions which are laid on me, and obey, as far as I am able, and if I am not able it is my own fault, every moral and religious duty. This particular line of conduct each of us must determine according to the best of his judgment, and, if my opinion in some few respects should differ from thine, and lead me, as at a future time it possibly may, into some slight variations, I hope our mutual charity will induce us not to doubt of the purity of each other's motives.

Young's satisfaction with his work on the accommodation of the eye was, however, short-lived. Home gave the Croonian Lecture on 13 November 1794, and it was published in 1795.[2] In the course of the lecture he described experiments which he had made with the assistance of Jesse Ramsden, the man whose name will be familiar to physicists as the inventor of Ramsden's eyepiece.[3] According to Home's paper their experiments refuted Young's conclusions, and showed that even in the case of

---

[1] Pettigrew, *op. cit.* p. 13.   [2] *Phil. Trans. Roy. Soc.* (1795), p. 1.
[3] He was a son-in-law of John Dollond, the inventor of the achromatic lens (which he manufactured), invented an eyepiece for telescopes, and was famous throughout the world for his telescopes and astronomical instruments.

subjects whose eyes had been 'couched'—i.e. had the lens removed—the power of accommodation was still retained. Young was temporarily convinced by the paper. In his Göttingen Dissertation in 1796 he says that his theory seems 'neither new nor true',[1] and in a letter to the Secretary of the Royal Society dated 8 July 1799[2] he closes with the words, 'but, should further experiments tend to confute any opinions that I have suggested, I shall relinquish them with as much readiness as I have long since abandoned the hypothesis which I once took the liberty of submitting to the Royal Society on the functions of the crystalline lens'. This, however, was by no means the end of the matter, as we shall see.

In May 1794 he met his uncle's patient, the Duke of Richmond, who wrote to Dr Brocklesby:

> But I must tell you how much pleased we all are with Mr Young. I really never saw a young man more pleasing and engaging. He seems to have already acquired much knowledge in most branches, and to be studious of obtaining more: it comes out without affectation on all subjects he talks upon. He is very cheerful and easy without assuming anything; and even on the peculiarity of his dress and Quakerism he talked so reasonably, that one cannot wish him to alter himself in any one particular. In short, I end as I began, by assuring you that the Duchess and I are quite charmed with him, and shall be happy to renew our acquaintance with him when we return to London.

This testimony from a man of the world is particularly interesting, as Young's letters sometimes border on the sententious and might well give a wrong impression.

Later in the same year Young visited William Herschel at Slough, where he had set up his great reflector telescope and was establishing his world-wide reputation as an astronomer. He visited Edmund Burke at Beaconsfield, where no doubt he discussed his own future. He also visited the Duke of Richmond at Goodwood. The Duke was Master-General of the Ordnance at the time, and offered to appoint Young as his private secretary.

---

[1] 'neque nova neque vera videtur' (Peacock, *op. cit.* p. 39).
[2] *Phil. Trans. Roy. Soc.* (1800), part I, p. 106.

The offer was an attractive one, but Young was advised against accepting it by Burke and Windham, who were in favour of his going to Cambridge to study law and abandoning the medical profession. He also felt that the appointment was precluded by his loyalty to the Society of Friends, whether by its connection with war or with the aristocracy is not clear. At any rate, he wrote to his mother:[1]

I have very lately refused the pressing offer of a situation which would have been the most favourable and flattering introduction to political life that a young man in my circumstances could desire. I might have lived at a duke's table, with a salary of £200 a year, as his secretary, and with hopes of a more lucrative appointment in a short time. I should have been in an agreeable family, have had time enough to study, a library, a laboratory, and philosophical apparatus at my service; and I was not ashamed to allege my regard for our Society as a principal reason for my not accepting the proposal.

It is not certain upon whose advice Young took the step of continuing his medical studies at Edinburgh, but it was, at any rate, a very natural one, as the prestige of the Edinburgh Medical School was very high at that time all over the world, and its students were a very cosmopolitan lot. It is said that in 1765 they included Americans and West Indians, Portuguese and Italians, Frenchmen and Englishmen, Irishmen and Dutchmen, Germans and Swiss, Russians and Danes among the students. 'Edinburgh already was not only an international medical centre, but also a highly esteemed, perhaps the most esteemed, place for a medical education.'[2] The school owed much to Alexander Monro, the first Professor of Anatomy, who studied at Leyden under Boerhaave, one of the greatest figures in the history of European medicine. He was appointed in 1720, and was succeeded by his son in 1758.

In 1725 the teaching was transferred from the Surgeons' Theatre to the University for reasons which have some historic interest. We have already seen that body-snatching was not

[1] Peacock, *op. cit.* p. 45.

[2] *Bicentenary of the Faculty of Medicine of the University of Edinburgh* (Edinburgh, 1926) p. 73.

unknown in London. In Edinburgh it was a public scandal. According to one authority, the Principal of the University 'engaged in this nefarious business' in 1626, 'and part of his spoil, consisting of the skull of George Buchanan,[1] is still preserved in the Museum of the Anatomical Department'.[2] In the Surgeons' Records, 20 May 1711, we find that,

of late there has been a violation of the sepulchres in the Greyfriars' churchyard, by some, who most unchristianly have been stealing, or at least attempting to carry away, the bodies of the dead out of their graves. But that which affects them most is a scandalous report, most maliciously spread about the town, that some of their number are accessory, which they cannot allow themselves to think, considering that the magistrates of Edinburgh have been always ready and willing to allow them what dead bodies fell under their gift, and thereby plentifully supplied their theatre for many years past.

It was the state of public feeling on this matter that led to the removal of the Anatomy Department from Surgeons' Square, where it was right in the midst of an indignant and hostile population, to the precincts of the University.[3]

It was to this seat of medical study that Young now set out, on horseback, as was usual in those days. He carried many letters of introduction, one of which said, 'He unites the scholar with the philosopher and the cultivation of modern arts with the simplicity of ancient manners.'[4] On the way he made a short tour in Derbyshire and Yorkshire. Peacock, who had read his journals and diaries, points out that he was always interested in natural history, natural phenomena, methods of manufacture and all sorts of curiosities, but not very much

---

[1] George Buchanan, 1506–82, historian and scholar.

[2] *Bicentenary of the Faculty of Medicine.*

[3] In Edinburgh and in Glasgow graves were not infrequently completely enclosed with strong iron railings, in one of which my grandfather was buried in 1895. In Edinburgh it was discovered in 1828 that Dr Robert Knox, the most famous anatomist of his day, was buying bodies from two Irish criminals, Burke and Hare, who were murdering unsuspecting victims to keep him supplied. Knox was acquitted at the trial of any complicity, but the public scandal created was one of the causes which led to the Anatomy Act of 1832. This Act made it necessary for all schools of anatomy to hold a Government licence, and it controlled the supply of subjects even if it did not augment it sufficiently to meet the whole demand.

[4] Peacock, *op. cit.* p. 52.

moved by scenery and natural beauty. His hereditary interest in sheep comes out in a reference in his diary to his visit to Robert Bakewell,[1] of Dishley near Ashbourne:

I viewed with pleasure his improvements in the various branches of his occupation; I felt his rams and sheep regularly as they were shorn, and went through all the forms of examination. What he has done is shown best by two sheep which have always lived together, one of his own improved breed, the other of his original breed from which all his stock was derived by selected mixture without crossing with any other breed. He entirely neglects the wool but has diminished the bone and increased the fat in a surprising degree.[2]

Travelling through Durham, where he notes a visit to the cathedral, he arrived in Edinburgh on 20 October 1794, and took lodgings in St James' Square.

The Professor of Anatomy was now Alexander Monro (secundus). He had a great reputation at home and abroad as a teacher, a practising physician and an anatomist. Young, however, was not impressed. Writing to his uncle he says: 'For anatomy I am very glad that I have done with it, for I should never learn it of Monro: I think him far inferior, as a lecturer, to Baillie,'[3] and again, 'some little information on chemistry I derive from Black's copious course—hardly anything from Monro—something considerable in the medical line from Gregory and Duncan'.[4] In the course of Monro's lectures the eye came under consideration, and Young writes:

When lecturing upon the eye, he noticed Hunter's having claimed the discovery of its being fibrous, and said that it had been known for a century and that he had always taught the same; this was received with applause from his pupils who always encouraged his avarice of priority; in this case, though Monro deserves nothing, I was not displeased that Hunter's pretended originality was disallowed. He is not yet come to the crystalline (lens) of the eye.

[1] 'The stock-breeding experiments at Dishley in Leicestershire made "the Leicester long-horns" and "the new Leicesters" famous in Europeand placed Robert Bakewell in the front of the agricultural pioneers' (C. Grant Robertson, *England under the Hanoverians* [London, 1930], p. 330).

[2] Peacock, *op. cit.* p. 48.   [3] *Ibid.* p. 52.   [4] *Ibid* p. 53.

I called upon him last night to show him my paper, which he said he had lately been reading, and thought it ingeniously treated, but he said he should study it more particularly and I left him my copy with a few additional notes for his perusal. . . . Monro was very polite, and asked me for my directions; I daresay he will think the better of me for having been opposed by Hunter.[1]

Meantime Young received the copy of Sir Everard Home's lecture, and at once let Monro know that he felt he could no longer hold the view set out in his own paper. Later he writes:

He then spoke of my paper with as much respect as it deserved, and took the pains to make some objections to it, which were partly worthy of attention and partly groundless; not making any use of the concession which I had to make to Home's opinion, but passing over in a very slight, and I think a very uncandid manner, the experiments stated in the Croonian lecture (by Home), insinuating, as is too common with him, that he had himself made observations of a similar nature.[2]

It is difficult to account for Young's disparagement of Monro. He had himself learned anatomy under great teachers, and this no doubt made him critical, but he seems to have conceived a personal dislike which was unusual with him.

The Black from whom he derived 'some little information' on chemistry was Joseph Black, now at the age of sixty-seven. Black did not complete the course, and retired the following year. He is best known for his work on latent heat, and for his co-operation with James Watt, the improver of the steam engine.[3]

---

[1] *Ibid.* p. 53.   [2] *Ibid.* p. 54.

[3] 'Dr Joseph Black had, at one time, a house near us, to the west. He was a striking and beautiful person; tall, very thin, and cadaverously pale; his hair carefully powdered, though there was little of it except what was collected into a long thin queue; his eyes dark, clear, and large, like deep pools of pure water. He wore black speckless clothes, silk stockings, silver buckles, and either a slim green silk umbrella, or a genteel brown cane. The general frame and air were feeble and slender. The wildest boy respected Black. No lad could be irreverent towards a man so pale, so gentle, so elegant and so illustrious. So he glided like a spirit through our rather mischievous sportiveness, unharmed. He died seated with a bowl of milk on his knee, of which his ceasing to live did not spill a drop; a departure which it seemed, after the event happened, might have been foretold of this attenuated philosophical gentleman' (Henry Cockburn, *Memorials of my Time* [Foulis, 1910], p. 46).

Dr James Gregory, to whom Young is more complimentary in the reference quoted, was Professor of the Practice of Medicine. He also had studied at Leyden, and was 'a great physician, a great lecturer, a great Latin Scholar and a great talker!'[1] He was also a great favourite with his students. According to Young, he 'is a very agreeable and well informed man; he seems to have vigorous and rapid thought'.[2] Coupled with his name for complimentary mention is that of Andrew Duncan,[3] who became Professor of the Theory of Medicine in 1789 when Gregory transferred from that chair to the chair of the Practice of Physic.

If Young was sparing in his praise of the Edinburgh teachers, he was, at least, impressed by the anatomy demonstrations of John Bell, 'the best surgeon that Scotland had then produced'.[4] Bell was a pupil of Monro's, but was struck with the neglect of the application of anatomy to surgery.

In Dr Monro's class, unless there be a fortunate succession of bloody murders, not three subjects are dissected in the year. On the remains of a subject fished up from the bottom of a tub of spirits, are demonstrated these delicate nerves, which are to be avoided or divided in our operations; and these are demonstrated once at the distance of one hundred feet! nerves and arteries which the surgeon has to dissect, at the peril of his patient's life.[5]

Young found his demonstrations to be 'of first class excellence'. The only other teacher whom Young mentions was Francis Home, the Professor of Materia Medica, 'who has some merit with something ridiculous in his manner'.

Several of these men were not only learned in their own subjects but were men of wide culture and accomplished classical scholars. Young's unenthusiastic and somewhat critical comments on his teachers must not be taken too seriously. In a letter to his uncle he says: 'I believe North[6] and Baker are prejudiced against Edinburgh: with respect to the study of

---

[1] Cockburn, *op. cit.* p. 97. [2] Peacock, *op. cit.* p. 51.
[3] Founded the Edinburgh Dispensary, 1776. [4] Cockburn, *op. cit.* p. 97.
[5] John Struthers, *Historical Sketch of the Edinburgh Anatomical School* (Edinburgh, 1867), p. 38. [6] The Hon Frederick North, afterwards Lord Guilford.

physic, it appears to me beyond comparison preferable to Oxford or Cambridge, and in other respects little inferior.'[1] He was convinced that Edinburgh ought to find a place in the course of every medical student, if not the actual place that it found in his own.

His own suggestions for medical study were set out many years later in his *Introduction to Medical Literature*, first published in 1813.[2] He was no believer in premature specialization, and recommended that an early beginning be made with languages, arithmetic and, later, mathematics. The University should be entered at sixteen, but medical study should not begin till nineteen, and should then continue for five or six years. The first winter of medical study should be at Edinburgh, which he specially commended for its elementary lectures as well as 'the excellence of the clinical and practical lectures'. The summer should be spent in Botany, Chemistry and other preliminary studies, followed by Anatomy and Physiology in London during the second winter, and hospital practice in the spring. The whole programme is set out thus:

If it were necessary to assign the age at which each of the studies which have been mentioned ought in general to commence we might prescribe for the preliminary education a form somewhat resembling this:

At 2, 3 or 4	Reading and reciting English
6	Latin, Writing
8	Arithmetic
10	Greek
12	French
14	Italian, Geometry
16	German, Mathematics
17	Natural Philosophy, Drawing
18	Chemistry, Botany.

The studies more strictly medical will be distributed nearly in this manner,

First Year.   Anatomy, Theory of Medicine (Clinical Lectures), Continuation of Chemistry and Botany, Mineralogy.

---

[1] Peacock, *op. cit.* p. 52.   [2] P. 18.

Second Year.   Practical Anatomy, Physiology. Hospital. Practice of Physic.

Third Year.   Comparative Anatomy.
Surgery, Midwifery, Materia Medica.
Clinical Lectures.

It may well be doubted whether a programme of this kind would be possible for any but those who shared to some extent Young's genius, but he put it forward as his mature view. His general idea was that of a wide literary education as the foundation on which the superstructure of medical training might be built. This has, of course, received wide support, and there must be many who regret the way in which the practitioner of wide education and culture has tended to become merged in the specialist. Dr Norman Moore[1] says:

Last, we may conclude that medicine in itself, with its essential preliminary, anatomy, contains sufficient opportunities of training in every form of observation and of logical deduction from what is observed, and that, for the rest, a mind which has been opened by a sound literary education is that best adapted to follow the life-long study of medicine which is the duty of every physician.

Of Young's fellow students we learn very little. 'I have found a much more select and desirable party of fellow students here, than I have met with before; there are five or six Oxford and Cambridge men, with most of whom I associate'.[2] It may well be that Young's tastes were somewhat different from those of the majority of his fellow students and his circle of friends restricted in consequence. He was friendly with two German students, and as he had already made up his mind to spend the following year in Göttingen, he got some help from one of them in his study of the language. None of the friends he mentions became famous, although three of them—John Bostock, E. N. Bancroft and Sir George Gibbes—became sufficiently distinguished to find a place in the *Dictionary of National Biography*.

But, of course, Young's interests were not confined to his

[1] Norman Moore, *History of Medicine in the British Isles* (Oxford, 1908), p. 82.
[2] Peacock, *op. cit.* p. 51.

professional studies. He was fortunate in securing as a friend Andrew Dalzel, Professor of Greek; and the two corresponded at intervals for many years afterwards. Dalzel was outstanding as a teacher and was the centre and focus of a group which represented much that was best in the culture of Edinburgh at that time. The enthusiasm for liberty awakened throughout the country by the French Revolution had begun to wane, and a strong reaction had set in. The Tories had never been very friendly to the Revolution, and Edmund Burke had led a section of the Whigs which had been consistently critical. The remainder of the Whigs under Charles Fox had defended the Revolution, and based high hopes upon it. The excesses of the revolutionaries in the end disappointed their friends and went far towards justifying their enemies, and the swing in public opinion was so strong that the most moderate ideas of democracy and liberty were in danger. So far as Edinburgh was concerned, Henry Cockburn says:

It was among them [the Whig Party] accordingly that independence found its only asylum. It had a few silent though devoted worshippers elsewhere, but the Whig Counsel were its only open champions. The Church can boast of Sir Harry Moncrieff alone as its contribution to the cause, but he was too faithful to his sacred functions to act as a political partisan. John Allen and John Thomson of the medical profession were active and fearless, and the College gave Dugald Stewart, John Playfair and Andrew Dalzel. Of these three, mathematics, which was his chair, enabled Playfair to come better off than his two colleagues; for Dalzel had to speak of Grecian liberty, and Stewart to explain the uses of liberty in general; and anxiously were they both watched.[1]

Among the group there were, in addition to those mentioned by Cockburn, Dr Adam Ferguson, historian of Rome; John Robison, Professor of Natural Philosophy; Professor Joseph Black, Dr James Gregory, and Dr Hutton, the first great British geologist.

Dalzel himself was a correspondent of Porson and of Parr. He took a special interest in Young during his stay in Edinburgh,

[1] Cockburn, *op. cit.* p. 97.

D

and enlisted his help in the preparation of the second volume of his *Analecta*, which was extensively used in classical teaching in the first half of the nineteenth century.

Writing to Professor Young of Glasgow, Dalzel says: 'There is a namesake of yours here at present from England, a great Grecian, who has translated into Greek verse Lear's imprecation from Shakspeare.'[1] Another famous Edinburgh 'Grecian' was James Bennett, who as a Lord of Session took the name of Lord Monboddo.[2] He had an enthusiastic veneration for the learning and philosophy of the Greeks. Young describes a night spent with Dalzel and Monboddo (then about eighty) on 13 November 1794:

Last night I was highly and unexpectedly gratified by meeting Lord Monboddo and Burgess of Oxford at Dr Gregory's; the Dr sent for me as a Grecian to meet them. We spent the evening in talking of ancient authors and their editions. I introduced the mention of Aristotle to Lord Monboddo as a favourite of his; he was warm on the subject. I do not think him a man either of the deepest learning or the finest taste, but as a singular character, and a wellknown writer,[3] I am pleased with being acquainted with him. We sat some time before my name was mentioned to Burgess, without literary conversation; but he said he had a presentiment that I was that nephew of Dr Brocklesby whose Greek writing Porson had shown him.[4]

With regard to Young's lighter reading and pursuits, he translated the whole of *Don Quixote* with the aid of a grammar and dictionary, and Ariosto's *Orlando Furioso* 'with no small satisfaction'. He also read Johnson's *Rasselas*, and as a preparation for a proposed tour in the Highlands of Scotland he read the *Journey to the Western Islands*.

14th May, 1795—I began, and the next day finished Johnson's Journey. It exhibits some strength of mental powers, but with a

---

[1] Andrew Dalzel, *History of the University of Edinburgh* (Edinburgh, 1862), p. 118.

[2] Classical learning, good conversation, excellent suppers, and ingenious though unsound metaphysics were the peculiarities of Monboddo. He was reputed a considerable lawyer in his own time; and his reports show that the reputation was well founded (Cockburn, *op. cit.* p. 102).

[3] Author of *Origin and Progress of Language and of Antient Metaphysics*.

[4] Peacock, *op. cit.* p. 55.

mixture of pedantry, bigotry and prejudice. I have not extracted from it much information of what I may find in the Highlands, but the manners of the country are well depicted.[1]

It was during his time at Edinburgh that he made a definite break with some of the Quaker traditions. Hudson Gurney says:

He now separated himself from the Society of Quakers and amidst his medical, scientific and classical labours, he determined on cultivating some of those arts in which he considered that his early education had left him deficient.[2]

Speaking of Dr Lettsom, a Quaker doctor of the preceding generation it was said:

Music, dancing, the theatre, the opera, wine, women and song, gambling, attendance at cock-fights, bull-baiting, race meetings, all the rough hearty joys of the Englishman of the time were incompatible with the Quaker costume he wore.[3]

From music, dancing and the theatre Young was no longer content to be cut off, although there is no indication that he ever had any desire to indulge in the other 'rough and hearty joys of the Englishman of the time' given in the list. He was very fond of feminine society, but his relations with women were unexceptionable. Of course, his reaction against the restrictions of the Society of Friends was widely shared. Of the Norwich Meeting in 1798 William Savery says there were 'very few of the middle-aged and young that had a consistent appearance in their dress. Indeed I thought it the gayest Friends' Meeting I ever sat in and was grieved to see it.'[4] And with this relaxation of the rules of dress went a new attitude to innocent amusements. Young's chief solicitude seems to have been for his mother's feelings, and his letter to her already quoted (p. 24) is designed to reassure her as to his fundamental attitude. At any rate he took lessons on the flute and in

[1] *Ibid.* p. 61.
[2] Memoir in Young's *Egyptian Dictionary*, pp. 16–17.
[3] J. J. Abraham, *Lettsom* (London, 1933), p. 47.
[4] Francis R. Taylor, *Life of William Savery of Philadelphia*.

dancing,[1] and became a patron of the theatre. Writing to his friend, Dr Bostock, soon after he left Edinburgh, he says:

I have seen Mrs Siddons in Douglas, The Grecian Daughter, The Mourning Bride, The Provoked Husband, The Fatal Marriage, Macbeth, and Venice Preserved. She was neither below nor much above, my expectation. I can form an idea of something more perfect. My friend Cruikshanks, when I went to take my leave of him, took me aside; and, after much preamble, told me he heard I had been at the play, and hoped that I should be able to contradict it. I told him I had been several times, and thought it right to go, etc. etc. as civilly as I could. I know you are determined to discourage my dancing and singing, and I am determined to pay no regard whatever to what you say. You think I shall never be able to play the flute well, and I am pretty sure that I may if I choose; as to dancing the die is cast.[2]

At the end of the University session he began to make careful preparations for his Highland tour, and on 5 June 1795 he set out. His diary describes his equipment:

I was mounted on a stout, well-made black horse, fourteen hands high, young and spirited, which I had purchased from my friend Cathcart; I had before me my oiled linens, the spencer with a separate camlet cover; under me a pair of saddle-bags, well filled with three or four changes of linen, a waistcoat and breeches, materials for writing and for drawing, paper, pens, ink, pencils and colours; packing paper and twine for minerals; soap, brushes, and a razor; a small edition of Thomson's Seasons, a third flute in a bag, some music, principally Scotch, bound with some blank music paper, wafers; a box for botanising; a thermometer; two little bottles with spirits for preserving insects; a bag for picking up stones; two maps of Scotland—Ainslie's small one and Sayer's; letters of recommendation. The bags had pockets at the end, one containing a pair of shoes, the other boards with straps and paper for drying plants.[3]

---

[1] 'And here were the last remains of the ballroom discipline of the preceding age. Martinet dowagers and venerable beaux acted as masters and mistresses of ceremonies, and made all the preliminary arrangements. No couple could dance unless each party was provided with a ticket prescribing the precise place in the precise dance' (Cockburn, *op. cit.* p. 27).

[2] Peacock, *op. cit.* p. 59.   [3] *Ibid.* p. 63.

One is torn between admiration of the varied interests of the traveller and pity for the beast of burden.

His letters of recommendation seem to have been numerous and very complimentary. Writing to Professor John Hunter of St Andrews, 3 June 1795, Dalzel says:

I use the freedom to introduce to your acquaintance Mr Thomas Young who is the bearer of this. He is nephew of Dr Brocklesby of London and has spent the last session in Edinburgh, chiefly in medical studies, though to these his attention formerly has by no means been confined. For, besides the great progress he has made in various branches of science, he is a most admirable classical scholar, and in particular has made surprising progress in the Greek, the mention of which will be a sufficient apology for my introducing him to you. His stay in St Andrew's will not be long, as he is on a tour to the North previous to his return to England, from whence he means to set off for Göttingen, with a view to prosecute his studies at that university. Though so young a man, he is already a Fellow of the Royal Society of London, and is known as an ingenious author in the Philosophical Transactions. The possession of such talents and accomplishments has not in the least affected his manners, which are simple, unassuming, and agreeable, and he is much esteemed by his literary friends here.[1]

Young's tour was an ambitious one. Starting from Edinburgh he made for St Andrews via Carron, Stirling, Kinross, Loch Leven and Falkland. Thence he made his way to Aberdeen passing through Dundee, Perth, Scone, Taymouth, Dunkeld, Killiecrankie, Blair, Falls of Bruar, Brechin, Findhaven, Arbroath, Montrose, Lawrence Kirk and Stonehaven. From Aberdeen he travelled to John o' Groats, the most northerly point in Scotland, going through Peterhead, Banff, Elgin, Fort George, Cromarty, Skibo and Wick, and returning to Elgin through Thurso, Skibo, Dingwall, Beauly, Inverness, Calder and Forres. Having visited Lochabers and Gordon Castle he proceeded through Inverness to Fort Augustus, and through the valley of the Caledonian Canal to Fort William, Ballachulish, Glencoe and Oban. From here he went by boat to the

[1] Dalzel, *op. cit.* pp. 118–19.

Island of Mull, crossed the island, and on by boat again to
Staffa and Iona. From thence he went to Inveraray, and
returned to Edinburgh by way of Dumbarton, Glasgow,
Hamilton and Lanark, arriving on 6 August. Some fragments of his journal are preserved by Peacock, including
references to St Andrews and Aberdeen, where he visited the
Universities, and to Gordon Castle and Inveraray Castle, where
he was the guest of the Duke of Gordon and of the Duke of
Argyll respectively. He was impressed by Scottish hospitality
and by the culture of the Gordon and Argyll households. He
fell a victim to the charms of the young ladies, and was surprised
to find himself so much at ease in the households of the great.
At Gordon Castle he 'could almost have wished to break or
dislocate a limb by chance, that I might be detained against
my will'.

His stay in Edinburgh was short, and soon he was on the
road again, heading for London, but diverging from time to
time from the direct route. Going south through Selkirk,
Hawick, Langholm and Longtown, he reached Carlisle and did
a tour of the Lakes. Next he visited North Wales, going by
Liverpool and Chester. He returned by Shrewsbury to Birmingham, and here he parted with the noble beast that had
carried him some hundreds of miles, and made his way to
London by coach, spending one night with Edmund Burke at
Beaconsfield. He was warmly welcomed by his uncle on his
arrival on 4 September, and after one or two visits to friends he
made his final preparations for a visit to Germany. The following letter,[1] written to his mother at the end of his time in
Edinburgh, is interesting as revealing his deep resolve to plan
his life wisely and prepare himself to the best of his ability for
his profession:

The present plan of my proceedings is this: to leave Edinburgh
early in the summer; to spend the summer in travelling through
Scotland, the north of England, Wales, and back by Shropshire, to
London; in the autumn to proceed either to Leyden, or more
probably by way of Hamburg to Göttingen; after graduating

[1] Pettigrew, *op. cit.* p. 6.

there, to take a circuit towards Vienna, and thence to Pavia, Rome, and Naples—after this I must be regulated by the state of politics—I expect many advantages from spending two years on the continent; not but that I believe almost all that can be known of physic might be learnt, if necessary, in London: this to one who reasoned only from speculation, and had observed but little of the actual state of society, might be deemed a sufficient reason for sparing ourselves the pains and danger of a long peregrination. But besides that I by no means wish to confine the cultivation of my mind to what is absolutely necessary for a trading physician, any one, who has been acquainted with the world, must have seen numbers of men, fully qualified for applying what little knowledge we have of the secrets of nature to the cure of diseases, linger (for want of some additional qualifications) between poverty and competence, having enough practice to induce them to continue in the profession, and too little to support them with comfort: every now and then, indeed, we see some of these emerge by mere accident from this state of obscurity, and persuade the credulous world that they leave their brethren infinitely behind them in all professional knowledge. There are many qualifications not immediately subservient to the practice of physic, which decidedly tend to advance the reputation of a practitioner; some by exercising his mental powers and giving acuteness to his faculties, some by showing his capacity to attain a knowledge of indifferent matters to which he may apply, and inducing the world to conclude that the same powers, applied with superior efforts to the science which makes his principal employment, will produce a proportionate degree of skill in this also; others again, by making a man fitter for passing through the various scenes of life with satisfaction to himself and pleasure to his acquaintance, and making his company and his friendship desirable to all lovers of virtue and elegance. If these qualifications have sometimes been thought incompatible with deep science, it is not so much to be attributed to the impossibility of their junction, as to the laziness and irresolution of those who have foolishly neglected the one to pursue the other. On these and similar grounds I have hitherto conducted my studies; on these principles I still regulate my employments; and for the same reason I think I cannot better spend the next two years of my life, than in attending (at the same time that I continue my scientific pursuits under the most eminent professors in different parts of Europe) to the various forms into which the customs and habits of

III

MEDICAL STUDY IN GÖTTINGEN AND CAMBRIDGE, 1795–9

'I find it [Göttingen] a very convenient place for study.'
'I must now make the best of Cambridge.' YOUNG

BEFORE his departure for Göttingen Young spent two days at Norwich with the Gurneys, and then, after a night at Yarmouth, left for Hamburg by 'packet' on 10 October 1795. The voyage took six days, and on arrival he was welcomed by Voght and Schmeisser, the two German students whom he had known in Edinburgh and who were residents of the town. They did the honours of the place until 21 October, when Young took the boat to Harburg to join the Stuhlwagen to Hanover.

It is a waggon with a leather covering, the back part like a coach, holding six, with curtains instead of glasses and without doors; the front seat holds three, with a curtain also to keep out the rain. I did not much dislike the conveyance, as the motion suited me better than that of a coach; but to be two nights and part of two days travelling less than ninety English miles would make any carriage disgusting.[1]

He carried a letter from Edmund Burke to Mr Brandes, the Secretary of the Regency, who was most helpful, and supplied him with introductions to the Professors at Göttingen. On 27 October he reached his destination, matriculated in the University on 29 October, and began his course on 3 November.

The reputation of Göttingen University at this time stood very high. It was founded in 1737 by George, Elector of Hanover and afterwards George II of England, and had a staff of distinguished Professors. It was a small University with about 800 students, of whom just over 100 were medical. Its

[1] Peacock, *op. cit.* p. 77.

library was one of the largest and best administered in Europe at this time and attracted students from all over the Continent.

> I am within a hundred yards of the second library in Europe, and can have any book I wish to consult on sending for it; this is the chief reason for my desiring to graduate here.

So writes Young to his mother.[1] In another letter he says:

> I am settled here for four or five months at least and perhaps for as much more: I find it a very convenient place for study; a number of professors of considerable merit in different branches. . . . My time is so portioned out to different instructions, that when I attend to them all, I have very few hours in the week unoccupied. I begin at eight with lectures on history; then follow others on medicine and natural history. I have taken two good rooms in the pleasantest part of the town, in a house which Professor Arnemann lets out to students: a man and his wife live in the house to wait on them all. I breakfast in my own room; dine at an 'ordinary' composed chiefly of students, at 12, which is the common hour throughout the University; and in the evening eat an egg alone.[2]

Young sets out his full programme as follows:

> At 8, I attend Spittler's courses on the History of the Principal States of Europe, exclusive of Germany.
> At 9, Arnemann on Materia Medica.
> At 10, Richter on Acute Diseases.
> At 11, Twice a week, private lessons from Blessman, the academical dancing-master.
> At 12, I dine at Ruhlander's table d'hôte.
> At 1, Twice a week, lessons on the Clavichord from Forkel; and twice a week, at home, from Fiorillo on Drawing.
> At 2, Lichtenberg on Physics.
> At 3, I ride in the academical *manége*, under the instructions of Ayrer, four times a week.
> At 4, Stromeyer on Diseases.
> At 5, Blumenbach on Natural History.
> At 6, Twice Blessman with other pupils, and twice Forkel.
> Spittler, Arnemann, and Blumenbach follow, in lecturing, their own compendiums, and Lichtenberg makes use of Erxleben's. I mean to study regularly beforehand.[3]

---

[1] Pettigrew, *op. cit.* p. 7.   [2] *Ibid.*   [3] Peacock, *op. cit.* p. 78

This admirable combination of the specialist training with the development of cultural and literary studies indicates his firm intention to prepare thoroughly for his medical career, and to develop the accomplishments which his Quaker upbringing had tended to suppress. He found it at first a little difficult to follow the lectures, being accustomed to reading the language but not hearing it. He and his three English companions, however, passed a self-denying ordinance and talked no English 'on pain of forfeiting twopence every half hour'.[1]

Of the professors then in residence at Göttingen the one whom Young most desired to meet was J. G. Heyne. He was partly responsible for the reintroduction of Greek into the University and for a new approach to classical authors. 'This was the viewpoint of the new humanism through which the study of antiquity once more acquired a reasonable and human purpose: the cultivation of a sense and taste for the beautiful and sublime in literature.'[2] Heyne was a classical scholar of international reputation, and Young, as we have seen, carried to him a letter of introduction from Dalzel. His first impression of Heyne is given in a letter to his uncle:[3]

He is very civil to me, and I had last week the honour of meeting him with his whole family at his brother-in-law Blumenbach's. I have not entered very deep into literary conversation with him, and have not had any opportunity of bringing forward any of my attempts in composition, except that he has seen a little compliment which I paid my drawing-master Fiorillo, in imitation of an ancient epigram, and expressed his approbation of it.[4]

Heyne's first impression of Young was appreciative in the extreme.

Although that delightful and erudite young man, Thomas Young [he writes to Dalzel] is sufficiently recommended by his own gifts of

[1] *Ibid.* p. 79.
[2] F. Paulsen, *The German Universities* (English trans. London, 1895), p. 47
[3] Peacock, *op. cit.* pp. 81–2.
[4] Three years afterwards S. T. Coleridge followed Young to Göttingen University where he 'called with my letters on the Professor Heyne, a little, hopping, over-civil sort of a thing who talks very fast and with fragments of coughing between every ten words. However he behaved very courteously to me' (*Letters of Samuel Taylor Coleridge*, ed. Ernest Hartley Coleridge, vol. I, pp. 280–1).

character and intellect, nevertheless it is impossible to tell you how greatly his arrival delighted me, and how the memory of you inclined me to affection for him, and also that charming letter from you which he handed over to me.[1]

Toward the end of his residence in Göttingen he attended Heyne's lectures on the history of art delivered in the University Library and illustrated by the extensive collection of prints housed there.

On one occasion Dr Brocklesby had accused Heyne of disparaging criticisms of the English public schools. Young counters this accusation with a quotation from one of Heyne's works in which he says:

The instruction at Eton is perhaps, in comparison with ours, in many respects very limited; it is, however, shown by experience, that a firm foundation in the ancient languages, much exercise in construing the classics, and a readiness in thought and expression in the manner of the originals, formed and derived from that exercise, accompanied also by mathematical studies, will always carry the mind to a higher degree of perfection than a premature knowledge, built upon a sandy bottom, and unfit for the foundation of a complete and regular academic education.[2]

It will readily be understood how warmly Young would endorse these sentiments.

Of the non-medical professors whose lectures Young attended the most outstanding was Spittler. To his course Young pays a high tribute as 'possessing very great merit', and says that, although the facts may later escape the memory, the students will still profit from the conclusions they are taught to draw. Rather more closely linked with his medical studies, but still quite distinct, were the lectures on Physics by Lichtenberg, to which we have no recorded reference.

Of the professors on the medical side, the most outstanding was J. F. Blumenbach, who 'has shown me many civilities'. He had become Curator of the Natural History Collection in 1776, and frequently visited France and England to add new

[1] Dalzel, *op. cit.* p. 120.   [2] Peacock, *op. cit.* p. 84.

specimens. He was almost the founder of the subject of Comparative Anatomy, and compared the human skull with that of animals as early as 1785. He lectured to Young on Natural History, using his own book as the textbook for the course. His lectures are described by Young with his usual detached and critical attitude of mind as 'not being very deep but containing much general information; their interest was not a little increased by the genial manner of the lecturer, and the amusing anecdotes with which they were occasionally interspersed'. Blumenbach was specially interested in anatomy, and made a very fine collection of skulls which was housed in the Anatomy department.

Clement Carlyon has put on record this rather illuminating little account of Professor Blumenbach in the lecture room and outside it.[1]

Whoever has met with the admirably arranged and useful manuals of Professor Blumenbach's Lectures on Natural History, Physiology, and Comparative Anatomy, of all which there have been good translations into our own language, will be able to appreciate the value of the complete courses, of which they do not profess to give more than a brief outline. His style of lecturing was clear and somewhat familiar; his sole object appearing to be to communicate information, which he enlivened by appropriate ancedote, and very often rendered still more interesting by a peculiar tone of voice and expression of countenance, and even sometimes by suitable action.

Arnemann, Professor of Materia Medica, was a brother-in-law of Blumenbach. He was Young's landlord, and was classed by him with Lichtenberg as being the most sociable among the professors. He was a prolific writer of medical books, and while rather overshadowed by his colleague, Blumenbach, he had a high reputation on the Continent. Richter's lectures on acute diseases Young followed 'with very exemplary regularity'.

There is no doubt that Young thoroughly enjoyed his opportunities as a student. We have already noticed the importance he attached to the library. He also appreciated the freedom from interruptions in the form of 'banquets, theatres and public or private meetings'.[1] In this respect Göttingen differed considerably both from London and from Edinburgh, and Young felt that there 'was a wonderful opportunity for the free pursuit of all studies'. At the same time social functions had their place in the scheme of things.

> We have every Saturday a public concert to which the ladies are admitted gratis, and the students make a tea party with a private concert on Wednesdays. . . . Sunday is the time appropriate for all sorts of company; in the morning the professors are at leisure to receive the visits of the students, and in the afternoon we have some-times a public assembly at the house of a professor, where the professors' wives and daughters and a few other families who reside here, generally with a majority of students, meet to play at cards and to talk, and on the alternate Sunday a dance. . . . The pro-fessors seldom invite the students to dine or sup with them; indeed they could not well afford, out of a fee of a louis or two, to give large entertainments; but the absence of the hospitality which prevails rather more in Britain, is compensated by the light in which the students are regarded; they are not the less, but perhaps the more, respected for being students, and indeed they behave in general like gentlemen, much more so than in some other German Universities.[2]

But there was one feature of the life he had enjoyed in London and in Edinburgh which he missed at Göttingen. He had previously been freely admitted as an equal into a group of men of culture and education who were leaders both in thought and in action in the communities to which they belonged. In London Dr Brocklesby was the focus of the group, in Edinburgh it centred in Professor Dalzel. In the case of Heyne, Young notes that 'he very seldom, if ever, has any parties at his house'. This was not true of other professors, however, as we have already seen. Both Blumenbach and Arnemann entertained students. But these occasions seem to have been more or less formal; and indeed this atmosphere of formality seems to have surrounded all the relations of students and professors. Carlyon brings this out in the following reference to Blumenbach:[3]

---

[1] Dalzel, *op. cit.* p. 121.   [2] Peacock, *op. cit.* p. 80.
[3] Carlyon, *op. cit.* p. 189.

No one could have been more easy of access than he invariably was, nor more ready to give a fuller explanation in private of any part of his lecture that might not have been well understood; he appeared to think that there was a peculiar debt of gratitude owing to the English on account of the liberal contributions of their countrymen to his different cabinets and particularly of the late Sir Joseph Banks, to whom he was indebted for numberless very valuable presents. It may not be irrelevant to remark here as a Göttingen peculiarity, that, however affable Professor Blumenbach may have been with his pupils at home, he strictly adhered to a rule, common to him with the other Professors of the University, of not taking the slightest notice of them in the public streets, or even when walking, as we occasionally met him, on the ramparts. He did not even return the compliment of a bow, but passed by as if he did not see us; a peculiarity the more remarkable, from occurring in a place where this species of politeness is thought a great deal of.[1]

Young summed the matter up in a letter to his uncle, in which he says:

Your idea of the German manners, as far as relates to Göttingen, is perfectly correct: partly from the nature of a University, crowded with young men, not always the most prudent nor the most temperate, and partly from the want of other inhabitants of respectability, the professors are the only established persons who form the society of the place; and having no superiors, being in the habit of a dogmatical delivery from the chair of instruction, and not being so absolutely dependent on their hearers for emolument as in some other seminaries, they are led to a formality and a distance which destroys the social pleasures. There are scarcely two families here who are sincerely cordial: either their pursuits are different, and they have no manner of connection, or they interfere and become rivals. There are, indeed, particular exceptions, and most of the professors receive visits with politeness, but scarcely in any case think of returning them; Arnemann, in whose house I live, and Lichtenberg, the lecturer on Natural Philosophy, are the most sociable. But on the whole, one must be content to be in Göttingen

---

[1] This was not without parallel at Cambridge. 'All communications to the Master are to be addressed through the College Tutor' said a Master of Trinity to an undergraduate who had the temerity to remark that the day was wet, when taking shelter from a rainstorm under the same archway with the Head of his House (A. E. Shipley, *John Willis Clark*, p. 17).

a mere student; as such one has many advantages, but the pleasure and improvement of free social communication must be sought elsewhere.[1]

Young formed a high opinion of German medicine, and was prepared to put up a spirited defence of it in correspondence with his uncle. Dr Brocklesby had been in Germany with the English army during part of the Seven Years War, and was inclined to be critical. Young replies:

The kindred sciences of anatomy, botany, and chymistry, are upon the whole, further advanced than in Britain; and the lectures here on physic and the materia medica are unquestionably better than those which I heard on the same subjects at Saint Bartholomew's Hospital.[2]

And again:

The English physicians are quoted as familiarly here as they are at home; the Germans know what London contains better than many of our own countrymen; but the reverse does not hold good; the German authors are very imperfectly or not at all known in Britain. . . .

so that

science here has one advantage that the doctrines of both countries are well known here, while the English attend little to any opinions but those of their own country.[3]

Young's original intention had been to take a diploma in Göttingen at the end of the winter session, and then 'to travel in Germany during the summer, reaching Vienna early in the autumn and having spent the winter there, in the further prosecution of my medical studies, to proceed through Switzerland to the North of Italy, Rome and Naples, and then to make the best of my way to England'.[4] In pursuance of the first part of this programme, and in accordance with the custom of the University of Göttingen, he applied to the Medical Faculty on 21 March 1795 to be examined, and passed the examination on 30 April. He draws a pleasant picture of the ordeal in these terms:

[1] Peacock, *op. cit.* pp. 82–3.   [2] *Ibid.* p. 87.
[3] *Ibid.*   [4] *Ibid.* p. 88.

I made no preparatory study, as is usual here, and also at Edinburgh not uncommon under the name of grinding. The examination lasted between four and five hours; the four examiners were seated round a table, well furnished with cakes, sweetmeats, and wine, which helped to pass the time agreeably; the questions were well calculated to sound the depth of a student's knowledge in practical physic, surgery, anatomy, chymistry, materia medica, and physiology; but the professors were not very severe in exacting accurate answers. Most of them were pleased to express their approbation of my replies. We were all previously obliged to give a summary account of the manner in which our lives had been spent.[1]

To the preparation of his dissertation—*De Corporis Humani Viribus Conservatricibus*—Young gave considerable time and attention. Its content and its Latinity had to be above reproach. Young made full use of the library and the dissertation shows that he consulted almost every volume that might have any bearing on his subject. The thesis was printed and circulated early in June, and received ready approval from the censor (the Dean of the Faculty), who gave it high praise. Finally, on 16 July 1796, he faced his public disputation. The ceremony is thus described for us by Peacock:

... he proceeded with his *praeses* ... and his two opponents ... to the summer auditorium, where he read a short thesis, called a *lectio cursoria*, the subject of which was the human voice; disputed according to the forms; was complimented on his performance; and after reading something like a prayer, was married to Hygeia, and created doctor of Physic, Surgery, and Midwifery.[2]

Thus ended Young's academical career at Göttingen and, it may be added, thus began his life's work in physics. Only a fragment of the *lectio* remains. It gives an alphabet of forty-seven letters designed to express, by their combination, every sound which the organs of the human voice are capable of forming, and thus available as a universal alphabet. Here we see his early and sustained interest in languages combined with his interest in anatomy. From this combination he developed an interest in the production and propagation of sound. Writing to Dalzel during his first year at Cambridge he says:[3]

[1] *Ibid.* p. 89.   [2] *Ibid.* p. 90.   [3] Dalzel, *op. cit.* pp. 143–4.

E

I am at present a good deal employed on the subject of the slight synoptic sketch at the end of my thesis, the definition and classification of the various sounds of all the languages that I can gain knowledge of; and have of late been diverging a little into the physical and mathematical theory of sound in general. I fancy I have made some singular observations on vibrating strings, and I mean to pursue my experiments.

This interest in sound led in turn to the work on Light which enabled him to restate, and to support with brilliantly original arguments and experiments, the wave theory of light.

The other part of Young's original programme, his scheme of European travel, was rendered impossible by the military situation on the Continent. British fortunes on land were at a low ebb. The British and Austrian armies had been driven out of the Low Countries in the campaign of 1793–4. Now Italy was conquered and Austria faced defeat; visits to Vienna, Rome and Naples were no longer feasible. But Young was unwilling completely to abandon his project and determined to see something of German centres of learning at least. In May, during a short vacation, he had joined two Britishers, afterwards well known, in a tour of the Harz Mountains and an ascent of the Brocken. One was Thomas Wedgwood, son of the Josiah Wedgwood of pottery fame. Wedgwood made the first attempt to use the effect of light on silver salts to obtain photographic records. The other was Sir John Leslie, a physicist whose researches in Heat were later to establish for him a considerable reputation.

On 23 July he went alone on another short excursion, this time to Brunswick (where he was presented at court, dressed in proper costume) and Helmstadt, returning to Göttingen on August 25th.

On 28 August he made his final departure from Göttingen, and set out on foot to visit various places of interest. Proceeding through Cassel, Gotha and Erfurt, he came to Weimar, where he visited Herder, one of the poets who at that time brought distinction to that city and court. At Jena he found the University in vacation, but was received by Butmer, the philologist.

He passed through Nuremberg to Leipzig, and then to Dresden, where he settled for a month, studying its various collections and enjoying the society of many acquaintances, both English and foreign. He visited Freiberg, where he was introduced to Werner.

On 19 November he started out for Berlin, reaching there three days later. Here he met Lord Elgin, the British Ambassador, and others, and remained until he set out for Hamburg on 14 January 1797, a journey of much discomfort which took four-and-a-half days in 'the coarsest and simplest open waggons, without any other seat than straw'. After a week in Hamburg he hurried off to Cuxhaven to join the packet for England, but his sailing was delayed by adverse winds for nearly a fortnight.

On the day of his arrival he was invited to dine with the Governor and Amtmann of the town, and again, on 6 February.

to spend the evening at the Castle with a large party to celebrate his birthday; it was the last that I passed in Germany, and one of the pleasantest; after supper we had a little dance, in which I was so fortunate as to have the two prettiest of his daughters and a prettier cousin for partners. The wind was already changing, and I took a final leave: the next morning we received the welcome summons. I went immediately to bed, and by this means avoided any material sickness till the third day, when the wind was a little high. I was imprisoned in the same disgusting hole the remaining five days, for if I attempted to sit up or go on deck I became giddy. On the eighth day we saw land, and made Yarmouth Roads about noon. We were several times alarmed lest we should meet with privateers; once I was in full expectation of an engagement, which was perhaps as bad as the thing itself. I could eat almost nothing but slept soundly and dreamt of feasting. The trouble and vexation at the custom-house was almost as bad as being at sea for the time; but I settled everything, and slept at Yarmouth that night, which was the conclusion of all dangers and difficulties.[1]

From Yarmouth it was natural that I should visit Norwich on my way to London. Mrs. Rich took me up after sleeping at Keswick (Hall); the next night we arrived at Wade's Mill; not that the fatigue

---

[1] Peacock, *op. cit.* pp. 109–10.

of travelling in England could be said, in comparison of Germany, to make rest necessary; but it was more convenient to sleep there; in the morning I took a walk up to the house at Youngsbury where I resided so many years, and we arrived about noon in London.[1]

There is much that is of interest in Young's comments on Germany and its people as they are given to us, from his journals, by Peacock. Of especial interest in view of the history of the last fifty years and the controversy about German nationalism is the following extract:[2]

have often been inclined to doubt whether a general character of a people can with any certainty be laid down; it is probable that a few distinguishing characteristics may in some cases be described, but there is scarcely any one common cause which can produce a similar effect over the whole of Germany. If we analyse the idea of countrymen, and look for the bond of mutual attachment, there is scarcely anything but the use of the same mother-tongue that can give any rational determination of the idea. The facility and prompt- ness of a mutual communication of ideas, and the habit of having absorbed from the earliest infancy similar principles from the same or similar writers, are perhaps the only marks of belonging to the same country that can be found throughout Germany; and indeed even the language can scarcely be said to be universally the same, except among those of the first ranks. Where the different parts of the same country are united by a community of government, of laws, and of opinions, the attachment is still closer and the resem- blance greater. But the liberal mind must rise above the little prejudices of local attachment; the love of our country sounds well in the mouth of an orator or in the lines of a poet, but it is one of the most dangerous tools in the hands of ambition, and has often been converted to the worst purposes. It is not to be expected, nor perhaps to be wished, that the vulgar should desert every principle but those which are founded in cool reason and philosophy; yet too little attention is paid by popular writers and speakers to the im- portant maxim conveyed in the short answer of Socrates to the men who inquired of what state he was a citizen. A man who has formed intimacies and friendships with inhabitants of different parts of the globe will find enough to love and to disapprove among every people; and perhaps one who has acquired the faculty of com-

[1] Peacock, *op. cit.* p. 114.   [2] *Ibid.* pp. 107–8.

municating his thoughts with equal ease and pleasure to the individuals of several nations, will find himself as much at home in the one as in the other. Certainly one who is totally destitute of this attainment can never be admitted to judge with impartiality of the character of any country. Many men of enlarged minds see clearly the want of common spirit in Germany, but it may be doubted whether they do not act unphilosophically in lamenting so much the absence of national attachment, with respect to its moral effects, however pernicious the political influence of so many jarring interests may be.

Peacock's own comment is:[1]

The reader who might be disposed to criticise the preceding views of the national character and literature of Germany should keep in mind the great changes which both of them have undergone since the time that they were written. The common calamities which nearly all the members of that vast empire suffered from the French occupation and the common exertions which were called forth in its defence, during the war of liberation, have created a common feeling for their fatherland, which no subsequent dismemberment, and we may likewise add, no subsequent misgovernment, has been able to destroy: whilst the rapid developments of every department of their national literature have tended to inspire, with a just pride, all those who have the privilege of using the language in which it is embodied.

Young's decision to continue his medical studies at Cambridge was made as a result of a number of considerations. In his early days in London, he had been urged by Burke and Windham to go to Cambridge to study law; and his uncle, Dr Brocklesby, although encouraging him in his desire to be a doctor, had also been in favour of Cambridge. Cambridge graduates, like Oxford graduates, had certain privileges in the medical profession. Indeed, it was a cause of bitter complaint in some quarters that the College of Physicians was run by Oxford and Cambridge, and this body, of course, ran the medical profession. In 1516 the physicians were

incorporated into a college with power to make statutes and ordinances for the government and correction of the College, and of

---

[1] *Ibid.* p. 114.

all persons practising physic within the city of London, and a circuit of seven miles round it. It is likewise enacted that no person shall be permitted to practise in any county of England or Wales without having first been examined by, and received letters testimonial from the president and three or more of the elects, unless he be a graduate of Oxford or Cambridge; but even a graduate of Oxford or Cambridge has no right to practise within seven miles of the city until he has been admitted to the College.[1]

In Young's time the members of the College were divided into three classes—Fellows, candidates and licentiates. All were free to practise, but only Fellows had any share in the management of the College. Physicians with degrees from Oxford or Cambridge were admitted as candidates, and, after a year's probation, as Fellows. Physicians holding degrees from other Universities were admitted as licentiates, and after a period of from seven to ten years were eligible as candidates for the Fellowship on the nomination of the President.

There seems in one respect to have been some confusion at this time as to the significance of changes which had recently been made in the Statutes of the College. Under the new Statute it was provided that 'candidates for the licentiate must, before graduating, have spent two whole years in some respectable University'.[2] It would appear that Young had expected his two years at Edinburgh and Göttingen to have qualified him in this respect. According to Hudson Gurney, new regulations of the College of Physicians, made in his absence, precluded him from immediate practice.[3] According to Peacock, he was wrongly advised by no less an authority than Sir George Baker, a friend of Dr Brocklesby and a distinguished physician, who had been President of the College almost continuously from 1785 to 1795.

Sir George Baker had told him that two years spent in different Universities in the study of physic, with a medical degree, would answer the purpose; and such would really appear to have been the intention of the framers of the regulation which had been recently

---

[1] *A Picture of the Present State of the Royal College of Physicians of London* (London, 1817), p. xxxix.   [2] *Ibid.* p. xxxiii.   [3] Memoir, p. 19.

adopted. The lawyers, however, who had been employed to put the regulation into a legal form, had given it a different construction, requiring that the two years immediately preceding the application for a licence should have been spent at the same University. The obvious effect of this unexpected reading of the Statute was to nullify any claim which he might have founded upon the year which he had passed at Edinburgh and thus to recall to his uncle's mind the expediency of his proceeding to Cambridge, and, by graduating there, to secure the full honours of his profession: to this scheme he had long been favourable, and was now enabled openly to urge it upon his nephew, when his religious principles no longer presented an insuperable obstacle to its adoption.[1]

Nevertheless, the choice of Cambridge was not made without some hesitations. Edinburgh still had strong attractions, and, writing to Dalzel on 27 March 1797 about a week after his admission to Cambridge, he says:[2]

I was not, till very lately, certain that I should not spend the ensuing winter in your neighbourhood, but I have now entered here at Emmanuel College and shall barely keep the terms for two years, which, as I wish to reside chiefly in London, will be more convenient to me than spending another whole year at Edinburgh; but I assure you that with respect to social pleasures, Cambridge is not to be compared to Edinburgh.

A month later, again in a letter to Dalzel, he expresses some regret that he had not graduated at Edinburgh, and continues, 'The foolish laws of the College in London are perplexed and ill-understood; but I must now make the best of Cambridge.'

So far as his 'religious principles' were concerned, it is probable that, in the first instance, Young had been attracted to Edinburgh not only by the prestige of its medical school, but also by its freedom from the religious tests which were operative at Cambridge. It is difficult to say when his attitude in this matter changed. Even while at Göttingen in 1796 he wrote to his mother about graduation, and said:

In anything which relates to this or to other proceedings I would not rashly give up the privileges of a member of the Society of

[1] Peacock, *op. cit.* pp. 88–9.   [2] Dalzel, *op. cit.* p. 137.

Friends, and I have already, on this ground, asked, and obtained leave to be admitted to a degree without an oath; a case which was here perfectly new.[1]

This definite stand, to which he refers again in connection with the actual ceremony of graduation, indicated some depth of conviction. We have reason to believe, however, that his attitude was in process of changing, and presumably when in the following year Cambridge was proposed, he was willing to become a member of the Church of England. He was not baptized till later, as the following entry from Hudson Gurney's diary, made shortly after Young's death, shows.

1829. May 25th.
Cd. Mrs Y.—and read her the commencement of the memoirs up to Y's settling in London—with which she was satisfied. It is a thing she is greatly set upon. She told me he was baptised at her mother's desire before their marriage, and had always taken the sacrament with her since—that he was a great studier of the scriptures and used, when her eyes failed, to read them to her—and was very careful in encouraging the religious practices of those about him. At the same time he himself, I gather, retained a good deal of his old creed, and carried to his scriptural studies his habit of inquisition of languages and manners—rather than the manner of the Bible people of the evangelical school.

Certainly then and for long afterwards (till 1871) every candidate for a bachelor degree at Cambridge was required to declare himself to be 'bona fide a member of the Church of England as by law established'. Hence the complaint of Dr Haviland, Regius Professor of Physic at Cambridge from 1817 to 1851, that as the degree of medicine was open only to those who had already taken the bachelor's degree, and as the practice at Oxford was the same as that at Cambridge, so 'no Dissenter can in England take the degree of M.D.'

Of Young's religious position very little is definitely known. The authority on whom we depend mainly for information about his life at Cambridge has left it on record that

[1] Pettigrew, *op. cit.* p. 7.

he never spoke of morals, of metaphysics or of religion. Of the last I never heard him say a word, nothing in favour of any sect, or in opposition to any doctrine; at the same time no sceptical doubt, no loose assertion, no idle scoff ever escaped him.[1]

Hudson Gurney in his Memoir[2] says that in his last lengthened interview with Young, when his illness was in its very last stage, Young assured him that 'perfectly aware of his situation, he had taken the sacraments of the church on the day preceding'. He adds later:[3]

His religious sentiments were by himself stated to be liberal, though orthodox. He had extensively studied the Scriptures, of which the precepts were deeply impressed upon his mind from his earliest years; and he evidenced the faith which he professed, in an unbending course of usefulness and rectitude.

In the eighteenth century the intellectual life of the English Universities had sunk to a very low ebb, and at the end of the century it was just beginning to recover. Trevelyan says:

At both Universities the undergraduates were entirely neglected by the great majority of the Fellows, though here and there a College Tutor zealously performed duties that ought to have been shared by the whole Society. Noblemen's sons and rich Fellow Commoners, who were much in evidence, and for whom large allowance was made in matters of discipline, were often accompanied by tutors of their own. The Professors of the University seldom performed any of their supposed functions. No lecture was delivered by any Regius Professor of Modern History (at Cambridge) between 1725 and 1773; the third and most scandalous of the holders of that chair died in 1768 from a fall while riding home drunk from his vicarage at Over.[4]

Compared with Edinburgh or with London the opportunities for instruction offered by the Cambridge Medical School were inadequate in the extreme; indeed nothing that could be called a school existed. A Regius Professorship of Physic had been founded in 1540, but even in Young's time the office was regarded as an additional perquisite to be held by a successful

[1] Peacock, *op. cit.* p. 119.   [2] Pp. 42–3.   [3] P. 47.
[4] G. M. Trevelyan, *Social History of England*, p. 366.

practitioner, and the Professor's duties did not involve any systematic teaching. In 1548 Edward VI had appointed a Royal Commission to visit the University and, among other things,

> to constitute a Medical College ... by designing one of the Colleges for the study of medicine, and to make such of the fellows thereof as were willing to apply themselves to that study and should be deemed fit, fellows of the King's Medical College, and to transfer to other Colleges those who were unwilling or should be considered unfit for that art.[1]

No action was taken by the Commission along these lines. In 1570, new Statutes by Elizabeth removed the requirement that candidates for medical degrees should previously have qualified in Arts. The requirement has never been replaced, but the Natural Sciences Tripos, introduced in 1851, was designed to make it easier for medical students to qualify for an Arts degree, and almost all of them now do. The Chair of Anatomy was instituted in 1707, but 'out of the first five professors three appear to have been absentees, and another held the Chair for one year only'.[2] Until the Chair of Anatomy was founded the Regius Professor of Physic was required to do one 'anatomy' per annum under penalty of a fine if he failed to fulfil his duties. Anatomies were usually carried out in the Regent House or in the Physic School (afterwards the South Library[3] and now the Council Room). Other anatomies were occasionally performed. In 1565 John Caius, founder of Caius College, obtained from Queen Elizabeth a 'formal yearly grant of two bodies, of criminals or unknown strangers dying in Cambridge, for dissection in Gonville and Caius College'.[4] Problems of supply gave the same difficulties in Cambridge in later years, however, that they gave in other places, and were solved in the same way. 'Laurence Sterne's body was discovered in the dissecting room in 1768.'[5]

In a sense the first physiological laboratory was that provided by Richard Bentley (1662–1742), Master of Trinity, in what is now the Bursary of the College. Here Stephen Hales (1677–

---

[1] Humphry D. Rolleston, *The Cambridge Medical School* (Cambridge, 1932), pp. 8–9.
[2] *Ibid.* p. 49.   [3] *Ibid.* p. 48.   [4] *Ibid.* p. 47.   [5] *Ibid.* p. 51.

1761) first measured blood pressure, and worked at animal and plant physiology before becoming perpetual curate of Teddington; but there was no organized Physiology Department until much later.

During Young's period the occupant of the Chair of Physic was Sir Isaac Pennington (1745–1817). He was Professor of Chemistry from 1773 to 1794, and held the Regius Professorship of Physic from 1794 to 1817. He was a successful practitioner in the town, and was knighted in 1795 on the occasion of the presentation by the University of a congratulatory address to George III on his escape from the attempt made on his life. He was the subject of the following epigram, attributed to W. L. Mansel, then Master of Trinity:

> For female ills, when Pennington indites,
> Not minding *what* but only *how* he writes,
> The ladies, while his graceful form they scan,
> Cry, with ill-omened rapture—*killing man.*

His official duties were very light. He had to read and expound Hippocrates and Galen, and to deliver 'at the end of the formal Physic Act a determination of speech in Latin on the subject, a duty which did not occur more than four times a year'.[1]

The occupant of the Chair of Anatomy was a very picturesque character of whom a good account is given by Gunning.[2] Busick Harwood was a native of Newmarket, and was apprenticed to an apothecary. Later he went to India as a surgeon and was reputed to have amassed considerable wealth by his treatment of the native princes. Returning to England, he was admitted to Christ's College as a Fellow Commoner in 1779, and was elected to the Fellowship of the Royal Society in 1784. He was a pioneer in blood transfusion, and not only wrote his thesis for the degree of M.B. on this subject in 1785, but demonstrated the subject publicly on animals on several occasions. He was elected to the Professorship of Anatomy in the same year as he took his degree; but the chair was not

---

[1] *Ibid.* p. 19.

[2] Henry Gunning, *Reminiscences of the University, Town and County of Cambridge from the Year 1780* (London, 1854), vol. I, pp. 52–5.

devoted exclusively to *human* anatomy, and he lectured to general audiences on comparative anatomy rather than to medical students on human anatomy. Attendance at his lectures was not compulsory for medical students.

He migrated from Christ's to Emmanuel before taking his M.D. in 1790. The prospect of a large garden, attached to his College rooms, was the declared motive; but it was generally supposed that political reasons had something to do with the move, Christ's being a Whig College, while Emmanuel under its then Master, Richard Farmer, was above reproach as a Tory institution. 'His evenings were generally spent in Emmanuel Parlour which, under the Presidency of Dr Farmer, was always open to those who loved pipes and tobacco and cheerful conversation.'[1] It was in this connection that he was chiefly associated with Young, who was a member of the Emmanuel Parlour throughout his Cambridge residence.

It is probable that Young's choice of Emmanuel as a College was largely determined by the friendship between Dr Brocklesby and the Master, Richard Farmer. Farmer was a distinguished Shakespeare scholar and a Fellow of the Royal Society. He had been one of Thomas Young's supporters when he was elected to the Fellowship of the Royal Society in 1794. He died just before Young was admitted to Emmanuel. His successor, the Rev. R. Towerson Cory, admitted Young as a Fellow Commoner on 18 March 1797, about a month after his return from Germany. A Fellow Commoner was so called because he was privileged to sit at the same table with the Fellows, and to enjoy their conversation. Fellow Commoners wore special gowns trimmed with gold or silver lace, and caps covered with velvet, the tassels to which were of gold or silver. They were usually of maturer years than the ordinary undergraduate, and were not subject to quite the same disciplinary rules.

Emmanuel had at this time, in addition to the Master and Tutor, fifteen Fellows. The University Calendar for 1799 gives, in addition, two University Professors (Harwood, of Anatomy,

[1] Gunning, *op. cit.* p. 54.

and Smithson Tennant, of Chemistry), eight noblemen, including the Earl of Westmorland, forty-six Masters of Arts, eighteen Fellow Commoners, twenty-two bachelor scholars, ten undergraduate scholars, twenty-five pensioners (ordinary undergraduates) and twelve sizars (undergraduates of limited means giving some service in return for their education).

The number of livings, some of which are very rich, is sixteen—one more than the number of Fellows. This is a superior College for such poor students as can get admission as Sizars. Gay men also consider it a gentlemanlike College, judging, I suppose, from the number of horses, dogs, and Fellow-Commoners, belonging to the society.[1]

The book which gives the Laws of the Emmanuel Parlour at this time (some of them still operative), and records the fines, the bets won and lost, and the bottles of wine given by the members, is still preserved. The record shows that Young was elected President of the Parlour on 4 November 1797, a signal honour for one who had only been a member six months. Some of the bets are topical, for example how long Pitt's Government would last; and whether Lady Hamilton would be received at court on her return. Some are personal, as when Sir Busick Harwood bet another member of the Parlour (Blackall) that he would disguise himself within a week so that Blackall would not know him, and won his bet in forty-eight hours by appearing in the guise of a bricklayer's labourer. Among Young's successful bets we find one on the angle subtended at the sun by the earth's semi-diameter; and at a later date two on the same night (a) that Young does not produce thirty pins the wires of which occupy less space than an inch, and (b) that Young does not draw with a pen one hundred lines in the space of an inch. Some of his bets were less successful. One of these was made on 14 March 1799: Young v. Pemberton—'Young will produce a pamphlet or paper on the theory of sound more satisfactory than any thing that has already appeared, before he takes his Bachelor's Degree.' Two of the other Fellows made the same bet with

[1] *Alma Mater*, by a Trinity Man (London, 1827), vol. II, p. 183.

one another. At the audit of 1802, Young's bet was given as undecided, but, on what grounds we do not know, it was decided against him later in that year. It is doubtful whether a competent tribunal would now uphold the decision on appeal.

A very detailed summary of Young's achievements, manners, habits, etc. is given by the Tutor of the College at that time. It is in some respects ungenerous and unduly critical, but it is of great interest, and is quoted by Peacock in full. Writing of Young's introduction to the College, the Tutor says:

When the Master introduced Young to his tutors he said, 'I have brought you a pupil qualified to read lectures to his tutors.' This, however, as might be concluded, he did not attempt, and the forbearance was mutual; he was never required to attend the common duties of the College.

Of his manners and his association with others he says:

In his manners he had something of the stiffness of the Quaker remaining; and though he never said or did a rude thing, he never made use of any of the forms of politeness. Not that he avoided them through affectation; his behaviour was natural without timidity, and easy without boldness. He rarely associated with the young men of the College, who called him, with a mixture of derision and respect, 'Phaenomenon Young'; but he lived on familiar terms with the Fellows in the Common Room. He had few friends of his own age or pursuits in the University, and not having been introduced to many of those who were distinguished either by their situation or talent, he did not seek their society, nor did they seek his; they did not like to admit the superiority of anyone *in statu pupillari*, and he would not converse with anyone but as an equal.[1]

Here we see again Young's desire for the kind of society he had enjoyed at Edinburgh. In letters he occasionally deplores 'barriers which custom opposes to a free interchange of society with the senior and more distinguished members of the University with whom the claims of a letter of introduction were considered to be generally discharged by a single dinner, to be succeeded afterwards by a formal and somewhat distant recognition'.[2] All the same, Young had some quite distinguished senior

---

[1] Peacock, *op. cit.* pp. 118–19.   [2] *Ibid.* p. 120.

friends, including Harwood, Pennington, and Dr Pearce, Master of Jesus and Dean of Ely. Among those more nearly his own age was William Gell, who was a Fellow of Emmanuel, an artist, archaeologist, and scholar, with whom he corresponded in later life.

Of his conversation we learn from the source already quoted that

he never obtruded his various learning in conversation; but if appealed to on the most difficult subject he answered in a quick, flippant, decisive way, as if he was speaking of the most easy; and in this mode of talking he differed from all the clever men that I ever saw. His reply never seemed to cost him an effort, and he did not appear to think there was any credit in being able to make it. He did not assert any superiority, or seem to suppose that he possessed it; but spoke as if he took it for granted that we all understood the matter as well as he did. He never spoke in praise of any of the writers of the day, even in his own peculiar department, and could not be persuaded to discuss their merits. He was never personal; he would speak of knowledge in itself, of what was known or what might be known, but never of himself or any other, as having discovered anything, or as likely to do so.[1]

This may have been true of Young's spoken word; it was by no means true of his written word. His very frank criticisms of contemporaries were sometimes resented as we shall see, and he was not slow to claim the credit of discoveries when he felt that credit to be his due.

Going on to speak of his classical learning the account says:

He had a high character for classical learning before he came to Cambridge; but I believe he did not pursue his classical studies in the latter part of his life—he seldom spoke of them; but I remember his meeting Dr Parr in the college Combination room, and when the Doctor had made, as was not unusual with him, some dogmatical observation on a point of scholarship, Young said firmly: 'Bentley, sir, was of a different opinion'; immediately quoting his authority, and showing his intimate knowledge of the subject. Parr said nothing; but, when Dr Young retired, asked who he was, and

[1] *Ibid.* pp. 117–18.

though he did not seem to have heard his name before, he said, 'A smart young man, that.'[1]

On Young's work the comment is:

It was difficult to say how he employed himself; he read little, and though he had access to the college and university libraries, he was seldom seen in them. There were no books piled on his floor, no papers scattered on his table, and his room had all the appearance of belonging to an idle man. I once found him blowing smoke through long tubes, and I afterwards saw a representation of the effect in the Transactions of the Royal Society to illustrate one of his papers upon sound; but he was not in the habit of making experiments.[2]

This account is a trifle misleading. Young was by no means idle. He was not reading medicine—he had already acquired all the knowledge in that field which he needed at the moment. But he read some books bearing on his own work with considerable profit, and he made a large number of experiments to which we shall refer presently. The account goes on to draw a rather ludicrous picture of Young's exercise:

He walked little, and rode less, but having learnt to ride the great horse abroad, he used to *pace* round Parker's Piece on a hackney: he once made an attempt to follow the hounds, but a severe fall prevented any future exhibition.[3]

It is difficult to reconcile this picture with Young's experience at Göttingen, one of the chief riding schools of Europe. He writes to his uncle:

I have been upon the back of the Springer. To mount this terrestrial Pegasus is considered here something like *summi in re equestri honores*, and is seldom attained without long practice. . . . We have another fashionable exercise, which I think adequately corresponds to the athletic schools of the ancients—vaulting on a wooden horse in various positions; and I am much more known among the students for excelling in this, than for writing Greek, of which they have little knowledge, and not much more respect.[4]

---

[1] Peacock, *op. cit.* p. 116.
[3] *Ibid.*
[2] *Ibid.* p. 119.
[4] *Ibid.* pp. 97–8.

Hudson Gurney confirms the fact that he was an accomplished horseman and gymnast.

It was March 1797 when Young was admitted to Emmanuel, and on 3 December of that year he visited his uncle in London. This visit was a tragic one, as his uncle died that same night, leaving to his nephew his house in Norfolk Street, Park Lane, with all the furniture, his library, his prints, his pictures (mostly selected by his friend, Sir Joshua Reynolds), and about £10,000 in money. Young retained some apartments in the house for his own use during vacations; but his summer vacations were largely spent at Worthing at the house of Mr John Ellis, a very rich West Indian planter. He also paid occasional visits to Bath, and to the Duke of Richmond at Goodwood.

In the early summer of 1798 he had a slight accident, and during his recovery he read some of the works of the contemporary French and German mathematicians. Writing to his friend Dr Bostock, he says:

I have been studying not the theory of the winds, but of the air, and I have made observations on harmonics which I believe are new. Several circumstances unknown to the English mathematicians which I thought I had first discovered, I since find to have been discovered and demonstrated by the foreign mathematicians; in fact Britain is very much behind its neighbours in many branches of the mathematics; were I to apply deeply to them I would become a disciple of the French and German school; but the field is too wide and too barren for me.[1]

Referring to the same subject, he writes to Dalzel (8 July 1798):

I am ashamed to find how much the foreign mathematicians for these forty years have surpassed the English in the higher branches of the sciences. Euler, Bernouilli and d'Alembert have given solutions of problems which have scarcely occurred to us in this country. I have had particular occasion to observe this in considering the figure of vibrating chords, the sounds of musical pipes and some other similar matters in which I fancied I had hit on some ideas entirely new, but I was glad to find them in part anticipated by

---

[1] *Ibid.* p. 127.

Bernouilli in 1753 and 1762. There are still several particulars respecting the gyration of chords, and formation of synchronous harmonics, the combination of sounds in the air, the phaenomena of beats, on which I flatter myself that I shall be able to throw some new light.

In the summer of 1799 he prepared the paper on 'Sound and Light' which was read to the Royal Society on 16 January 1800, and published in the *Philosophical Transactions*. Its full title is 'Outline of Experiments and Enquiries respecting Sound and Light from the Philosophical Transactions, in a letter addressed to Edward Whitaker Grey, M.D., Secretary, Royal Society.' It is obviously the paper which was the subject of the Parlour bet to which reference was made earlier. Posterity would hardly dare to support the decision of the Emmanuel Parlour against Young's claim. For the paper covers a large range of phenomena, gives an account of numerous original experimental observations and measurements, and shows a wide knowledge of contemporary writers on sound, including Bernoulli, Euler and Lagrange. But it also stresses the analogies between sound and light, and indicates clearly how Young's mind had already begun to grapple with the evidence for the wave theory of light. This aspect of the paper will be considered later. Meanwhile let us note that it contains measurements of the quantity of air discharged through an aperture and of the direction and velocity of a stream of air; measurement of the pressure required to make various organ pipes 'speak'; measurements of the frequencies of vibration corresponding to audible notes; and observations and measurements on vibrating strings. These records show that he *did* spend some of his Cambridge days in experiments. He remarks that the note produced by footsteps in a passage between two walls is the note appropriate to a vibrating air column whose length is the distance between the walls. He connects this with the note of an organ pipe of the same length and with notes produced by the air between the opposite walls of a room. 'The appropriate notes of a room may readily be discovered by singing the scale in it.'

Of special interest is the section on the vibration of chords. He points out that chords may vibrate as a whole or in two, three, four, etc. parts, and that each mode of vibration has its appropriate note. When the stretched chord is bowed or struck a mixture of these modes is produced and the ear can hear a series of 'partial tones' which give quality to the note. The relative strength of the partial tones will depend to some extent on the point at which the bow or hammer is applied to the string. Thus in the mode giving the second partial the string vibrates in two segments with a 'node' or point of minimum motion at the centre. If then the centre is bowed or struck, this particular partial tone will tend to be absent. The paper itself, which is dated 'Emmanuel College, Cambridge, 8th July 1799', concludes with the following paragraph, part of which has already been quoted.

Thus, sir, I have endeavoured to advance a few steps only, in the investigation of some very obscure but interesting subjects. As far as I know, most of these observations are new; but if they should be found to have been already made by any other person, their repetition in a connected chain of inference may still be excusable. I am persuaded also, that at least some of the positions maintained are incontrovertibly consistent with truth and nature; but, should further experiments tend to confute any opinions that I have suggested, I shall relinquish them with as much readiness as I have long since abandoned the hypothesis which I once took the liberty of submitting to the Royal Society on the functions of the crystalline lens [of the eye].

In the spring of 1799, when Young had kept the six terms necessary for his degree, he left Cambridge, took a house at No. 48 Welbeck Street, London, and began his medical practice. Thus was he launched on the career for which he had prepared himself with unusual care in London, Edinburgh, Göttingen, and Cambridge.

IV

PHYSICIAN AND MEDICAL AUTHOR

'My profession goes on quietly but with tolerable success.'

YOUNG

As soon as Young had established himself in London he made some contacts with the hospitals, and settled down in medical practice. He found his professional progress somewhat slow, and had a good deal of time on his hands which he was able to devote to his interests in other fields. He was anxious not to prejudice his reputation in medicine by seeming to devote too much time to other activities, and his numerous contributions to scientific and other journals were written over a pseudonym. The veil was a thin one, however, and the authorship of the articles in question was pretty widely known. In 1800 he was offered the Professorship of Physics at the Royal Institution, and accepted it; but in 1802 he resigned it again on the ground that continuing to hold it might be detrimental to his advancement in his profession. This period was, as we shall see, one of his most productive periods in the field of optical research, and it was during these early years in medical practice that he developed the wave theory of light.

In the field of medicine great changes were in progress. In the treatment of infectious diseases the revolution in protective treatment had just reached its climax. Smallpox was a widespread scourge in this and other countries in the seventeenth and early eighteenth centuries. In 1796 Edward Jenner successfully protected a boy against smallpox by inoculating him with cowpox, and vaccination became an established method of producing immunity. Important as was this discovery in itself, it was almost more important by virtue of the whole new train of work and thought which was opened out by it.

About this time also there began an attempt to improve the

hygienic conditions in the towns, and attention was directed to 'public health'. Westminster obtained an Improvement Act in 1762, Birmingham in 1765, and the City of London and Manchester in 1776. These Acts dealt with the disposal of sewage and kindred matters. At the same time the importance of personal cleanliness came to be more widely recognized, baths were introduced, into the houses of the wealthy at least, and the advantages of good ventilation and of fresh air were more widely recognized. Among aids to diagnosis, the clinical thermometer and the stethoscope had just been invented.

In these circumstances, it was not unnatural that there should be a general reaction against the more drastic methods for the treatment of disease which had till then been current. Of J. Lettsom, a well-known and greatly respected Quaker physician who practised some years earlier than Young, a scurrilous person wrote:

> When any sick to me apply
> I physics, bleeds and sweats 'em,
> If, after that, they choose to die,
> Why verily,
>
> I. Lettsom[1]

Certainly, the eighteenth-century physicians believed in purging, bleeding and sweating as almost universal remedies.

In this matter of rigour of treatment Young held a middle position. He was in sympathy with the reaction against it and in favour of the milder remedies; but he was of opinion that the reaction was in danger of going too far. With reference to a case of smallpox in which bleeding had been used, he writes:

There was nothing to regret from his having been bled at the beginning before the disease was recognised. A patient of mine in St George's Hospital was bled under similar circumstances, and I saw no reason to think that he was the worse for it, though I had not ordered it.[2]

and again:

I have no *horror* of bleeding in the epidemic fever, unless when it

---

[1] J. J. Abraham, *Lettsom* (London, 1933), title-page.
[2] To Hudson Gurney, 24 Aug. 1824.

is carried to the excess that some surgeon butchers have done. I have bled, I think with advantage, in a case or two which I thought clearly seemed to require it, at least they recovered. . . . On the whole, there was certainly too much dread of the lance when I was a young man, and when we were told that it had destroyed more in the last century than the sword.[1]

As part of the new attitude to health came an increased demand for the seaside and the country holiday. Richard Russell (1687–1759)[2] had popularized sea-bathing as a cure for glands, and made the reputation of Brighton. 'Everyone rushed coastwards to be cured, like tongues, by dipping into brine.' During Young's period the English watering-place and spa became even more popular with the wealthy and the aristocratic, owing to the restrictions on travel occasioned by the Napoleonic wars.[3] First Brighton, and later Worthing, acquired a reputation for sea-bathing. From the *New Worthing Guide*, 1810 we learn that:

The practice of sea-bathing with its concomitant exercise on the coast is very refreshing and agreeable to the robust, as well as salutary to invalids; and growing fashionable, the inhabitants of Worthing availing themselves of its favourable situation, and following the example of other places, have used great exertions for the improvement of their town, so that now in point of conveniences and elegant accommodation for visitors it may in most respects vie with the best resorted watering places in the kingdom.

In *A Sketch of Worthing and its Environs*,[4] we find the bathing strongly recommended, and high praise given to the 'bathing women':

And here we should not forget the extreme tenderness and attention of the bathing women, particularly towards the children and invalids. We may venture to assert, that in this point of view, they are not to be equalled at any other watering place in the kingdom, and what may have a powerful recommendation in their favour, you have not to encounter that grim harshness of visage so peculiarly striking, and so strongly depicted as in the countenance of the celebrated bathing women of Brighton.

[1] To Hudson Gurney, 6 Jan. 1825.   [2] Abraham, *op. cit.* p. 279.
[3] *Ibid.* p. 280.   [4] By J. Mackcoull (Worthing, 1811).

Young evidently decided to take advantage of this situation. He had friends at Worthing and in 1805 he spent the summer there, and repeated this practice annually until 1820. By this arrangement he was able to spend the summer out of town, to make professional contacts which he could maintain in London during the winter, and to enjoy the cultural society which, all through his life, meant so much to him. He acquired a house of his own in Steyne Row in 1808, and in the *Sketch of Worthing* already referred to we find a warning against medical quacks, followed by the assurance that:

in this particular we feel indescribable pleasure and hesitate not a moment to declare, with gratitude and sincerity, that Dr Young of Steyne Row, the practising physician of the place, is entitled to our unlimited confidence in the healing art, and to whom we particularly recommend the valetudinarian visitor, where he will meet with all the relief that the Materia Medica can possibly afford, added to which the tender conciliating manners of a well-bred gentleman.

In a later edition in 1813, Young is referred to as 'the resident physician'.

Young took his M.B. degree at Cambridge in March 1803, and his M.D. degree in July 1808, the dates in both cases being the earliest at which the regulations would permit him to proceed to the degree. He submitted dissertations for both degrees.[1]

On 14 June 1804, he was married to Eliza Maxwell, second daughter of J. P. Maxwell of Cavendish Square and of Trippendence, near Farnborough, Kent. The marriage seems to have been in every way a singularly happy one, and his wife, who was 'extremely young'[2] at the time, survived him. His relations with his wife's family were also most happy and cordial.

In May 1806 the office of Physician to the Middlesex Hospital fell vacant, and Young decided to become a candidate. As a result of a preliminary canvass of the electors, however, he came to the conclusion that he had no chance, and that his prospects even for the next vacancy were none too good. He

---

[1] Peacock, *op. cit.* pp. 211–12. [2] *Ibid.* p. 212.

therefore withdrew his candidature. Writing to Lord Hard-wicke from Welbeck Street on 10 December 1806, he says:

Dr Young returns his sincere thanks to Lord Hardwicke for his obliging promise of his vote at the approaching election of a physician to the Middlesex Hospital; but finding that, notwith-standing the very flattering manner in which his applications have been generally received, Dr Satterley's connexion with the medical gentlemen of the house, by giving him the advantage of an early canvass, has secured him a decided majority, Dr Young wishes to decline for the present giving his friends the trouble of attending the election; especially as he hopes to prevail on them to grant him a similar favour on a future occasion.[1]

In 1809 he was appointed to deliver a course of lectures at the Middlesex Hospital, and did so in the winter 1809–10. He took the preparation of these lectures very seriously, and writing to a friend in April 1809, he says:

I have been absorbed in Physic day and night—not altogether in the practice, but more in the theory—having a course of lectures to prepare for next winter on which I am to rest, in some degree, my medical reputation.[2]

The thoroughness with which he did his work is indicated in a letter[3] in which he says:

I have been spending a month on some chemical investigations, which I have just completed, merely because I was asked to give a few lectures on chemistry and pharmacy; but then I consider that I should have no right to give lectures on chemistry if I had done absolutely nothing to prove myself capable of it. Certainly twenty or even fifty pupils would be scarcely an inducement to take all the pains I have taken and shall take in the business, but for the very important advantage you mention. The longer a person has lived the less he gains by reading and the more likely he is to forget what he has read and learnt of old; and the only remedy that I know of is to write upon every subject that he wishes to understand, even if he burns what he has written.

In June we find him not only preparing the lectures, but getting

---

[1] British Museum Manuscripts, 35646 f. 91.
[2] Peacock, *op. cit.* p. 219.   [3] *Ibid.*

ready also for the necessary examination for admission to the Fellowship of the College of Physicians, and writing a medical essay on the Effects of Climate.

The course consisted of thirty-six lectures in all—six on Physiology, six on Chemistry, twenty on Nosology (the systematic classification and study of diseases) and General Practice, and four on Materia Medica. The material included a new and original system of classifying diseases, and most of it was embodied in his *Introduction to Medical Literature* published later. The course was repeated in the following winter (1810–11), but was not conspicuously successful as a lecture course, owing to the demands which Young made on his students. Like many other great men he provided a repast much too rich for the average intellectual digestion, and gave his hearers much more than they were able to carry away.

On 22 December 1809, he was elected to the Fellowship of the Royal College of Physicians, and in 1810 was appointed to deliver the Gulston Lecture. Early in 1811 there was a vacancy on the staff of St George's Hospital, and Young was persuaded to become a candidate. There were three other candidates, and friends were active in their support. Writing to Hudson Gurney on 7 January 1811, Lord Aberdeen says:

It is impossible for me, however, to accede to your request respecting Dr Young. Cabbell is a man who was with me in Scotland and whom it was impossible to refuse to support. I fear that I have even been the means of procuring him votes. It is necessary for me to say that I did not know what Dr Young it was who opposed him or I would have taken no active part in the affair but merely given my own vote. As it is I shall now cease.

Young himself was not inactive, and in the event he was successful by a rather narrow margin. The election was held on 24 January 1811, and the voting was:

Dr Young	100
Dr Cabbell	92
Dr Roget	51
Dr Harrison	4

The election had excited a great deal of interest, and commenting on it Young writes:[1]

There never was anything like the total number, and the contest has been almost unparalleled: any of the three candidates had advantages which would have secured him in any common case. Local interest and the protracted efforts of a whole family made the Cabbells very naturally confident of triumphant success; parliamentary influence and the natural wish to serve a man who is likely to be Lord Chancellor, made Sir S. Romilly's nephew very formidable; and for myself the event speaks. But it is remarkable what a variety of interests I have been obliged to bring into play; scarcely any one of my friends having procured for me more than two or three favourable answers, so that every one lamented how very little he could do; yet the aggregate was sufficient for the purpose. Mrs Young has emerged from death to life by the event of this contest.

Young seems to have been very happy in his relations with St George's Hospital. It was the hospital of the Hunters, with a great reputation, and contained about 250 beds. Young's portrait was painted by Sir Thomas Lawrence at the request of Hudson Gurney, and a copy of this picture by Brigstocke was presented to the Governors of St George's Hospital, and hangs in the Board Room. He retained his position as Physician until his death; and after he had abandoned private practice, he still did his regular round of patients.

It is interesting to note that, although he was on the staff for eighteen years, there is no mention of his name in the records of Governors' meetings until we come to the curt announcement on 13 May 1829 that 'the death of Dr Young, one of the Physicians to this Institution, having been announced, *ordered* That a special Court for the election of a Physician to this Institution in the place of Dr Young, deceased, be held. . . .'

There can be no doubt at all that Young was disappointed with what he regarded as his comparative failure as a medical practitioner, and that he was irritated by the popularity and success of some of his contemporaries, who seemed to achieve a success which, in his view, their attainments did not merit. This

[1] Peacock, *op. cit.* p. 221.

is amply borne out by his letters to Hudson Gurney, the earlier of which give expression to a moderate satisfaction, while the later ones indicate a deep sense of disappointment. Writing from London on 23 January 1816, he says:

It is singular how much you and I are contrasted in everything: you are generally out of humour with yourself, though you have great reason to be satisfied with others: I am abundantly disposed to give due weight to my own merits, but I feel nothing like an obligation to the world in general whom I cannot persuade to swallow my prescriptions with as much docility as they drink your beer; and in this point I must allow myself for your inferior: wisdom, like charity, begins at home; and I have no right to the consolation even of complaining of the public; for the public judgment must be influenced by some motives which have an extensive foundation in human nature, and which ought, therefore, to be foreseen and to regulate the conduct of those who are dependent on the public. I am not however quite so much humbled as to allow that I have miscalculated, on the great scale; it is only the magnitude of the fluctuations on each side of the average that surprises me; and although one knows that the ship is safe, it requires some nerve to be carried up and down so rapidly as will sometimes happen, without a little apprehension of touching bottom on some of the descents.

He sometimes remained in Worthing till very late in the season. Writing on 6 November 1816,[1] he says

I have had a tolerably prosperous season at Worthing, both in a professional point of view, and from having made several agreeable acquaintances; although I have every now and then been ashamed of the absurd motives from which people have shown me civilities: . . . I shall probably stay here just a fortnight longer, unless any good patient should choose to be very ill and detain me an additional week—but I shall certainly be in town by the end of the month.

Again he writes from Worthing on 21 October 1817:[2]

On the whole, however, I do not profess to be altogether discontented: my profession goes on quietly, but with tolerable success; I have no manner of motive for writing any more *medical* books. I am very well satisfied with those I have written; they have brought

---

[1] To Hudson Gurney.   [2] *Ibid.*

me some credit, but no new patients worth mentioning: though I suppose they will in due time if I persevere:

From this date there is a noticeable change in attitude. His connection with Worthing ceased in 1820. On 22 August of that year he finishes a letter[1] with the sentence:

Worthing is more dull than ever—I have been here 6 or 7 whole days only—and I find it quite a consolation to be without a single patient, except paupers.

On 4 September he writes from Tunbridge Wells:[2]

If I had any patients at Tunbridge I should not refuse to prescribe for them: but when I left Worthing it was upon the supposition that I had profited as much by a watering place as I was likely to do, and that it was time to consider myself as stationary in London the whole year round—so that I am now supposed to be taking a holiday for a few weeks. Besides, there are plenty of patient hunters here already.

Young's disillusionment with medical practice and his sense of disappointment comes out very clearly in a letter of 30 November 1822. Hudson Gurney had evidently written to him suggesting that he should write a popular book on the work he had done in Egyptian hieroglyphics, suggesting that if he did this under his own name instead of under a pseudonym it would enhance his reputation, and this would reflect itself in an increased medical practice. He replied:[3]

Well, I am not sure that I may not take your advice and for once throw away my cane and wig, and show my bare forehead to the public undefended and without disguise. But do not flatter yourself that I am persuaded by your arguments—though I daresay you are a very good arguer in the House of Commons. In my case I cannot think but that you are mistaken and if I do publish, as you suggest, a popular work on the Hieroglyphics—it will not be that I expect advantage from it in the pursuit of physic: but because I have *so little* to lose and so little to hope that the one is not worth keeping and the other not worth looking after. If I could only prolong my life to a few hundred years instead of fourscore or less, your view of

[1] To Hudson Gurney, 22 Aug. 1820.   [2] *Ibid.* 4 Sept. 1820.
[3] *Ibid.* 30 Nov. 1822.

the generalship to be adopted might be a very correct one, and it might be possible to force the public to believe me to be the most eligible physician to be consulted—and the profession to admit that the public is in the right. But it has taken me thirty or forty years to become at all known as a man of science and a scholar—it would take me fifty more to be allowed to be a good gentleman and lady's physician—and in the second century of my life the advantages would pour in upon me as rapidly as I could possibly devise for the comfort of my *third* century. But at the middle of the only century which concerns me, so far as relates to about two thirds or three fourths of its whole duration—when instead of a progressive advancement, in spite of all my subservience to the opinion of the public and the jealousy of my competitors, I have been for a few years gradually losing the little practice that the kindness of a few partial friends had procured me—would you have me go back to an attempt to establish a popularity upon general grounds, with the idea that it might *hereafter* be converted into a golden shower when I have had such ample experience of the effect of a partial and suppressed celebrity only?—No—if I do change my mode of proceeding—it will be from the intoxication of some occurrence like the present which will make me *throw away the camphor bag* and give way to the simple impulse of nature, even without much prospect of pleasure far less of any advantage to be obtained by my temerity.

Gurney's rejoinder to this letter thoroughly roused Young, and he replied[1] on 16 January 1823:

Your letter has so filled me with indignation that I cannot begin my *breakfast* till I have set an answer to it on the stocks. To think that we have lived so long together, and that you know me so little as to suppose that I am *irritated* because I have not *taken* with the public as an author—or that I ever wished to be as well known as Grimaldi or as Parson Sidney Smith—or in short that I care any other way for the *public* than as wishing them to take my *physic* as willingly and as universally as they take your *beer*. I do not pretend to be wholly without *vanity*—but I trust I have pride enough to combat its excess—and certainly if I seek for the approbation of others I hope I shall always feel that *satis est equitem mihi plaudere*.

It is difficult rightly to assess Young's real merit as a medical

---

[1] *Ibid.* 16 January 1823.

practitioner. Clearly his official position on the staff of St George's Hospital gave him every advantage; some of his predecessors and some of his successors had very large practices. He was widely read in medical literature, and had sat under some of the best teachers. He was also a man of undoubted ability. What then was lacking?

Peacock[1] quotes the apothecary of the Hospital as saying that a greater proportion of the patients admitted under Young were discharged cured, or perhaps in more correct language, relieved, than of those who were subjected to a more fashionable and energetic treatment. It is said also that an examination of the records of the Hospital showed that the prescriptions which were given by Young were such as 'approximated to the best practice of the day'. He attributes the lack of popularity to Young's manner, which he describes as 'gentle and gentlemanly but not genial', and to the fact that he would not use the many perfectly justifiable arts by which some physicians recommend themselves to their patients.

This analysis of the situation, with its implications, roused the indignation of Sir Benjamin Brodie, a colleague of Young on the staff of St George's. In his autobiography he writes:[2]

Young, one of the greatest philosophers of the age, and indeed second to none but Davy, never prospered as a physician. His biographer, Dr Peacock, has ascribed his failure to his being too good for his profession, and to his being above certain ignoble arts, which were, as he believed, made use of by his competitors, and he has availed himself of this opportunity of publishing a very illiberal tirade against those who belong to this division of the medical profession. Nothing can be more unjust than the whole of Dr Peacock's observations on this subject. There may be among physicians, as well as in other professions, some individuals who acquire a reputation to which they have no claim, but my experience justifies me in asserting that no physician acquires a *large* reputation, or retains what may be called an extensive practice, who is really unworthy of it. The public are, on the whole, pretty good judges in

---

[1] *Op. cit.* p. 224.
[2] *The Works of Sir Benjamin Collins Brodie*, collected and arranged by Charles Hawkins (London, 1865), pp. 91–2.

a matter in which they are so much interested, and if by any accident they have been led to give their confidence to a wrong person, they are seldom long in discovering and correcting their mistake. With regard to Dr Young, the truth is that either his mind, from it having been so long trained by the study of the more exact sciences, was not fitted for the profession which he had chosen, or that it was so much engrossed by other, and to him more interesting pursuits, that he never bestowed on it that constant and patient attention without which no one can be a great physician or a great statesman. The students at the hospital complained that they learned nothing from him. I never could discern that he kept any written notes of cases, and I doubt whether he ever thought of his cases in the hospital after he had left the wards. His medical writings were little more than compilations from books, with no indication of original research. I offer these observations as a matter of justice to others, and not in depreciation of Dr Young, for whom I had a great personal regard, whose vast and varied attainments out of his profession, and whose great original genius displayed in other ways, place him in the foremost rank of those whose names adorn the annals of our country. Dr Peacock mentions as a proof of his superiority as a physician, that the list of his hospital patients presented a larger proportion of cures than that of any of his colleagues. I doubt not that the statement is true, but the conclusion from it is wrong. Hospital patients as well as private patients have their preferences, and those who labour under dangerous diseases will take some trouble to be admitted under the care of the physician or surgeon in whom they repose the greatest confidence; while those whose ailments are less important are contented to take their chance of being admitted under one person or under another. Moreover, many patients are sent to a hospital by private practitioners, and it is no matter of wonder that those who, if they themselves laboured under severe illness, would consult not Young, but Chambers or Nevinson, showed the same preference as to poor persons in whom they were interested.

This rather unsympathetic judgment is supported by Munk.[1] Dr Young

did not shine at the bedside or in the practical work of his profession, and was but little followed by pupils in the wards. His colleagues

[1] William Munk, *Roll of the Royal College of Physicians of London* (2nd ed., London, 1878), vol. III, p. 82.

and contemporaries failed to discover that success and excellence in
his treatment of disease, which his biographer, Dr Peacock, would
claim for him.

Perhaps the most balanced judgment is that of Pettigrew:[1]

He was not a popular physician. He wanted that confidence or
assurance which is so necessary to the successful exercise of his
profession. He was perhaps too deeply informed, and therefore too
sensible of the difficulty of arriving at true knowledge in the
profession of medicine, hastily to form a judgment; and his great
love of and adherence to truth made him often hesitate where others
felt no difficulty whatever in the expression of their opinion. He is,
therefore, not celebrated as a medical practitioner; nor did he ever
enjoy an extensive practice; but in information upon the subjects of
his profession, in depth of research into the history of diseases and
the opinions of all who have preceded him it would be difficult to
find his equal.

When Young published his *Lectures in Natural Philosophy* in
1807 (see pp. 128-42), he devoted the second volume to an annotated catalogue of all the important works that had been published dealing with each part of the subject. He conceived the
idea of a similar work on medicine about the same time, and in
the intervening years he collected his material. In 1813 there
appeared his *Introduction to Medical Literature*. It was dedicated
to the Governors of St George's Hospital, and nothing like it
had appeared before in English. Ploucquet's *Literatura medica
digesta*, of which a second edition had appeared in 1810 published at Tübingen, was very comprehensive, but quite undis-
criminating. Works good and bad, old and new, were included
without any guidance to the prospective reader. Nor was it a
classified list. The basis of Young's book was a new Nosology,
or systematic classification of all known diseases. He was
dissatisfied with the existing classification devised by Cullen,
and set himself to apply the general principles used by Linnaeus
in Botany. It was characterized by the *Quarterly Review*[2] as
'the most exact and practical nosology which has hitherto been
submitted to public attention'. Under each disease is set out a

[1] Pettigrew, *op. cit.* p. 9.   [2] *Quarterly Review*, IX (1813), p. 117.

list of the important works, pamphlets, papers, etc. bearing on it. The list runs into thousands, and is an interesting indication of the scope of Young's reading, for the works referred to are not only listed, but assessed and sometimes summarized.

I have inserted no books but such as I conceive to be necessary to a complete medical library: those which are of the most established importance are distinguished by an asterisk; and those which every student ought to think himself obliged to peruse, in the course of his regular studies, by capital letters. Perhaps both of these distinctions ought to have been somewhat more liberally bestowed. . . . I have also distinguished another class of books and papers, by printing the names of their authors in Italics; these I consider as extremely deserving of attention, although not absolutely indispensable to every medical student.[1]

Occasionally we find notes interpolated based on his own clinical experience, and it is interesting to find his judgment on his own books. The syllabus of his lectures at the Middlesex Hospital appears as 'Young's syllabus of a course of lectures on the elements of the medical sciences, 8. Lond. 1809'[2]—no capitals, no asterisk, no italics! On the other hand, we find also 'Young's course of lectures on natural philosophy 2v. 4. Lond. 1807.' This time the author's name appears in italics, and this note is added:

Probably contains as much of natural philosophy as is absolutely necessary for a medical student; and with respect to the fundamental doctrines of chemistry, enters into an examination of the constitution of matter, of the phenomenon of heat and of electrochemical science.

This is a very modest estimate of the scope of his *Lectures*, as we shall see; and the medical student of today would be appalled at the suggestion that he should cover this ground for the Physics of his First M.B.

At the end of the general list of diseases there is a short section of what might be called occupational diseases, where works are quoted which deal with the diseases of Princes, Men of the World, Men of Letters, Comedians, Artisans, Labourers,

---

[1] T. Young, *Introduction to Medical Literature* (London, 1813), Preface, p. xv.
[2] *Ibid.* p. 52.

G

Poor, Army, Seamen and Prisoners. There follows a short section on drugs, a series of chemical tables, and a 'Sketch of Animal Chemistry', with extracts translated from the works of the Swedish chemist, Berzelius.

One of the most interesting sections of the book is that entitled 'Remarks on the Measurement of Minute Particles, especially those of blood and of pus'. In the course of his work on optics he had studied the coloured rings—sometimes called haloes or coronae or glories—which may be observed surrounding a small bright source of light when seen through a cloud or fog of small drops or particles. The more uniform the particles the more distinct are the rings; the smaller the particles the larger are the rings. The same appearance is produced by a collection of fine fibres, for example, in a lock of wool, and in this case the size of the rings is a measure of the thickness of the fibres. Young thus describes the phenomenon and the instrument based on it:[1]

Where, however, the greater number of the particles are nearly equal in dimensions, the luminous object viewed through them exhibits a much more striking appearance, for it is surrounded by rings of colours, somewhat resembling those of the rainbow, but differently arranged, and often beautifully brilliant. The blood, a little diluted, always exhibits them in great perfection. . . . A minute quantity of the fluid to be examined in this manner may be put between two small pieces of plate glass, and if we hold the glass close to the eye, and look through it at a distant candle with a dark object behind it, the appearance, if the globules are present, will be so conspicuous as to leave no doubt respecting their existence. . . . The rings of colour, which are here employed to discover the existence of a number of equal particles, may also be employed for measuring the comparative and the real dimensions of these particles, or of any pulverised or fibrous substances which are sufficiently uniform in their diameters. Immediately about the luminous object we see a light area, terminating in a reddish dark margin, then a ring of bluish green, and without it a ring of red; and the alternations of green and red are often repeated several times, where the particles or fibres are sufficiently uniform. I observed some years ago that

[1] Young, *op. cit.* pp. 574–5.

these rings were the larger as the particles or fibres affording them were smaller, but that they were always of the same magnitude for the same particles. It is therefore only necessary to measure the angular magnitude of these rings, or of any one of them, in order to identify the size of the particles which afford them: and having once established a scale, from an examination of a sufficient number of substances of known dimensions, we may thus determine the actual magnitude of any other substances which exhibit the colours. The limit between the first green ring and the red which surrounds it, affords the best standard of comparison. . . . Such an instrument I have called an Eriometer, from its utility in measuring the fibres of wool, and I have given directions for making it to Mr Fidler of Foley St. . . . The luminous point is afforded by a perforation of a brass plate, which is surrounded by a circle of minute holes; the substance to be examined is fixed on some wires, which are carried by a slider. . . . The slider is drawn out to such a distance as to exhibit the required coincidence, and the index then shows the number representing the magnitude of the substance examined.[1]

A similar account of the instrument appears in a letter from Young to Sir Joseph Banks written from Worthing, 10 September 1810.[2] It begins:

'Dear Sir—Observing from the papers that you have been interesting yourself respecting the arrangement of a micrometer for the purpose of measuring the diameter of the fibres of different kinds of wool, I beg leave to trouble you with the description of a very simple instrument which I invented some time ago for a similar purpose, and which I propose to call an agricultural micrometer.

The instrument has also been described by W. H. Bragg.[3]

Fig. 1 illustrates the arrangement when in adjustment. *A* is the specimen, and *B* is the brass plate; *b* is the central perforation, and *C C* two of the small perforations. *S* is the source of light. The eye is placed close to *A* so as to view *B* through it.

---

[1] Three of these instruments are now in the possession of Mr Philip Young of Mangotsfield.

[2] Bence Jones, *The Royal Institution, its Founder and its first Professors* (1871). The original letter (British Museum Add. MSS, 33982, f.9.) contains a very simple form of the instrument composed of two pieces of card and a tape measure.

[3] *Universe of Light*, p. 152, and *Proc. Roy. Inst.*, vol. XXVI, p. 492.

The distance between *A* and *B* is varied until the required coloured ring coincides with the ring of perforations.

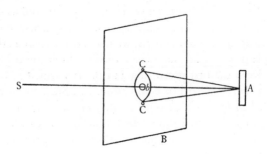

Fig. 1. Diagram of Eriometer

In Fig. 1 if *d* is the distance between *A* and *B*, and *a* the radius of the circle of small perforations, then *d* is what Young chooses as his scale number (i.e. the cotangent of the angular radius of the ring). He gives a series of values for milk, blood, various fine seeds such as *Lycoperdon bovista* (puff ball) and *Lycopodium*, and also a series of values for wools. Of these the one for the blood corpuscles, diluted by serum only, which he finds to be 8, is the most interesting.

When it comes to a matter of translating these comparative measurements into actual values, he says:

The theory, which suggested to me the construction of the eriometer, requires some corrections in its immediate applications, which depend upon circumstances not completely understood: at present therefore I shall only employ, for the determination of the true value of the numbers of its scale, an experimental comparison of its indications with some microscopical measurements, which Dr Wollaston has been so good as to perform for me, with an admirably accurate micrometer of his own invention![1]

From Wollaston's observations on the seed of *Lycoperdon bovista*, on blood, and on a coil of very fine wire, which gave a series of consistent results, Young found that, to get the measure-

[1] *Op. cit.* p. 577.

PLATE I

ERIOMETER

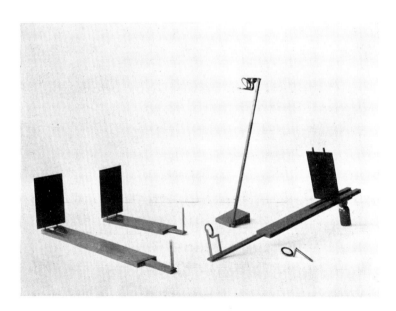

ERIOMETERS MADE AND USED BY YOUNG

ments in inches, he had to divide the scale number by 28,800. Taking his figure of 8 for the red corpuscles of human blood, we find the value .000226 in. or .00072 cm. This simple, original and ingenious method of measuring the size of particles has since been applied by other investigators. It was used by A. Pijper[1] and W. G. Millar.[2] More recently, W. F. Emmons[3] has adapted the principle for clinical use, and has devised the very simple and portable form of the instrument shown in Fig. 2.[4]

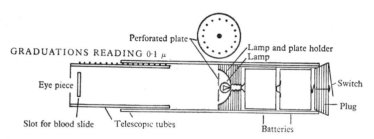

Fig. 2. Emmons's adapted Eriometer

It consists of two telescopic tubes. The larger, 10 inches in length, is fitted with two small dry cells, and with electric bulb and switch, like an ordinary flashlight. Immediately in front of the electric filament is placed a disk perforated near its periphery centre. The other tube, which telescopes completely into the first, carries the blood-slide and is graduated to read directly the diameter of the cells in the smear.

Emmons's value for the normal blood cells by this method is .00079 cm., checked by another method .000795 cm., and he gives the textbook value as .00078 cm. Further clinical studies, using the eriometer, are given by Emmons.[5] It will be seen how close to these values Young's figure of .00072 cm. lies.

Wool fibres differ in diameter from point to point, and differ among themselves. There is therefore a great deal to be said for an instrument which automatically gives an *average*, as the

[1] *Lancet*, 2 (1924), 367. [2] *Proc. Roy. Soc.* B 99 (1926), 264.
[3] *Quarterly Journal of Medicine*, 21 (1927), 83. [4] *Ibid.* 21 (1927), 86, Fig. 4.
[5] *Journal of Physiology*, 64 (1927), 215.

eriometer does. Yet no use seems to have been made of the
eriometer for the purpose after which it was named. In Young's
own article on Chromatics[1] (see pp. 284-306) we find a suggested
explanation of the neglect of the instrument.

Dr Young has made this appearance the foundation of a mode of
measuring the fineness of wool, which he has recommended for
agricultural purposes, though it seems hitherto to have been found
much too delicate to be employed by 'the hard hands of peasants'
with any advantage.

The last section of the book is a very interesting essay on the
Medical Effects of Climates, in which, however, there is
nothing very new or striking.

This summary will perhaps give some idea of the importance
and scope of Young's *Introduction to Medical Literature*, and when
we come to consider the other achievements of his first thirteen
years after leaving Emmanuel, we shall begin to see him in his
true proportions.

The book was favourably but not uncritically reviewed in
the *Quarterly Review* for March 1813. After dealing with the
contents at some length the article ended with what was undoubtedly very high praise, but not altogether undeserved.

The style throughout is clear and polished; refined without affectation, and easy without the sacrifice of dignity and correctness. It
may be regarded both as an example and incitement to the introduction of a more finished mode of writing in medical compositions.
We are not pronouncing too favourably of this work, when we
express our confidence that, stored with such valuable learning and
information, and enriched with such advantages of method and
composition, it will not only be resorted to as a direction to students,
but will find its way, as a book of reference, into the hand of the
enlightened physician. It is no less a guide to youth, than a staff to
age; and both descriptions of practitioners are under great obligations
to the author for this productive effort of talent, labour and
erudition.

Even had the praise been much more exaggerated and fulsome
than in point of fact it was, it offered no excuse for the attitude

---

[1] *Works of Young*, vol. I, pp. 284 ff.

of the *Edinburgh Medical and Surgical Journal*, one of the leading medical periodicals of the time. This journal had been rather depreciatory and quite unfair in its notice of his Croonian Lecture of 1808:[1]

The little that is known on this subject, however, has not been derived from the mathematical school, but from the experiments of Hales, Haller, Senac, Hunter and Jones; who not content with calculating upon what has been already known, determined to discover something new.

It now published a long review of the *Introduction to Medical Literature*, beginning with this rather ill-natured paragraph:[2]

If we have experienced considerable disappointment in the perusal of this elaborate volume, it may partly be attributed to the circumstance, that our expectations had been previously raised to a high pitch, by the splendid eulogium which some injudicious friend, apparently possessed of more zeal in favour of the author, than of sound medical knowledge, has thought proper to pass upon the work, in a recent London review. Such partial and exaggerated praise is pregnant with injustice both to the author and the public, and savours much of the vulgar art of puffing, which is so well understood in these venal times. The author himself, indeed, has disclaimed all pretensions to that perfection, which his friend ascribes to his publication, as 'absolutely unattainable in a work of this kind'; and he cannot, therefore, be gratified, or even flattered, by what himself has averred to be untrue.

It ended a very critical review, in which some quite unfounded charges were levelled against Young, with the words:

At the same time, they [i.e. Young's professional brethren] cannot but be thankful to the author for the useful compilation with which his industry has now supplied them.

Although Young was himself a trenchant and even merciless critic of others, he was peculiarly sensitive to criticism himself. We have seen how critical he was of his teachers, and we shall see later that his sweeping criticism of others created difficulties and raised enmities that had serious consequences. Yet any

[1] *Edinburgh Medical and Surgical Journal*, VI (1810), 190.
[2] *Ibid.* IX (1813), 463.

criticism of his own work which seemed to him in the least degree unjust provoked in him a desire to refute it, and involved him in controversy. He was not a good controversialist. His style was too laboured and too ponderous, as the following extracts will show. They are taken from 'A letter to the Editors of *A Medical and Surgical Journal*.'[1] Whether the letter was ever sent is uncertain.

Gentlemen,

Notwithstanding that I have been so unfortunate as to incur your displeasure, by involuntarily becoming the object of some very high encomiums, which have been bestowed on me, perhaps too lavishly, in a popular review, while, as you have clearly proved from my own words, the nature of the subject itself rendered perfection unattainable, I still depend so much on your regard for your own general character, which I am by no means disposed to depreciate, as to believe that you will take the earliest opportunity to correct a very important error, into which you have fallen, in asserting, that I have recommended to a student of physic to attend an hospital 'in the second year *only*' of his medical studies. Now, in the 18th page of my Essay you will find these words: 'As the spring advances, he must become a pupil of an hospital, which must continue to be his principle and *daily* object at *every subsequent* period, *while* practical lectures should be attended with diligence'; and these lectures are enumerated in the following page, among the pursuits of the third year. The public must be the judges between us: and how you will be able to exculpate yourselves before them for so unaccountable a misrepresentation, which you have expanded into a whole page of argument, I am utterly at a loss to foresee. You have either censured what you have not read, or what you have read and forgotten: for I cannot believe you both mischievous and foolish enough to advance such an accusation, at the moment that you were fully aware of its falsehood.

Whether or no you were in the same happy predicament of inattention or oblivion when you asserted that I spoke '*lightly* of the clinical lectures of Edinburgh', I will not pretend to determine: perhaps you will solemnly maintain that to mention in express terms their '*excellence*', and their '*acknowledged superiority*' (p. 15) is to speak lightly of them; but this is more a matter of opinion than

[1] Printed as an appendix in the second edition of the book.

the former, and therefore I shall not expect you to retract it. It is, however, an absolute mis-statement to say that I have considered the affections comprehended under the term PNEUSIS as one DISEASE; for I have most carefully remarked (p. 28) that I have intentionally united *different* diseases, as species constituting the same *genus*, according to their natural analogies, and to the most convenient mode of treating of them; nor have you been more correct in insinuating that the gout is to be found in two places, without *any* reference from one to the other; for in fact there are references in *both* the passages, in which I have thought it necessary to mention respectively the different forms of this very anomalous disease. . . . I have not indeed professed myself by any means satisfied with the arrangement of this division of my work, which, however, I am happy to find you have thought more deserving of your indulgence than the rest; for, however I may think the value of your commendations diminished by the want of a sounder spirit of criticism, and a greater power of discrimination, than you appear to me to have displayed in your censures, I do not profess to be altogether indifferent to your good opinion.

I am, Gentlemen,
Your very obedient Servant,

Worthing, 21 Oct. 1813.　　　　　THOMAS YOUNG

At this time he had in mind to follow up this general work with a series of special treatises on the various classes of diseases, but even before the first of these was published, he had come to the conclusion that the task was beyond even his powers, and must be left to be completed by others. He did make a beginning, however, with his work on *Consumptive Diseases*. The exhaustive nature of this little treatise is strongly emphasized by Pettigrew:[1]

There is not an author of any note or celebrity—there is not a point connected with the disease which merits attention, that is not there most carefully, most accurately put forth. It is a medical library upon the subject of which it treats; the whole body of ancient and modern medicine in relation to Consumption is included within the small compass of an octavo volume. There are but two medical works in the English language entitled to this distinction, Dr Young's

---

[1] Pettigrew, *op. cit.* pp. 9–10.

on Consumptive Diseases, and Dr Cooke's on Nervous Diseases. Each has proceeded from a most distinguished scholar, and each gives in a condensed form an original and authentic abstract of all preceding authors on the subject of the particular diseases which form the topics of their consideration.

Even the *Edinburgh Medical and Surgical Journal* forgot its old animosities, and gave the book high praise. It concluded its review with this tribute:[1]

The second part of our author's production, which occupies more than three-fourths of the volume, admits of no analysis or abridgment, but stands unrivalled in the literary history of medicine, for its accuracy and utility. It is not a mere catalogue of dissertations or titles of books, copied from preceding compilers for the twentieth time, but is a real condensation or selection from the original authors, of every fact worth preserving on the subject. It thus almost supersedes the necessity of perusing any of the preceding authors, and is, in itself, a complete library in regard to consumption.

Referring to this book, he writes to Hudson Gurney:

My friends say what friends usually do on such occasions; but I have not had a greater proportion of consumptive cases among my patients than usual, though the season has been a tolerably fair one.

In 1821 we find him preparing a second edition of his *Introduction to Medical Literature*. Writing to Hudson Gurney on 3 January 1821, he says:

I am in no very urgent haste, having plenty of employment for a month or two in preparing my Medical Literature for a second edition. I have sold the copyright to William Phillips for the vast sum of £100—which as I got nothing by the first edition, I was very ready to accept—though friend Phillips himself said he was ashamed to offer a sum so disproportionate to the intrinsic merit of the work, and the labour of compiling it, especially as he said authors very often very *sensitive* upon such points—but I told him I was not at all sensitive, and closed immediately with his proposal. The lectures [? the Royal Institution Lectures] he said were too good a book, and that was the true reason why they did not sell. In

---

[1] *Edinburgh Medical and Surgical Journal*, XIII (1817), p. 501.

short, I think if I happen to live to be about 200, I shall begin to reap some little credit and emolument from the labours of my youth—but at 100 I shall be still a boy in public opinion.

The book was published in 1823, and contained two important additions, one being the Croonian Lecture for 1808 brought up to date, and the other an essay on 'Palpitation'.

When Young took his M.D. degree at Cambridge in 1808 the subject of his thesis was 'Inflamation'. It has not been preserved, but it gave rise to the Croonian Lecture just referred to. He found that to discuss the subject adequately he required more knowledge of the motion of fluids in pipes than he had so far acquired. He therefore devoted himself for a short period to this subject, and on 5 May 1808 read a paper to the Royal Society called 'Hydraulic Investigations'. In this he examines critically an empirical formula for the flow of a liquid in a pipe, which had just then been published by Dubuat. The experiments on which the formula was based are re-examined, and the results of some other investigators brought under consideration. As a result a new formula is suggested. The resistance to fluid motion due to a bend in a pipe or river and the propagation of an impulse through an elastic tube form the subjects of two other sections. The paper is a closely reasoned one, based for the most part on the work of other observers. No account of any work of his own is given, although the results of some experiments he made are quoted. The whole paper, however, was avowedly a preparation for the Croonian Lecture which he delivered to the Royal Society on 10 November of the same year (1808), 'On the Functions of the Heart and Arteries'. Here he applied the results of his excursions into the subject of hydraulics to a development of our knowledge of the circulation of the blood, and in particular to controvert the view then widely held that the peristaltic contraction of the walls of the arteries was an important cause of the circulation. It concludes with this modest claim:

Although the arguments, which I have advanced, appear to me sufficient to prove that, in the ordinary state of the circulation, the muscular powers of the arteries have very little effect in propelling

V

THE HUMAN EYE

'An organ that exhibits to an attentive observer, an arrangement of various substances, so correctly and delicately adapted to the purposes of the sense of vision, that we cannot help admiring, at every step, the wisdom by which each part is adjusted to the rest.' YOUNG

YOUNG has been hailed as the father of physiological optics. Perhaps this is a little unfair to some of his distinguished predecessors. The eye was first described in considerable detail by Alhazen in his *Opticae Thesaurus*, and many of the Latin names which he gave to the parts of the eye are still universally used. Among other early workers who made some contribution to the subject are Franciscus Maurolycus (1494–1577), Johann Kepler (1571–1630), C. Scheiner (1575–1650), René Descartes (1596–1650), and Christian Huygens (1629–95). It may be more fairly said that these predecessors cleared the site, and that Young, in his paper on 'The Mechanism of the Eye', read to the Royal Society on 27 November 1800, and published in 1801,[1] laid the foundations. It is a remarkable paper, breaking quite new ground in many respects and recording practical measurements whose accuracy has stood the test of time.

It will be remembered that Young's earliest scientific paper dealt with the accommodation of the eye for vision at different distances, and the circumstances in which he returned to this subject are set out in the opening sentences of his paper.

In the year 1793, I had the honour of laying before the Royal Society some observations on the faculty by which the eye accommodates itself to the perception of objects at different distances. The opinion which I then entertained, although it had never been placed exactly in the same light, was neither so new, nor so much forgotten,

---

[1] *Phil. Trans.* 92 (1801), 23.

as was supposed by myself, and by most of those with whom I had any intercourse on the subject. Mr Hunter, who had long before formed a similar opinion, was still less aware of having been anticipated in it, and was engaged, at the time of his death, in an investigation of the facts relative to it; an investigation for which, as far as physiology was concerned, he was undoubtedly well qualified. Mr Home, with the assistance of Mr Ramsden, continued the inquiry which Mr Hunter had begun; and the results of his experiments appeared very satisfactorily to confute the hypothesis of the muscularity of the crystalline lens. I therefore thought it incumbent on me to take the earliest opportunity of testifying my persuasion of the justice of Mr Home's conclusions, which I accordingly mentioned in a Dissertation published at Göttingen in 1796 and also an Essay presented to the Society last year. About three months ago, I was induced to resume the subject, by perusing Dr Porterfield's paper on the internal motions of the eye; and I have very unexpectedly made some observations, which I think I may venture to say, appear to be finally conclusive in favour of my former opinion, as far as that opinion attributed to the lens a power of changing its figure.

In order to understand the work of Young on the eye it is necessary to have a clear idea of its optical structure. The essential parts for our purpose are shown in Fig. 3.

A, B, C and D all play their part in focusing on the retina E an image of any object to which the eye is directed, and ideally all the rays which leave any one point on the object and pass through the pupil are brought to coincide at one point on the retina; so that there is a point-to-point correspondence between object and image.

Young's paper begins with the discussion of some general theorems on the refraction of light, and then proceeds to describe his special form of the optometer, earlier forms of which had been used by Scheiner and by Porterfield. If the eye be focused on the middle point B of three points, A, B and C at different distances on its axis, and a card D with two pinholes close together be held close to the eye, then two rays from B will enter the eye through the pinholes and converge to its image B' on the retina. If this focus be maintained the retina will not be at the right distance from the lens to focus *A*. Its image *A'* will be formed in front of the retina, and the two rays will fall on the retina at different points, thus making

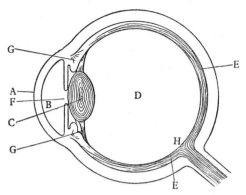

Fig. 3. The Eye

A is the outer transparent cover, the *cornea*.

B is a space filled with a fluid called the *aqueous humour*.

C is the *crystalline lens*, an elastic, jelly-like body.

D is a space filled with another fluid, the *vitreous humour*.

E is the sensitive coating of the inside of the eye—the *retina*.

F is the *pupil*, an adjustable diaphragm which regulates the amount of light entering the system.

G are the *ciliary muscles* which adjust the power of the lens, but whose function was unknown to Young.

H is the blind spot where the optic nerve enters the retina.

A appear double. Similarly the image *C'* of the point *C* will be formed behind the retina, and the rays will converge towards this point again meeting the retina in two points and making *C* appear double.

If the object be at the point of perfect vision, the image on the retina will be single; but in every other case, the image being double, we shall appear to see a double object: and if we look at a line pointed nearly to the eye, it will appear as two lines, crossing each other in the point of perfect vision. For this purpose, the holes may be converted into slits, which render the images nearly as distinct, at the same time that they admit more light.

The normal eye in repose is focused for distance, and to observe an object close to the eye an effort is required. The normal eye cannot comfortably focus for an object much

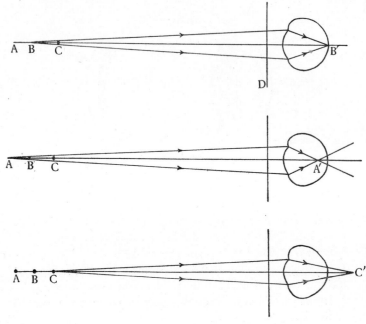

Fig. 4. Action of Optometer

closer than 10 in. (25 cm.), and this is now usually regarded as the 'near-point' or nearest point of comfortably distinct vision.

In principle the use of the optometer is simple. The subject places the eye to be tested close to the slits and allows the eye to relax. The point on which his eye is now focused is the farthest point which he can see distinctly—i.e. his 'far-point'. It is the point at which the two lines he sees intersect and as the instrument is graduated he can read off this distance. He now endeavours to focus on a nearer point and as he does so the intersection of the two lines approaches him. When he has brought it as near as he comfortably can he reads its position on the graduated scale. This is his 'near-point', and this, with his 'far-point', determines his range of accommodation.

In practice, two difficulties arise—one easily overcome and one inherent in the use of all optometers. The first is the difficulty that normally the 'far-point' is at an infinite distance and we cannot have a base line to look at which is infinitely long. To deal with this difficulty a converging lens is used close to the slits. Light coming from a point at the focus of this lens will enter the eye as a parallel beam—i.e. as if it came from an infinite distance. If then the lines seen when the lens is used intersect at a distance equal to the focal length of the lens then the 'far-point' is at infinity and the eye is, in this respect, normal. The scale is then graduated so as to show the equivalent distance of each point, as modified by the lens, and not merely its actual distance. The second difficulty very disturbing to the subject is that of maintaining the eye relaxed and preventing involuntary changes of focus. Young obviously met this difficulty because he says: 'Few can bring their eyes at pleasure to the state of full action, or of perfect relaxation.'

The instrument is shown in Fig. 5, taken from Young's paper. He used a lens of four inches focus, so that the infinitely distant point is four inches from the lens. One scale gives actual distances and one equivalent distances calculated for the use of the lens. The two outside scales give focal lengths of spectacle lenses required to give an abnormal eye the normal near-point and the normal far-point. Young took the normal near-point to be at 8 inches from the eye instead of the 10 inches now usually adopted.

To measure the range of accommodation he calculated the focal length of the spectacle lens which, when the eye remained

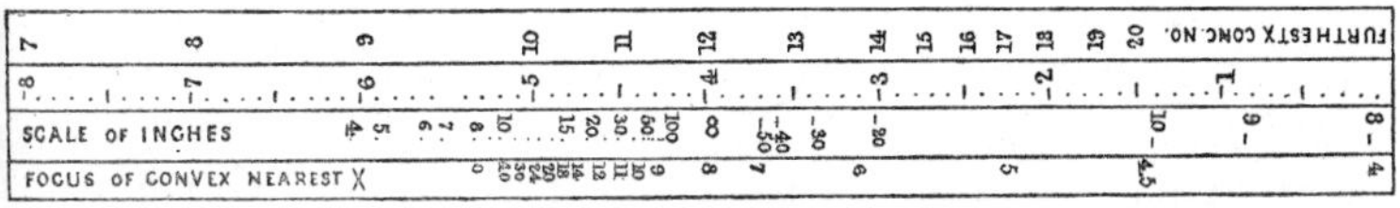

Fig. 5. The Optometer

relaxed, would be required to change from the far-point to the near-point. It is usual now to specify range of accommodation by the *power* of the lens required rather than by its *focal length*.

H

To calculate the power we state the focal length in metres and take its reciprocal and this gives us the power in 'dioptres'. Thus Young finds the focal length of lens required for his own eye to be 4 inches. This is a little over 0.1 metre and the power is therefore 10 dioptres. He notes, quite rightly, that the faculty 'diminishes in some degree as persons advance in life'. It is, as a matter of fact, as high as 12 or 14 in children, drops to about 2 at age 50 and has almost disappeared at age 70. The change takes place mainly in the distance of the near-point.

I have not given Young's own description of his optometer, having been warned by a letter which appeared in the *Philosophical Magazine* some 45 years later. It reads as follows:[1]

However eminent the abilities of the late Dr Young, he certainly did not study the art of writing in such a style, that not only he *might possibly be understood* by those of his readers who comprehended the subject nearly as well as himself, but that he *could not possibly be misunderstood* by any one of ordinary capacity and attention—an invaluable art, too little attended to by English philosophers. . . . To use a homely but forcible comparison, I would say, Dr Young, being himself 'in the ship of science', seems to expect that 'the disciple can arrive there without a boat'. A few lucid paragraphs would furnish the boats on this occasion. . . .

I cannot find that anyone attempted to respond to this appeal so I have tried to 'furnish the boats'.

Having described his optometer, Young's next step was to give measurements of the various dimensions of the eye.

Being convinced of the advantage of making every observation with as little assistance as possible, I have endeavoured to confine most of my experiments to my own eyes; and I shall, in general, ground my calculations on the supposition of an eye similar to my own. I shall, therefore, first endeavour to ascertain all its dimensions, and all its faculties. For measuring the diameters, I fix a small key on each point of a pair of compasses; and I can venture to bring the rings into immediate contact with the sclerotica (the covering of the eye). . . . With an eye less prominent, this method might not have succeeded!

This rather drastic method of measurement in which he turned

[1] *Phil. Mag.* 26 (1845), 436.

his eye inwards as far as possible, pushed the ring of one key in at the back until the phantom (the bright ring produced by its pressure on the retina) was central, and then adjusted the other key to touch the front of the cornea, could not have been either pleasant or easy. By means of it he measured the length of the eyeball and the curvature of the cornea, and his measurements were extraordinarily accurate. The following table compares Young's results with those given by Southall.[1]

	Young	Southall
Length of Optic Axis	23 mm.	24 mm.
Radius of Curvature of Cornea	7.87 mm.	7. 70 mm.

Going on to experiment with the optometer to determine the far-point of his own eye, Young made an important discovery:

My eye, in a state of relaxation, collects to a focus on the retina, those rays which diverge vertically from an object at the distance of ten inches from the cornea, and the rays which diverge horizontally from an object at seven inches distance. For, if I hold the plane of the optometer vertically, the images of the line appear to cross at ten inches; if horizontally at seven. I have never experienced any inconvenience from this imperfection, nor did I ever discover it till I made these experiments; and I believe I can examine minute objects with as much accuracy as most of those whose eyes are differently formed.

This is the first recognition of that painfully common defect known as astigmatism. According to the statistical information compiled in recent years, at least half of all the cases of poor eyesight with less than normal acuity of vision are due to this defect.[2] It becomes a source of eye-strain with all its unpleasant consequences. Where, as in Young's case, the far-point is at a different distance when measured with the plane of the optometer horizontal from what it is with the plane of the optometer vertical, then the pencil of light that passes from the lens of the eye to the retina is 'astigmatic'—i.e. cannot be brought to a point, and so the image of an object is always fuzzy. If it is

[1] J. P. C. Southall, *Introduction to Physical Optics* (Oxford, 1937).
[2] *Ibid.* p. 144.

possible to focus a vertical line sharply, then all horizontal lines will be fuzzy, and vice-versa. The two lines of which this is true are usually horizontal and vertical, but not always so. They are, however, always at right angles to one another and this forms the basis of the common test applied by the optician. He presents the patient with a card showing a series of radiating black lines. Most patients find that one particular line seems sharp and the line at right angles seems fuzzy. Not many of the millions who now have their astigmatism corrected by spectacles realize that they owe the discovery of the defect from which they suffer to Thomas Young.

Young showed that the defect would be produced if the lens of the eye was oblique to the axis and that it could be corrected by using spectacle lenses set obliquely in such a way as to counteract the obliquity of the lens of the eye. He found that some people were in the habit of improving their vision by this device. The defect is most commonly due to the fact that some of the refracting surfaces of the eye are not spherical. Sir George Airy had one eye so badly astigmatic as to be unusable, and showed in 1825 that astigmatism could be corrected by the use of cylindrical lenses. He had such a lens made for himself by Fuller, an Ipswich optician, in 1827. Cylindrical lenses (as now used) were seldom prescribed or supplied, however, until the second half of the nineteenth century.[1]

Young showed further that where light rays fell obliquely on the eye they gave rise to astigmatism even if all the refracting surfaces were truly spherical and correctly orientated. Perfect vision is therefore only possible near the centre of the field of vision. He measured the degree of astigmatism for his own eye, using pencils of various obliquities.

Two other defects which the eye shares with all lenses he investigated. The first of these—known as spherical aberration —is due to the fact that the peripheral portions of a lens act as if they belonged to a lens of greater power. Thus rays coming through the marginal portions are focused nearer the lens than those coming through the central portions. It is for this reason

[1] *Encyc. Brit.* (14th ed.), vol. XXI, p. 178.

that we 'stop down' a camera lens to improve the definition. Young adapted the optometer to test for this defect but found his own eyes fairly free.

The other—known as chromatic aberration—is due to the fact that violet rays are more strongly refracted than red rays so that the lens splits up the white light coming from a point and focuses the violet nearer to the lens than the red. It is this defect that accounts for the red and blue coloured borders which sometimes surround objects seen through cheap or old-fashioned field glasses. Young established the existence of this phenomenon in the case of the eye and obtained a rough measurement of its magnitude.

From this point Young proceeds to the most important section of the paper—the reconsideration of the explanation of the process of accommodation put forward in his earlier communication. Taking the range of accommodation, measured with the optometer, for his own eyes and for those of a number of other subjects, he calculates the changes necessary to produce this effect on four hypotheses: (a) that the curvature of the cornea changes; (b) that the length of the eyeball changes; (c) that changes (a) and (b) occur at the same time; (d) that the crystalline lens changes its shape. Starting with (a) he quotes the results of a series of experiments all indicating that no change in the cornea takes place. He then adds his most conclusive experiment. The cornea acts as a refracting surface and adds to the power of the lens of the eye because at that surface the light rays pass from air to the 'aqueous humour' contained between the cornea and the lens. If there were aqueous humour on both sides of the cornea it would cause no refraction and contribute nothing to the power of the lens system. Now optically the aqueous humour is very nearly equivalent to water, so that if the eye is immersed in water the refraction of the cornea is eliminated. Young found that when his eye was immersed in water he could no longer focus sharply (as those who swim under water well know); but when he placed in front of his eye a lens of the same power as the cornea whose action he had eliminated he could again focus sharply. He found that the power of accommodation was the same as before. It could not, therefore, be due to changes taking place in the cornea. He thus describes this crucial experiment:

But a much more accurate and decisive experiment remains. I take out of a small botanical microscope, a double convex lens, of eight-tenths radius and focal distance, fixed in a socket one-fifth of an inch in depth; securing its edges with wax, I drop into it a little water, nearly cold, till it is three fourths full, and then apply it to my eye, so that the cornea enters halfway into the socket, and is every-where in contact with the water. My eye immediately becomes presbyopic,[1] and the refractive power of the lens, which is reduced by the water to a focal length of about 16 tenths is not sufficient to supply the place of the cornea, rendered inefficacious by the inter-ventions of the water; but the addition of another lens of five inches and a half focus, restores my eye to its natural state and somewhat more. I then apply the optometer, and I find the same inequality in the horizontal and vertical refractions as without the water;[2] and I have, in both directions, a power of accommodation equivalent to a focal length of four inches, as before. . . . After this it is almost necessary to apologize for having stated the former experiments; but, in so delicate a subject, we cannot have too great a variety of concurring evidence.

Having thus ruled out the cornea as an effective agent in the process of accommodation, Young now goes on to consider the possibility of a change in the length of the eyeball. Among other experiments to test this point we find the following:

Another test, and a much more delicate one, was the application of the ring of a key at the external angle, when the eye was turned as much inwards as possible, and confined at the same time by a strong oval iron ring, pressed against it at the internal angle. The key was forced in as far as the sensibility of the integuments would admit, and was wedged, by a moderate pressure, between the eye and the bone. In this situation the phantom[3] caused by the pressure extended within the field of perfect vision, and was very accurately defined.

[1] Young uses the term *presbyopic* for long sight instead of the modern term *hyper-metropic. Presbyopic* is now used to indicate loss of the power of accommodation.

[2] Showing that his astigmatism was not due to the cornea.

[3] The bright ring produced by pressure on the retina.

With the eye thus confined, so that extension of the axis was impossible, Young found the power of accommodation un-impaired. Any tendency of the eyeball to lengthen would have increased the pressure on the retina and altered the size or shape of the 'phantom'. 'But no such circumstance took place; the power of accommodation was as extensive as ever; and there was no perceptible change either in the size or in the figure of the oval spot.'

This then throws the burden of explanation on hypothesis (d), (c) being ruled out by the conclusion reached on (a). Here Young is thrown back on the evidence adduced by Home and Ramsden in their paper of 1794, according to which the power of accommodation remained even when the crystalline lens had been removed:

I must here acknowledge my great obligation to Mr Ware for the readiness and liberality with which he introduced me to such of his numerous patients as he thought most likely to furnish a satis-factory determination. It is unnecessary to enumerate every par-ticular experiment; but the universal result is, contrary to the expectations with which I entered on the enquiry, that in an eye, deprived of the crystalline lens, the actual focal distance is totally unchangeable.[1]

After some further discussion, in which Young wrongly attributes the power of the crystalline lens to change its focus to the muscularity of the lens itself instead of to the ciliary muscles whose function was then unknown, he proceeds to summarize his results:

First, the determination of the refractive power of a variable medium, and its application to the constitution of the crystalline lens. Secondly, the construction of an instrument for ascertaining,

---

[1] One patient had played a special part in earlier discussions—a certain Benjamin Clark. In the *Introduction to Medical Literature*, 2nd ed. p. 96, Young writes: 'Mr Home, in his last Croonian lecture on vision, laments that Benjamin Clark could not then be found: he has, however, since returned to this country, and experiments have been made on his sight, in the presence of the late Mr Cavendish, Mr Home, Mr Brodie, and Dr Young; after the most patient examination, it appeared that the imperfect eye, from which the crystalline lens had been extracted, possessed no power whatever of altering its focus, while the same tests exhibited a very considerable change in the focal distance of the perfect eye.' The changes in curvature of the lens surfaces have since been demonstrated.

upon inspection, the exact focal distance of every eye, and the remedy for its imperfections. Thirdly, to show the accurate adjustment of every part of the eye, for seeing with distinctness the greatest possible extent of objects at the same instant. Fourthly, to measure the collective dispersion of coloured rays in the eye. Fifthly, by immersing the eye in water, to demonstrate that its accommodation does not depend on any change in the curvature of the cornea. Sixthly, by confining the eye at the extremities of its axis, to prove that no material change in its length can take place. Seventhly, to examine what inference can be drawn from the experiments hitherto made on persons deprived of the lens; to pursue the inquiry on the principles suggested by Dr Porterfield: and to confirm his opinion of the utter inability of such persons to change the refractive state of the organ. Eighthly, to deduce, from the aberration of the lateral rays, a decisive argument in favour of a change in the quantity of this aberration, the form into which the lens appears to be thrown in my own eye, and the mode by which the change must be produced in that of every other person. And I flatter myself that I shall not be deemed too precipitate, in denominating this series of experiments satisfactorily demonstrative.

This paper shows Young at his best. The essential theoretical relations are first worked out. Then follows a set of careful measurements with an instrument specially designed. Next the possible hypotheses are clearly set out, and the erroneous ones eliminated by convincing experiments carefully chosen and executed. Lastly, the correct hypothesis is established by confirmatory observations. Speaking of this 'masterly monograph' Sir John Parsons has said:[1] 'But I agree myself with Tscherning that Young's greatest and most original contributions to science are contained in his paper on the Mechanism of the Eye.'

The other outstanding contribution of Young in the field of physiological optics is the Young-Helmholtz theory of colour vision.

The scientific study of colour may be said to start with the work of Newton on the spectrum of the sun.

In a very dark chamber, at a round Hole, about one third Part of an Inch broad, made in the shut of a Window, I placed a Glass

---

[1] *Trans. Optical Soc.* 32 (1930-1), 162.

Prism, whereby the Beam of the Sun's Light, which came in at that Hole, might be refracted upwards towards the opposite Wall of the Chamber, and there form a colour'd Image of the Sun.[1]

In these words Newton begins the account of his researches. In the coloured band thrown on the wall of his room in Trinity College, Cambridge, he fancied he could distinguish seven distinct colours—red, orange, yellow, green, blue, indigo and violet—and recombining these he found that he could reproduce white light. White light, as ordinarily found, was therefore a mixture of all the colours. He further showed that all the spectrum colours were 'pure' (i.e. that they came through a second prism unchanged). Proceeding to mix pure colours, he discovered that certain pure colours could be matched by a mixture of other pure colours. Pure orange, for instance, could be matched by a mixture of pure red and pure yellow, containing no orange at all. Thus the same sensation, orange, can be produced by two quite different physical stimuli, (*a*) pure orange or (*b*) a mixture of pure red and pure yellow with no orange present.

He devised a colour diagram to represent the results of his experiments, and to enable him to predict the colour resulting from any given mixture. It is shown in Fig. 6.

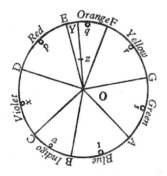

Fig. 6. Colour Diagram

The circumference of a circle is divided into seven parts in

[1] Sir Isaac Newton, *Opticks* (1704), reprinted from 4th ed. (London, 1931), p. 26.

proportion to the intervals of the musical scale. *BC* and *EF* are the semitones, the other parts are the tones. The pure colours are then represented by the intervals as shown. To find the colour resulting from a mixture, proceed as follows. Imagine at *p* (the mid-point of the arc representing red) a small mass proportional to the amount of pure red in the mixture, and at *q* a small mass proportional to the orange in the mixture, and so for all the other colours. Now find the position of the centre of gravity of the masses. Suppose it to be at *z*. Join *Oz* and produce it to meet the circumference at *Y*. Then *Y* represents the colour or hue of the mixture—in this case a reddish orange. Also, since *O* represents white (an equal mixture of all the colours) the distance of *z* from *O* indicates the purity of the colour—*Y* being the pure colour with no white.

'This rule', says Newton, 'I conceive accurate enough for practice, though not mathematically accurate.'[1] Newton regarded the seven colours as 'primary', and noted that he 'could never yet by mixing only two primary colours produce a perfect white. Whether it may be compounded of a mixture of three taken at equal distances in the circumference I do not know, but of four or five I do not much question that it may.'[2] These researches were first published in 1704.

Interest in the perception of colour was further stimulated about seventy years later by an account of the first recorded case of colour-blindness. Presumably the defect must have existed for centuries previously, but no reference to it has been found. On 13 February 1777, a paper was read to the Royal Society with the title 'An Account of Persons who could not distinguish colours. By Mr Joseph Huddart, in a letter to the Rev. Joseph Priestley, LL.D., F.R.S.'[3] The principal subject of the letter was a shoemaker named Harris who, as a child, had been much puzzled by people describing as a 'red' stocking what seemed to him to be merely a stocking. He also noticed that other children could distinguish ripe cherries from the leaves of the tree much more easily than he. This interesting discovery was followed soon after by a paper read to the

---

[1] Newton, *op. cit.* p. 158.   [2] *Ibid.* pp. 156–7.   [3] *Phil. Trans.* 67 (1777), 260.

Literary and Philosophical Society of Manchester in 1798.[1] In this paper the famous chemist, John Dalton, gave an account of his own colour vision. To him blood appeared bottle-green, and a laurel leaf was a good match for red sealing-wax. Red, orange, yellow and green were much alike, but he could distinguish blue and purple. Dalton's case attracted so much attention that the phenomenon was for a time called 'Daltonism', and there was a real danger that Dalton would be remembered for his optical defect and not for his contributions to atomic theory. Considering that of men about 8 per cent and of women about 0.5 per cent have abnormal colour vision, it seems rather extraordinary that the defect should not have been discovered earlier, although in some cases it is not so marked as in those just recorded.

Such then was the state of knowledge of colour perception when Young's attention was directed to the subject, probably by a study of Newton's *Opticks*. In the Bakerian Lecture to the Royal Society 'On the Theory of Light and Colours', read 12 November 1801,[2] he starts from the great variety of colours in the spectrum. Careful experiment has shown since that there are some 150 to 170 distinguishable hues. It seems to Young impossible to imagine that each point on the retina of the eye where the image of a coloured object may be thrown there is a separate kind of nerve fibre for each possible hue. He writes:

Now, as it is almost impossible to conceive each sensitive point of the retina to contain an infinite number of particles, each capable of vibrating in perfect unison with every possible undulation, it becomes necessary to suppose the number limited, for instance, to the three principal colours, red, yellow and blue, of which the undulations are related in magnitude nearly as the numbers 8, 7, and 6; and that each of the particles is capable of being put in motion less or more forcibly by undulations differing less or more from a perfect unison; for instance, the undulations of green light being nearly in the ratio of $6\frac{1}{2}$, will affect equally the particles in unison with yellow and blue, and produce the same effect as a light composed of those two species; and each sensitive filament of the nerve may consist of three portions, one for each principal colour.

[1] *Memoirs Lit. and Phil. Soc. Manchester* 5 (1798), 28. [2] *Phil. Trans.* 92 (1802), 12.

He develops this view further in his Royal Institution Lectures. He still holds to the three 'principal' colours but he substitutes green for yellow and violet for blue, retaining red as before. His reason for this change is 'that the perfect sensations of yellow and of blue are produced respectively by mixtures of red and green and of green and violet light.' Thus, in discarding yellow as a principal colour and substituting green, he asserts that a yellow sensation can be produced by mixing green light and red light. The artist is so accustomed to produce green by mixing yellow and blue pigments that he is much more likely to agree with Young's first judgment than with his second. But we must distinguish between mixing paints and mixing lights. Blue paint appears blue because it absorbs the red end of the spectrum and returns blue and some green to the eye. Yellow paint appears yellow because it absorbs the blue end of the spectrum and returns red and some green to the eye. The only colour returned by both paints when they are mixed is green. But this is not due to mixing blue and yellow, but to subtracting from white light the blue (absorbed by the yellow) and the red (absorbed by the blue), and returning to the eye what is not absorbed by either paint, i.e. green. Young indicates that he was alive to this objection to the use of pigments, and he uses a method of experiment which avoids it. A mixture of green light with red light produces the sensation yellow, and a mixture of blue light with yellow light, a near white.

In commenting on Young's theory at a much later date Clerk Maxwell writes:[1]

It seems almost a truism to say that colour is a sensation; and yet Young, by honestly recognising this elementary truth, established the first consistent theory of colour. So far as I know, Thomas Young was the first who, starting from the well-known fact that there are three primary colours, sought for the explanation of this fact, not in the nature of light, but in the constitution of man.

Now Young refers to 'principal' colours not to 'primary' colours. And I doubt whether in Young's time the fact that

[1] James Clerk Maxwell, *Scientific Papers* (Cambridge, 1890), vol. II, p. 267.

any spectrum colour could be matched by a suitable mixture of three pure colours was indeed a well-known fact. As I read his short and rather incidental references to his theory, to which he himself does not seem to have attached any great importance, the conviction that three colours were sufficient was of the nature of an intuition which, no doubt, his experimental work tended to confirm.

It is not clear how much experimental work Young did on the subject. He only once indicates a numerical result, and gives no account of any experiments. He does, however, suggest a method.

The sensations of various kinds of light may also be combined in a still more satisfactory manner by painting the surface of a circle (i.e. circular disc) with different colours (i.e. coloured sectors) in any way that may be desired, and causing it to revolve with such rapidity that the whole may assume the appearance of a single tint or of a combination of tints resulting from the mixture of colours.[1]

The colour top is said to have been used by Ptolemy[2] in the second century, although Young seems to have been the first to suggest its use for scientific colour mixture. It was subsequently developed by Clerk Maxwell, and the illustration, fig. 7,

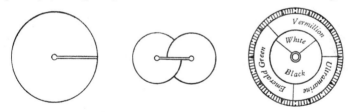

Fig. 7. Development of the Colour Top

is taken from one of his papers.[3] One colour succeeds another so rapidly that the image of one colour on the retina is succeeded by the images of the other two before the first has time to die away. Thus the images are superposed on the retina, and the colours mixed. In the centre of the top is the smaller disk of

---

[1] *Lectures*, vol. I, p. 440.
[2] R. A. Houston, *Light and Colour* (London, 1923), p. 73.
[3] Clerk Maxwell, *op. cit.* vol. I, Plate I, figs. 3, 4 and 5.

colour to be matched, overlapping, by a variable amount, a black disk to be adjusted if the colour is too light.

In Young's published lectures he gives a coloured diagram showing his modification of Newton's coloured circle. For Newton's circle with seven arcs Young substitutes a triangle with the three primary colours at the vertices. At the midpoints of the sides are the colours produced by mixing the primary colours in pairs—yellow from red and green, purple from violet and red, blue from green and violet.

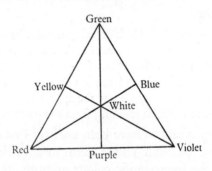

Fig. 8 Young's modification of Newton's colour circle

If we choose the exact hues of the primary colours so that they have to be mixed in equal quantities to produce white, then the corresponding point will be as marked—equidistant from the three vertices. This method of representation has been widely used as a basis by subsequent workers.

Young returns to the subject in his article 'Chromatics', written in 1817 for the Supplement to the *Encyclopaedia Britannica*. He adds little that is new, but brings out the essentials of his theory and its status as follows:

If we seek for the simplest arrangement, which would enable it [the eye] to receive and discriminate the impressions of the different parts of the spectrum, we may suppose three distinct sensations only to be excited by the rays of the three principal pure colours, falling on any given point of the retina, the red, the green, and the violet; while the rays occupying the intermediate spaces are capable of producing mixed sensations, the yellow those which belong to the red and green, and the blue those which belong to the green and violet.

The theory then is a very simple one. We are capable of feeling three different colour-sensations. Light of different kinds excites these sensations in different proportions, and it is by the different combinations of these three primary sensations that all the varieties of visible colour are produced. In Young's own account two phrases are worth repeating, (a) 'at least this supposition simplifies the theory of colours; it may, therefore, be adopted with advantage, until it be found inconsistent with any of the phenomena', and (b) 'if we seek for the simplest arrangement, which would enable the eye to receive and discriminate, etc.'

This theory, like every other, is an induction which goes beyond the facts, an intuition, an inspired guess. Nothing was then known of the existence of three different kinds of fibres or receiving mechanisms of any kind in the retina of the eye. And like every other theory it must be judged by the *simplicity* of its representation of the known facts, and by the way in which it can direct into lines of fruitful discovery the workers who, using it as a starting point, try to answer the further questions it suggests. Young's brilliant intuition stands up to these tests admirably. Its simplicity is obvious, and it is no exaggeration to say that it has been not only the starting point, but the guide, of nearly all subsequent research. It gives not only a simple representation of the facts of colour-mixing, but also a simple representation of the facts of colour-blindness. Young was quick to apply it in the case of Dalton, whose own explanation of his deficiency was that it was due to the fact that the fluid in his eye absorbed red before it reached the retina. Young has a different explanation.

He [Dalton] thinks it probable that the vitreous humour (of his eye) is of a deep blue tinge (thus absorbing the red); but this has never been observed by anatomists, and it is much more simple to suppose the absence or paralysis of those fibres of the retina, which are calculated to perceive red. . . .

Herschel, after experimenting on Dalton, supported Young's view; but Dalton persisted in his own view, and was not proved to be wrong until after his death in 1844.

Young's work on colour sensation attracted no immediate attention. It was not until Helmholtz rediscovered it, nearly fifty years later, that it became effective.[1] He adopted Young's theory with some modifications, and it has since come to be known as the Young-Helmholtz theory. Referring to the original theory, Helmholtz says:[2]

The theory of colours, with all these marvellous and complicated relations, was a riddle which Goethe in vain attempted to solve; nor were we physicists and physiologists more successful. I include myself among the number; for I long toiled at the task, without getting any nearer my object, until I at last discovered that a wonderfully simple solution had been discovered at the beginning of this century, and had been in print ever since for any one to read who chose. This solution was found and published by the same Thomas Young who first showed the right method of arriving at the interpretations of Egyptian hieroglyphics. He was one of the most acute men who ever lived, but had the misfortune to be too far in advance of his contemporaries. They looked on him with astonishment, but could not follow his bold speculations, and thus a mass of his most important thoughts remained buried and forgotten in the Transactions of the Royal Society until a later generation by slow degrees arrived at the rediscovery of his discoveries, and came to appreciate the force of his arguments and the accuracy of his conclusions.

Even in relation to the modifications which he himself felt to be necessary, he said:

But the form of this hypothesis as originally proposed by Young is clearer in both conception and expression than it would be if it were modified as suggested, and hence it will be retained in its original concrete form, for the sake of exposition if for nothing else.[3]

Young's work was taken up about the same time by Clerk Maxwell. He began experimenting both with the colour top

[1] *Phil. Mag.* 4 (1852), 519.

[2] H. Helmholtz, *Popular Lectures* (London, 1873), p. 249.

[3] H. Helmholtz, *Treatise on Physiological Optics*, ed. Southall (*Optical Society of America*, 1924), vol. II, p. 144.

method and with the mixing of coloured light by an ingenious colour-box. These experiments, started in the study of his home at Glenlair as early as 1850,[1] were continued in the large room of the house at Palace Gardens Terrace in Kensington where he lived while professor at King's College, London. The subject became one of his main interests, and the apparatus with which he worked is still preserved at the Cavendish Laboratory, Cambridge. The experiments were made on normal and on colour-blind observers. His work established the fact that all colours may be matched by suitable mixtures of three primary colours and so supported the Young-Helmholtz theory, and he used Young's triangle of colours to represent his results.

So far as colour-blindness is concerned, Young's theory offers much the simplest basis of classification. Normal observers are tri-chromats and need to use three primary colours if they are to be able to match all the various possible hues. These have all three primary sensations. Some colour-blind observers are di-chromats and can match every hue by a mixture in various proportions of *two* primary colours. They are subdivided into protanopes, in whom the red sensation is missing, tritanopes, in whom the blue sensation is missing, and deuteranopes, in whom the red and green sensations are combined to form one. There are also monochromats, for whom any colour matches any other. These presumably have only one primary sensation.

The facts of abnormal colour vision are much more complex than this short summary would suggest and require corresponding modifications of the theory, but they are not in conflict with Young's basic assumptions. During the last century or so every worker in the field of colour sensation has had to come to grips with the Young-Helmholtz theory. The theory itself has been modified in certain directions by those who have accepted it as a basis. It has been rejected by others who have suggested alternatives. But most of these alternatives have been short-lived, and none of them looks like supplanting Young's theory. Indeed, the latest work strengthens our confidence in the essential features of the theory.

[1] L. Campbell and W. Garnett, *Life of James Clerk Maxwell* (London, 1882), p. 198.

J

Polyak, from an examination of the retina,[1] has come to the conclusion that there are three specific types of path for the electrical impulses generated when the retina is stimulated, and these three kinds of path might correspond to the three primary sensations.

Hartridge,[2] by stimulating very minute areas of the retina with white light, found that the resulting sensation was sometimes red, sometimes green and sometimes blue. Discussing his results he concludes that 'Thomas Young's trichromatic theory of colour vision is substantially correct, since the above tests are held to prove the existence of red receptors, green receptors and blue receptors, in the human fovea'.

By work on the electrical response of single nerve fibres in the retina Granit has found two different types of response. One is a response with a broad maximum about the centre of the spectrum and diminishing towards both ends. This he called the dominator and associated it with the reception of ordinary white light. The other type of response was a sharply selective response, evoked by light of a particular colour and closely neighbouring wave-lengths. These he called modulators and he found six or seven of them, but these 'narrow bands of sensitivity were located in three preferential regions of the spectrum, red-yellow, green and blue'.

In his Thomas Young Memorial Lecture[3] he sums up the results of his work thus:

It is characteristic of those whom we revere as classics of science that their ideas have been formulated with a curious insight into how nature might be expected to behave and so have preserved lasting creative power. What greater tribute could one scientist pay to another than to perform an experiment suggested by his ideas, 140 years after they have been formulated, and come to the conclusion that these ideas were fundamentally correct? The mechanism of colour reception is organised by the peripheral visual apparatus (i.e. in the eye), the number of colour sensitive elements is relatively limited, and these elements represent widely different regions of the

[1] S. L. Polyak, *The Retina* (Chicago, 1941).   [2] *Nature* (London), 158 (1946), 97.
[3] *Proc. Phys. Soc.* (1945), 462.

visible spectrum. Those were Young's three fundamental assumptions. He was right even in assuming three main types of colour-receiving apparatus. These are the three preferential regions within which modulators are found. The electro-physiological work may indeed be said to have confirmed the view he gave of the framework of a mechanism of colour perception. Its finished picture looks somewhat different, but the old framework was solid enough and shines through.

VI

PROFESSOR AT THE ROYAL INSTITUTION

'I am willing to undertake the various charges which you have the goodness to detail, and I flatter myself that you will have no reason to complain of any want of zeal on my part in the services of the Royal Institution.' YOUNG

SHORTLY after leaving Cambridge Young found his fortunes linked with a rather striking venture which had then just been started, mainly through the efforts of Benjamin Thompson, Count Rumford. This remarkable man was a native of New England who became unpopular because of his British sympathies and who afterwards fought on the British side in the American War of Independence. He came subsequently to this country and then went to Bavaria, where he entered the government service. It was while superintending the boring of cannon at Munich in the prosecution of his official duties that he made the observations which led him to the view that the work done by the horses on the boring machine was being transformed into heat and made him a pioneer in the theory that work and heat were equivalent manifestations of the same thing, *energy*.

But Thompson, besides being a soldier and a scientist, was an extremely capable administrator, with a sensitive social conscience. He set to work to improve the condition of the poor and to stamp out vagrancy, and it was for his services in this connection that he was made a Count of the Holy Roman Empire with the title of Baron Rumford. The monument erected to his memory refers to him as one 'who eradicated the most scandalous of public evils, idleness and mendicity; who gave to the poor, help, occupation and morals, and to the youth of the Fatherland so many schools of culture'.

It was in 1796 that plans for the founding of the Royal

Institution began to take shape in his mind, and in 1798 he propounded the idea of an Institution which would combine under one roof all the many interests of his own versatile genius, social and scientific. He made his proposals known to a selected group at a time when there was general scarcity, anxiety and even alarm. The House of Commons and the Board of Agriculture were earnestly engaged with measures for relieving distress and averting famine.

After several consultations that were held in Mr Bernard's apartments in the Foundling Hospital and at the London house of the Bishop of Durham, at which several gentlemen assisted who are well known as zealous promotors of useful improvements, it was agreed that Mr Bernard should report to the Committee of the Society for Bettering the Condition of the Poor, the general result of these consultations and the unanimous desire of the gentlemen who assisted at them that means might be devised for making an attempt to carry the scheme proposed into execution.[1]

In 1799 Rumford issued a fifty-page pamphlet containing

Proposals for forming by subscription, in the Metropolis of the British Empire, a Public Institution for diffusing the knowledge and facilitating the general introduction of Useful Mechanical Inventions and Improvements, and for teaching, by courses of Philosophical Lectures and Experiments, the Application of Science to the Common Purposes of Life.

The introduction to this pamphlet is dated from Rumford's residence in Brompton Row, 4 March 1799. His purpose involves establishing 'relations between philosophers and workmen' and bringing their united efforts to bear 'in the improvement of agriculture, manufactures, commerce, and the augmentation of domestic comforts.'

The first formal meeting of the managers was held at the house of Sir Joseph Banks, President of the Royal Society, on 9 March 1799, and arrangements were made to prepare a draft Charter and to put the proposals before 'His Majesty, the Royal Family, the Ministers, the great Officers of State, the members

---

[1] George E. Ellis, *Memoir of Sir Benjamin Thompson, Count Rumford* (Philadelphia), p. 384.

of both Houses of Parliament, of the Privy Council and before the twelve judges'. About a year later (13 January 1800) the Royal Seal was attached to the Charter and with a great flourish of trumpets the scheme was inaugurated. The King became the Patron of the Institution and the first officers were appointed by him. The premises in Albemarle Street, still occupied by the Institution, were acquired, and bit by bit Rumford's ambitious plans were put into execution. There was to be an industrial school for artisans; a collection of models of fireplaces, grates, stoves, steam engines, spinning wheels, etc.; a professor was to be appointed and provided with a well-equipped lecture room; and a convenient club with a restaurant and school of cookery was to be included. The first professor, Garnett, was appointed to the Chair of 'Chemistry and Natural Philosophy' in 1799.

The *Journal* of the Institution was at first edited by Rumford and it gives some idea of the early progress of the Institution and the way in which its scope and purpose altered as it developed. A minute of the Managers of 31 March 1800 sets out that the *Journal* is to be

exclusively devoted to the diffusion of the knowledge of new and interesting scientific discoveries and of useful improvements in mechanics, arts and manufactures; and particularly of making known all such new inventions and contrivances as tend to facilitate labour and render it more productive; to promote domestic economy and increase the conveniences, comforts and enjoyments of life.

In the same number of the *Journal* in which this minute is recorded it is also reported that a 'Committee of Natural Philosophy and Chemistry' was set up. This included Henry Cavendish, Neville Maskelyne (Astronomer Royal), Sir Charles Blagden (Secretary of the Royal Society), Samuel Vince (Professor of Experimental Philosophy at Cambridge), and William Farish (Professor of Chemistry, also at Cambridge). What this Committee did is not very clear and the same obscurity attaches to the work of the other committees set up at the same meeting. These were for the study of: (*a*) the making of bread; (*b*) cheap and nutritious soups for feeding the poor; (c) cottages and cottage fireplaces; (d) kitchen fireplaces and kitchen utensils; and numerous other similar purposes.

On 25 May 1801 Rumford is able to report that the small kitchen and the large kitchen have both been fitted with new contrivances and that a dining room for 'experimental' dinners has been opened.

The early numbers of the *Journal* contain two papers by Rumford, one on 'Observations relative to the means of increasing the Quantities of heat obtained in the combustion of Fuel' and one on 'The use of steam as a Vehicle for conveying heat from one place to another'.

Garnett, the first professor, resigned in 1801 and in the same year Sir Humphry Davy, who had been first assistant lecturer and subsequently lecturer in Chemistry, was appointed to succeed him, and Sir Joseph Banks was consulted as to the possible candidates for a chair of Natural Philosophy. The outcome of this consultation was an interview between Rumford and Young, when certain proposals were made by Rumford, the nature of which is made pretty clear by a letter from Young which follows. Rumford had evidently suggested that Young should allow himself to be considered for the professorship at a salary less than that paid to Garnett. Young's reply is very characteristic, especially in the way he presses his claim for the full salary without either arrogance or mock-modesty.[1]

Welbeck Street,
Thursday, July 9, 1801

Sir,—I have received your obliging letter and beg leave to return you and the managers thanks for the honour you do me.

I am willing to undertake the various charges which you have the goodness to detail, and I flatter myself that you will have no reason to complain of any want of zeal on my part in the service of the Royal Institution.

But I confess I think it would be in some measure degrading both to me and to the Institution that the salary which appears to me to

[1] H. Bence Jones, *History of the Royal Institution* (London, 1871), p. 417.

have been no more than moderate before, should now be reduced by one-fourth, at the same time that the labour and responsibility of the employment are rather increased than lessened. For, whatever might have been expected of the late professor respecting the Journals and the superintendence of the house, I do not apprehend that any specific stipulation was made on the subject; and, as I am determined to devote a greater share of attention to the Institution than he ever appears to have done, I do not see that my education and opportunities of literary acquirement have been such as to render me less worthy than he was of a salary which, when compared with the emoluments of other situations of a similar nature, is by no means exorbitant.

It would not be my wish, and the duties of the professorship would certainly render it impossible for me to attempt any extent of medical practice; but I should be sorry to bind myself to reject the little that might accidentally fall in my way. I do not mention this as a matter of any consequence, but to avoid having it understood, from the conversation I had with you, that I should be obliged to refuse my advice to a friend who might consult me.

As to the Journals, I should not much object to engage that a sheet or more should be ready for publication every week; but I conceive that it would give them additional importance if it were left to the direction of the professor, with the approbation of the Committee, with proper notice, to publish a number at the end of a fortnight, instead of a week, whenever there might appear to be a real deficiency of matter to fill it. And I think I should want little or no assistance, either in translating or in transcribing except what Mr Davy might have the goodness to give me.

I hope that, when you have reconsidered what I have stated, you will not much differ from me in opinion, and that you will favour me with a further communication of your sentiments on the subject.

I am, Sir, your obliged and obedient humble Servant,

THOMAS YOUNG

Count Rumford,
Royal Institution

The very next day the matter came before the Managers and it is clear that Young's representations had prevailed, for we read in the minutes of 10 July 1801:

Count Rumford reported that at the recommendation of Sir

Joseph Banks he had had a conversation with Doctor Young, respecting his engaging as Professor of Natural Philosophy at the Royal Institution, and Editor of the Journals, together with a general superintendency of the House and it appearing from the report of Count Rumford, that Dr Young is a man of ability equal to these undertakings:

RESOLVED that Count Rumford be authorised to engage Dr Young in the aforesaid capacities at a salary of £300 per annum.

At a meeting on 3 August 1801, Count Rumford reported that he had engaged Dr Young, and laid before the managers

a copy of his letter to Dr Young expressive of the conditions of his engagement.

RESOLVED that the Managers approve the measures taken by Count Rumford—That the appointment of Dr Young be confirmed —and that the Count's letter be deposited with the rough minutes of the Meeting.

The letter has, unfortunately, not been preserved.

Young at once took up the editorship of the *Journal* in the autumn of 1801 and published a number chiefly devoted to Davy's lectures on 'Galvanic Phenomena'. Later numbers contain references to Young's Bakerian Lecture to the Royal Society in that year and to his own and Davy's lectures to the Institution. Early in 1802 Young was joined in the editorship by Davy and the joint responsibility was maintained until 1803, when the publication of the *Journal* was interrupted and not resumed till 1830.

Young also set about the preparation of his lectures. He began his course on 20 January 1802 and finished it on 17 May, having delivered thirty-one lectures. The syllabus was printed at the Press of the Institution and issued on 19 January 1802. He announces that the lectures will be divided into three semi-independent series, of which two will be delivered on Mondays and on Wednesdays respectively at 2 o'clock and the third on Friday evenings at 8.0 so as to suit as far as possible the convenience of different persons; and that in future winters each series will, in turn, be taken on the Friday evenings.

Another part of the syllabus 'contains all the preliminary knowledge that is necessary for those who may wish to enter mathematically on the various subjects of the lectures'.

Young's own ideas about the purpose of the Institution are indicated briefly in his Introductory Lecture:

The primary and peculiar object of the Royal Institution of Great Britain is to apply to domestic convenience the improvements which have been made in Science, and to introduce into general practice such mechanical inventions as are of decided utility.

At the same time he guards against a too rigid interpretation of this practical object and puts in a plea for science for its own sake.

Those who possess the genuine spirit of investigation, and who have tasted the pure satisfaction arising from an advancement in intellectual acquirements, are contented to proceed on their researches, without inquiring at every step, what they can gain by their newly discovered lights and to what purposes they are applicable; they receive a sufficient gratification from the enlargment of their views of the constitution of the universe and experience in the immediate pursuit of knowledge that pleasure which others wish to obtain more circuitously by its means.

His views are more systematically set out in a document prepared at the same time with a view to publication in the *Journal*. This document was never published owing to the uncertainty which had already crept into the counsels of the Managers about the future of the Institution. The difficulty of holding together all the diverse interests which had been inherited from Rumford was already becoming apparent and Young's account[1] indicates a very definite narrowing of scope. He defines the 'professed object' of the Institution as 'the diffusion of useful knowledge, derived from Science and applicable to the purposes of life'. He continues:

The means proposed for attaining this end are, first, an annual delivery of lectures in the various branches of natural philosophy and chemistry, familiar enough to be intelligible to moderate

[1] Bence Jones, *op. cit.* p. 206.

capacities, and extensive enough to comprehend the most important applications of theory to practice; secondly the furnishing of a spacious repository with models of such machines, instruments, and utensils, as, after sufficient experimental examination, can with confidence be recommended for introduction into common use; thirdly the establishing of a chemical laboratory, with proper apparatus and materials to be employed in such investigations as are of the greatest practical utility; fourthly, the provision of reading rooms, supplied as well with periodical publications as with works of acknowledged merit, particularly relative to the sciences and arts, and lastly, the extension of the benefits derived from the Institution by publishing from time to time, in its Journals, such improvements as may either have been otherwise suggested by individuals in foreign countries or in our own.

It will be noticed that in this scheme the lectures are given pride of place. It is true that they are to be 'familiar enough to be intelligible to moderate capacities', but there is no indication that they were to be specially designed for artisans as Rumford had proposed. Nor is there any mention of workshops or of those efforts to improve the lot of the poor into which Rumford had thrown himself with so much enthusiasm in Austria and with which he had engaged the interest of the Society for Bettering the Condition of the Poor in London. These had evidently been abandoned. Writing to Rumford's biographer, Bence Jones says:[1]

The fact was that Rumford's idea of workshops and kitchen, industrial school, model exhibition, social clubhouse and scientific committees to do everything, etc. etc. was much too big and unworkable for a private body. . . . Rumford, seeing he could not have his way, went to Paris.

Unfortunately only the dynamic influence of Rumford could have integrated the activities which he had attempted to initiate. It was he who gave life to the projects which interested the Society for Bettering the Condition of the Poor and soon after he left England for Munich in 1802 these projects died. Young was not the man to develop them. They did not lie at

[1] Ellis, *op. cit.* p. 434.

all along the line of his own interests. His sole recorded contribution in this direction appears in the *Journal* in 1802.

Experiment made by Dr Young. Bones taken from a piece of beef which has been roasted, reduced to smooth paste, and made into a quart of broth with proper vegetables. Broth showed no tendency to jelly when cold, tasted only of vegetables, nothing disagreeable in its insipidity.

On 5 July 1802 Young applied for leave of absence for August and September and provided in advance sufficient material for the publication of the *Journal* in the meantime. The application was granted and Young went to Rouen in a professional capacity with the Duke of Richmond and his brother Lord George Lennox. While there he went to Paris and attended a meeting of the National Institute of France, where he met Napoleon, the First Consul.[1]

Before leaving for France he applied to the Managers for permission to order a Whirling Table and a Solar Microscope for lecture illustrations, and this was granted on 3 August. On 7 September he asked permission to spend from £30 to £50 on a Planetarium; he also suggested that the *Literary Newspaper of Jena* and Gilbert's *Journal of Natural Philosophy* should be 'procured by contract with the Post Office by each mail'. He added certain recommendations for additions to the library, among them the *Méchanique Céleste* of Laplace, then just published.

Of the lectures as an intellectual achievement it is impossible to speak too highly. We shall consider them in some detail in their published form. Suffice it to say at this stage that for their immense scope, their grasp of the subjects and their originality they are quite unique in the history of Natural Philosophy or Physics. It is difficult to understand how, in the comparatively short time available, Young was able to make himself master of the earlier and contemporary literature of the wide field of knowledge embraced in the lectures. Only the habits of industry and application which he had acquired could have made it possible, and it seems fairly certain that while at

[1] H. Gurney, *op. cit.* p. 22.

Cambridge he must have read a great deal and preserved, as had been his early custom, his notes on what he read. When he repeated his course in the spring of 1803 he increased the number of lectures from thirty-one to sixty, and his published lectures are based on this extended course. It was the last course he delivered at the Royal Institution.

All this is not meant to imply that his lectures were successful *as lectures*. He undertook his task with a high resolve to bring his subject-matter within the grasp of the ordinary member of his audience. He foresees his difficulties. In his introductory lecture he asks his audience

to pardon the formality of a written discourse in favour of the advantage of a superior degree of order and perspicuity. It would unquestionably be desirable that every syllable advanced should be rendered perfectly easy and comprehensible even to the most uninformed, that the most inattentive might find sufficient variety and entertainment in what is submitted to them to excite their curiosity, and that in all cases the pleasing, and sometimes even the surprising, should be united with the instructive and the important. But, whenever there appears to be a real impossibility of reconciling these various objects, I shall esteem it better to seek for substantial utility than temporary amusement; for if we fail of being useful, for want of being sufficiently popular, we remain at least respectable; but if we are unsuccessful in our attempts to amuse, we immediately appear trifling and contemptible. It shall, however, at all times be my endeavour to avoid each extreme, and I trust that I shall then only be condemned when I am found abstruse from ostentation or uninteresting from supineness. The most difficult thing for a teacher is to recollect how much it cost himself to learn, and to accommodate his instruction to the apprehension of the uniformed. By bearing in mind this observation I hope to be able to render my lectures more and more intelligible and familiar, not by passing over difficulties, but by endeavouring to facilitate the task of overcoming them; and if at any time I appear to have failed in this attempt, I shall think myself honoured by any subsequent inquiries that my audience may be disposed to make.

With great courage he undertakes to cater for the ladies and promises them special attention and consideration.

A considerable portion of my audience, to whose information it will be my particular ambition to accommodate my lectures, consists of that sex, which, by the custom of civilised society, is in some measure exempted from the more laborious duties that occupy the time and attention of the other sex. The many leisure hours, which are at the command of females in the superior orders of society, may surely be appropriated, with greater satisfaction, to the improvement of the mind, and to the acquisition of knowledge, than to such amusements as are only designed for facilitating the insipid consumption of superfluous time. . . . In this point of view the Royal Institution may in some degree supply the place of a subordinate University, to those whose sex or situation in life has denied them the advantage of an academical education in the national seminaries of learning.

It is, alas, only too clear that Young failed in his declared purpose. To some extent this was no doubt due to defects of style. Although parts of the lectures are written in a beautifully clear and elegant style, easy to read, and probably easy to understand when heard, there is much that is lacking in clearness of exposition. But the cause of his failure lies largely in the inappropriateness of his subject-matter. Even in our day, with its widespread interest in science and its nodding acquaintance with fundamental scientific ideas, few members of the general public could have assimilated the subject-matter of these lectures.

The writer of the rather critical account of his College days, whom we have already quoted, says:[1]

His language was correct, his utterance rapid and his sentences, though without any affectations, were never left unfinished. But his words were not those in familiar use, and the arrangement of his ideas seldom the same as those he conversed with. He was, therefore, worse calculated than any man I ever knew for the communication of knowledge.

I remember him taking me with him to the Royal Institution to hear him lecture to a number of silly women and dilettante philosophers. But nothing could show less judgment than the method he adopted; for he presumed, like many other lecturers and preachers, on the knowledge and not on the ignorance of his hearers.

[1] Peacock, *op. cit.* p. 118.

His friend Hudson Gurney says:[1]

As a lecturer at the Royal Institution, Dr Young . . . passed the capacities of his audience, who . . . were led to their attendance more as a matter of fashion, than from love of research, and who for the most part had little previous knowledge. His style was compressed and laconic; he went into the depths of science, and indeed gave more matter than it would perhaps have been possible . . . to have followed at the moment without considerable difficulty.

Dr Paris thus contrasts Davy's lectures with those of Young:[2]

Dr Young, whose profound knowledge of the subjects he taught no one will venture to question, lectured in the same theatre and to an audience similarly constituted to that which was attracted to Davy, but he found the number of his attendants diminish daily and for no other reason than that he adopted too severe and didactic a style.

It is clear that the contrast here set out was not unfairly drawn. Davy's lectures were undoubtedly the more popular but had nothing like the scope and originality of Young's.

On 26 April 1803 a further recommendation for the library was submitted by Young to the Managers, together with a letter making certain requests. As this letter has not been preserved we do not know what these requests were. They were refused, but the decision was apparently not communicated to Young until 6 June. On receipt of it he intimated his wish to resign. The Managers parried this move by inviting him to deliver twenty lectures in the forthcoming season and to state his subject and his terms. At the next meeting on 4 July, however, it was agreed to pay Young the balance of salary to terminate his engagement. There is no doubt that one factor in Young's decision was his fear that to continue his tenure of the professorship would prejudice his professional prospects, and in this view he had the support of his friends.[3] That the negotiations were harmonious is made clear by the fact that at the meeting of the Managers on 3 October he was elected a life member of the Institution. This honour he acknowledged in

[1] Gurney, *Memoir*, p. 21.   [2] Bence Jones, *op. cit.* p. 240.
[3] Gurney, *Memoir*, p. 22.

the following letter,[1] dated from 40 Welbeck Street on 6 November 1803.

I beg to return you my sincere thanks for the privilege of a life subscriber to the Royal Institution which you have conferred upon me. I consider this honour both as a flattering mark of your approbation of the unremitting attention which it was my endeavour to pay to the objects of the Institution while I was employed in its service, and as a substantial advantage in giving me access to a collection of books so valuable as that which is now forming in it. For this privilege I cannot show my gratitude better than by endeavouring to make such use of it as to render the publication of my lectures, which I am preparing, more and more worthy of the Institution in which they were delivered, and fitted to co-operate in its exertions for the advancement and dissemination of mechanical knowledge.

Young's *Lectures on Natural Philosophy* appeared in two quarto volumes in 1807. The first volume contains the lectures with diagrams and illustrations; the second volume contains a classified list of references to the relevant literature and a reprint of several original papers. Together they form a more complete account of the subject than has appeared in English either before or since. To turn over the pages is a liberal education, for the subject of them is not Physics in the narrow sense but Natural Philosophy with a breadth of interpretation unknown today, even in Scotland. Sir Joseph Larmor[2] has described the lectures as the 'greatest and most original of all lecture courses' and has said of the bibliography that 'no such authoritative catalogue, even of the select classical works of modern science of personal origin, is likely to appear again'.

Let us look then at the contents of these two volumes and at the way in which the exposition of the subject is planned. The course is divided into three parts with twenty lectures in each part. The first part is headed 'Mechanics', and, in addition to matter which would now be included under such a title, comprises lectures on drawing, writing, and measuring; and on architecture and carpentry. The second part is entitled 'Hydro-

[1] Bence Jones, *op. cit.* p. 246.   [2] *Nature* (London), 133 (1934), 276.

dynamics'. It includes a systematic treatment of the physical properties of liquids and gases; a discussion of reservoirs, canals, piers and harbours; the theory of the sailing boat and a description of the common forms of water pump and of air pump. In this section also is included the subjects of acoustics and optics with all Young's original contributions to these subjects —some of which have already been noticed while others will be discussed later. The third part, headed 'Physics', deals with astronomy, gravitation, tides, cohesion, the phenomena of heat and electricity, climates and winds, vegetation and animal life.

Young's lectures were originally written for delivery and in their published form had evidently been rewritten for publication so as to embody the fresh material acquired during his compilation of the bibliography. But the spacious treatment of the subject in these lectures is not merely the result of wide reading in the literature of the subject. They are full of original contributions—original methods of presentation, original design of apparatus and major contributions in the realm of scientific discovery.

In the first part he shows that he has clearly grasped the importance of what we now call the kinetic energy of a moving body and he is the first to apply the term *energy* in this connection.[1] The quantity mass (velocity) has been

conveyed by the term living or ascending force. . . . The same idea is somewhat more concisely expressed by the term *energy*, which indicates the tendency of a body to ascend or to penetrate to a certain distance in opposition to a retarding force (p. 44).

In discussing the work of Archimedes on the lever, he shows his gift for illuminating illustration of principles.

The boast of Archimedes was therefore accompanied by an unnecessary condition. 'Give me', said he, 'but a firm support, and I will move the earth'; but granting him his support, he could only have displaced the earth insensibly by the properties of his machines; and without any support, when he threw rocks upon the ships of Marcellus he actually caused the walls of Syracuse and the island of

[1] J. Clerk Maxwell, *Theory of Heat* (London, 1899), p. 91.

K

Sicily to move northwards, with as much momentum as carried his projectiles southwards against the Roman armaments (p. 58).

Young devotes a good deal of space both in this volume and in volume II to a discussion of standards of length, mass and time; but as he was, in the later years of his life, particularly interested in this matter in an official capacity, the subject can be more appropriately considered in a later chapter.[1]

He gives a very clear exposition of the economics of mechanical power, comparing a man, a horse, a mule and a steam engine. He concludes that 'the daily work of a horse' (which he sets rather high as judged by later standards) 'is equal to that of five or six men' (p. 132). 'The strength of a mule is equal to that of three or four men' (p. 133). 'The expense of keeping a horse is in general about twice or thrice as great as the hire of a day labourer, so that the force of horses may be reckoned about half as expensive as that of men.' As regards the steam engine, he states on the authority of 'Mr Boulton' that 84 lb. of coal is equivalent to the daily labour of $8\frac{1}{3}$ men, or perhaps more; the value of this quantity of coal is seldom more than that of the work of a single labourer for a day; but the expense of the machinery generally renders a steam engine somewhat more than half as expensive as the number of horses for which it it substituted (p. 133).

Young claims in his preface that the 'passive strength' (by which he means the elasticity) 'of materials of all kinds has been very fully investigated, and many new conclusions formed respecting it, which are of immediate importance to the architect and to the engineer'. This claim is very fully substantiated in the text.

He defines for the first time a quantity which measures the resistance of a rod of any material to compression. This he calls a modulus of elasticity and it now bears his name. 'Young's Modulus' is probably the student's first association with the name of Young. It is a very important quantity involved in the bending of beams as well as in extension and compression, and therefore of great importance in the study of the strength

[1] Chapter XII, pp. 289–94.

of materials. The physicist today defines the quantity very concisely as the ratio of the applied stress to the resulting strain, where the stress is the compressing force per unit area of cross-section and the strain is the contraction per unit length. Young's definition is a model of cumbersome obscurity.

We may express the elasticity of any substance which may be denominated the modulus of its elasticity, and of which the weight is such that any addition to it would increase it in the same proportion as the weight added would shorten, by its pressure, a portion of the substance of equal diameter (p. 137).

This definition is only slightly improved in the second volume, where it runs thus (vol. II, p. 46):

The modulus of elasticity of any substance is a column of the same substance, capable of producing a pressure upon its base which is to the weight causing a certain degree of compression as the length of the substance is to the diminution of its length.

Young shows that the modulus applies both to compression and to extension of rods and he extends its application to liquids also. He knew that a liquid column could sustain a tension without breaking and instances the way in which the mercury in a barometer tube which has been completely filled will adhere to the top of the tube, on inverting it with the open end below a trough of mercury. The column is then much longer than that which the atmosphere would support. Tait regarded the application of the modulus to liquids as 'one of the few really imperfect portions of his (Young's) great work'. Rayleigh;[1] however, comes to the defence of Young:

A deficiency of explanation must be admitted, but I am not sure that Young's ideas were really confused. The modulus for solids corresponds to a condition of no lateral force, that for liquid to no lateral extension. The distinction should certainly have been pointed out; but the moduli are really comparable in respect of very important effects, which Young probably had in his mind—viz. the propagation of sound along a bar in one case, and in the other through a fluid, whether unlimited or contained in an unyielding tube.

[1] Lord Rayleigh, *Collected Papers*, vol. IV, p. 425.

Closely related to this discussion of Young's Modulus is his explanation of the 'Sandblast effect'. On p. 144 he points out that 'there is, however, a limit beyond which the velocity of a body striking another cannot be increased without overcoming its resilience, and breaking it, however small the bulk of the first body may be'. In other words, even a grain of sand projected with sufficient velocity against a hard surface will disintegrate it. This Rayleigh regards as 'among the many remarkable anticipations' contained in Young's lectures.

The optical lectures (xxxv-xl) contain an account of his work on the eye and on the perception of colour as set out in the earlier papers discussed in chapters vii and viii. But they also contain what was undoubtedly his greatest contribution to physical science—an admirable account of the wave theory of light, with an exposition of the principle of interference and a description of the experiments by means of which he demonstrated its application to light. Referring to this in his Preface he says:

Some new cases of the production of colours have been pointed out and have been referred to the general law of double lights (phenomena of interference) by which a great variety of the experiments of former opticians have also been explained; and this law has been applied to the establishment of a theory of the nature of light which satisfactorily removes almost every difficulty that has hitherto attended the subject.

These matters will occupy our attention in the next chapter.

At the time when Young's lectures were given, the nature of heat was in dispute. The theory that it was an imponderable fluid called caloric was strongly held in this country and very strongly held in France. The rival theory that it consisted in the agitation of the minute particles of a body and so was a 'mode of motion' had its supporters, but was not established until some forty years later. Young was one of the most clear-sighted of these. He accepted the theory without hesitation and linked it up with his wave theory of light and with the discoveries which had just been made by Herschel in England and Ritter in Germany. Herschel had discovered that, when a spectrum of sunlight was thrown by a prism, a thermometer showed a rise of temperature beyond the red end of the spectrum, where the spectrum was invisible. Ritter showed that the silver salts blackened by light were affected not only at the extreme violet end of the spectrum but beyond it, where, again, no spectrum was visible. Young brings these phenomena into relation with the dynamical theory of heat and with the wave theory of light in the following passage:

If heat is not a substance, it must be a quality; and this quality can only be motion. It was Newton's opinion that heat consists in a minute vibratory motion of the particles of bodies and that this motion is communicated through an apparent vacuum by the undulations of an elastic medium which is also concerned in the phenomena of light. If the arguments which have been lately advanced in favour of the undulatory theory of light be deemed valid, there will be still stronger reasons for admitting this doctrine respecting heat; and it will only be necessary to suppose the vibrations and undulations principally constituting it to be larger and stronger than those of light, while at the same time the smaller vibrations of light, and even the blackening rays derived from still more minute vibrations may, perhaps, when sufficiently condensed, concur in producing the effect of heat. These effects beginning from the blackening rays, which are invisible, are a little more perceptible in the violet, which still possess but a faint power of illumination; the yellow-green afford the most light; the red give less light, but more heat; while the still larger and less frequent vibrations, which have no effect upon the sense of sight can be supposed to give rise to the least refrangible rays and to constitute invisible heat (p. 564).

In this passage we have Young clearly enunciating the idea of a continuous spectrum passing from the ultra-violet through the visible to the infra-red, the radiations having a gradually increasing wave-length and a gradually diminishing frequency, and the sharp distinction between the visible and the invisible radiations being purely one of physiological effect. In this he was again much ahead of his time.

He treats the tides at some length, without making any notable advance on contemporary knowledge except in two respects. He was the first to facilitate the study of the tides by the compilation of a co-tidal map.[1] This map of the English

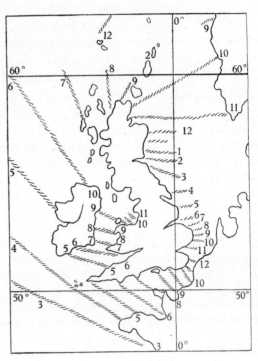

Fig. 9. Co-tidal Map

Channel shows lines joining the places where high-water is simultaneous. By his treatment of tides in canals he also gave an important clue to a line of development which was likely to be more fruitful for the treatment of the problems arising in the theory of tides. Before Young's time it was usual to postulate an ideal sphere completely covered with water.

In later lectures he discusses the cohesion and the capillary action of liquids. He derives the general expression relating the surface tension of a film to the curvature imposed on it by a difference of pressure on its two sides. The particular case of

[1] Vol. I, Plate XXXVIII, Fig. 521.

the relation for a cylinder had been derived by Segner and wrongly applied to a sphere. Young also discussed the constant 'angle of contact' at which a surface film of liquid meets a solid. He obtained an equation for this angle which is still in use.[1]

No doubt the equilibrium existing in the line of contact between a solid and a liquid involves in reality the balancing of forces directed towards individual molecular centres. In the absence of detailed knowledge of such forces, however, we must be content with a more limited account of the phenomenon in terms of Young's energy equation.

In his work in this field Young anticipated in many respects that of his great French contemporary, Laplace, and became involved in controversy with him. Young's work had originally appeared as 'An Essay on the Cohesion of Fluids', read to the Royal Society on 20 December 1804. Laplace read his paper to the Institute of France in 1805 and published it in 1806 as a Supplement to his *Méchanique Céleste*. He subsequently admitted that one of his results had been anticipated by Young, but made no reference to the other conclusions which Young had reached by independent methods. Laplace complained that Young had not attempted to derive his hypotheses from the law of the attraction of molecules—i.e. that he had not gone to the root of the matter. This, however, was unfair to Young, as Rayleigh[2] has pointed out. Young assumes a force of cohesion and a force of repulsion to balance it:

It is simplest to suppose the force of cohesion nearly or perfectly constant in its magnitude, throughout the minute distance to which it extends, and owing its apparent diversity to the contrary action of the repulsive force which varies with the distance.

Young's views were subsequently developed more fully in an article written for the Supplement to the fourth edition of the *Encyclopaedia Britannica*. It is one of his most remarkable efforts. In it he calculates the magnitude of the 'intrinsic pressure'—the balanced pressure in the interior of a liquid. His calculation agrees well with more recent values and he uses it

[1] *Proc. Phys. Soc. London*, 62 (1949), 122.   [2] *Collected Papers*, vol. III, p. 397.

to calculate the distance over which molecular forces are appreciable. Writing in 1890, Rayleigh says:

One of the most remarkable features of Young's treatise is his estimate of the range of the attractive force. . . . Never once have I seen it alluded to; and it is, I believe, generally supposed that the first attempt of the kind is not more than twenty years old.[1]

Going on from this point, Young makes the first estimate ever made of the diameter of a molecule. He gets it about a hundred times too large, but this detracts very little from the merit of this acute piece of reasoning.

Lord Kelvin referred to this work of Young's in his *Baltimore Lectures*:[2]

The first suggestion, so far as we now know, for estimating the dimensions of molecular structure in ordinary matter was given in 1805 by Thomas Young as derived from his and Laplace's substantially identical theories of capillary attraction.

It will be noted that Lord Kelvin refers to Young's and Laplace's theories as substantially identical.

A feature of volume 1 is the series of plates, forty-three in number, with which the volume closes. These illustrate the apparatus used in the lectures and the 'execution of the engravings has been minutely superintended'. There is much that is original here also. Plate XV shows various modes of communicating motion by the employment of wheel work. The most interesting figure is Fig. 198. It is thus described in the notes to the plate:

A chronometer for measuring minute portions of time. The axis AB being turned, either by the handle A or by the weight C. The balls D, E fly out and carry the weights F, G further from the axis; in consequence of which the increased effect of friction retards the motion, when it becomes too rapid. The barrel H is turned in the meantime, with the axis, and is allowed to descend as the thread at I is uncoiled, so that the point K, which is pressed against it by a spring, describes on it a spiral, which is interrupted whenever the pin K is touched.

---

[1] *Collected Papers*, p. 423.   [2] Lord Kelvin, *Baltimore Lectures*, pp. 279–80.

The principle on which this instrument of Young's is designed has since been widely applied. It is found in the familiar recording barometer and recording thermometer. It has been

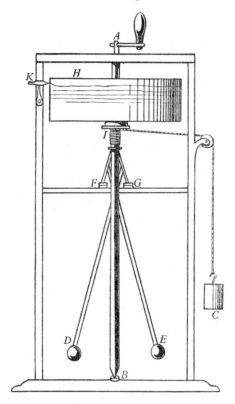

Fig. 10. Forerunner of Recording Barometer

used in acoustics for the determination of frequencies. It was adapted by Ludwig to indicate the movements of respiration and the variations in arterial pressure. Known originally as the kymograph, it has since been used for the investigation of animal movements of every conceivable kind and even 'for the transient and delicate electrical changes which are associated with vital action'.[1]

[1] Charles Joseph Singer, *Short History of Medicine* (Oxford, 1928), p. 216.

Another Plate of special interest is Plate XX. Fig. 265 is thus described:

An apparatus for observing the motions of waves excited, in a fluid poured into the trough AB, by the vibrations of the elastic wire C, loaded with moveable weight D; the shadow of the waves being thrown on a screen E and by the lamp F, through the bottom of the trough, which is of glass.

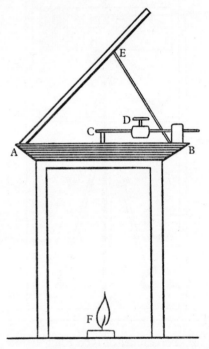

Fig. 11. Ripple Tank

This apparatus was used by Young in his lectures to illustrate the phenomena of wave motion. Fig 266 shows the divergence or 'diffraction' of a series of waves after passing through an aperture; Fig. 267 illustrates the phenomenon of the interference of waves, with which we shall be specially concerned in the next chapter. This actual ripple-tank was subsequently used by Faraday, and apparatus of the kind has become part of the stock-in-trade of every lecturer in physics. It was used to clarify the properties of waves in general and so to elucidate the wave theory of light.

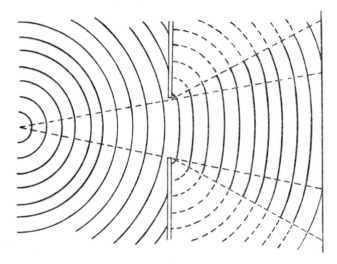

Fig. 12. Diffraction of Water Waves

It must, of course, be admitted that the style of the lectures and the presentation of the subject leaves much to be desired. As lectures they are obviously unsuited to the mixed general audience of a Royal Institution lecture. Even regarded as a written treatise they are very difficult reading. Pettigrew says very truly that:

The style of them is not adapted for general perusal, nor calculated to excite the attention of youthful minds so strongly as more elementary works. The author is too laconic, the matter is too abundant and too much condensed for minds that do not surpass the ordinary degree of power, and the professor gives credit to his readers for more knowledge than they can fairly be generally estimated to possess.[1]

The second volume of the *Lectures* opens with a short section on 'The Mathematical Elements of Natural Philosophy', covering propositions and demonstrations in pure mathematics,

[1] Pettigrew, *op. cit.* p. 7.

mechanics, hydrostatics, sound and light. The treatment is concise and in some cases obscure. In the part dealing with light he makes advances in the field of geometrical optics which have received little recognition. Here we find for the first time a geometrical construction for the refracted ray due to any incident ray falling on a spherical surface—a construction now to be found in every textbook on 'Light'. It was rediscovered by Amici (1784–1860) and has become of fundamental importance in the design of high-power microscopes. Using Young's graphical construction it is possible to obtain a very fair idea of the defects of the image in any optical instrument. In a recent lecture[1] it was said that 'the real testimony to the importance of Young's work in the field of geometrical optics is the fact that his equations are still used by optical designers one hundred and fifty years after he obtained them'.

This opening section of the volume is followed by a catalogue of 'works relating to natural philosophy and the mechanical arts; with references to particular passages, and occasional abstracts and remarks'. This catalogue extends over about 450 quarto pages. It formed the model for his *Medical Dictionary* described in Chapter IV. It was compiled in just over three years after the resignation of his professorship. Of this catalogue of references he says that

the labour of arranging about twenty thousand articles, in a systematic form, was by no means less considerable than that of collecting them. The transactions of scientific societies, and the best and latest periodical publications, which have so much multiplied the number of sources of information, constituted no small part of the collection, which was thus to be reduced into one body of science.[2]

It is indeed a remarkable achievement—sufficiently remarkable if it had been the uninterrupted task of the three years of its preparation, but doubly so as a task which shared with other projects the scanty leisure of a busy life.

Volume II concludes with a series of reprinted articles—his

[1] T. Smith, 'Contributions of Thomas Young to Geometrical Optics', *Proc. Phys. Soc. Lond.* 62 (1949), 629.   [2] Preface to vol. I, p. vi.

early paper 'Observations on Vision', his later 'Outlines of Experiments and Inquiries respecting Sound and Light' and his paper 'On the Mechanism of the Eye', with all of which we have already dealt. The series includes also his important papers on the wave theory of light, 'Letter to Mr Nicholson respecting Sound and Light'; 'On the Theory of Light and Colours'; and 'An Account of some cases of the Production of Colours'. To these are added 'An Essay on Cycloidal Curves', 'An Essay on Music' and 'An Essay on the Cohesion of Fluids'. At the very end comes an 'Account of the Proceedings of the Royal Society from November 1801 to July 1802' from the *Journal of the Royal Institution*.

It was not Young's original intention to produce a second edition of this work. The volume of material increased as the preparation of the volumes proceeded; there was considerable difficulty over the engravings, and the appearance of the work was delayed beyond the time Young had planned for. This preoccupation he felt to be prejudicing his medical career:

Whatever the deficiencies of this work may be, I think it right to observe that my present pursuits will not allow me to look forward to any period, at which I shall be able to remove them, or even to attend to the correction of the press, or the revision of the engravings, in case of the necessity of a second edition.

In this matter he seems slightly to have weakened. A copy of the book bought recently[1] contained a sheet in Young's hand-writing which consists of a list of corrections. Another copy now in the possession of the Royal Institution was given to Professor Henry S. Meiers between 1890 and 1895 by a student who bought the two volumes from a bookstall in Whitechapel for one shilling! This copy is annotated in Young's inimitable penmanship, some of which is undecipherable without a lens. The notes are clearly meant for a second edition, but the proposed changes are not for the most part material.

The sum agreed between Young and the publisher for the production of the two volumes was £1000, but the publisher failed and Young never received the money. A second edition

[1] By Professor Robinson of Queen Mary College, London.

did appear, however, after his death. It was edited by the Rev. P. Kelland, Professor of Mathematics in the University of Edinburgh, and was published in 1845. Perhaps we cannot do better than conclude this chapter with his valuation of the *Lectures* as set out in his preface:

Whether we regard the depth of Dr Young's learning, the extent of his research, the accuracy of his statements, or the beauty and originality of his theoretical views, in whatever way we contemplate these Lectures, our admiration is equally excited. They embody a complete system of Mechanical Philosophy, drawn from original sources, and illustrated by a hand capable of reducing them to the most perfect subjection. Unlike other popular writers, who, for the most part, either take the sciences at second hand, or content themselves simply with extracting the discoveries and adopting the hypotheses of more distinguished philosophers, Dr Young travelled over the whole literature of science, and whilst we are astonished at the rich store of materials which he has collected, we find nothing more prominent than the impress of his own acute and powerful mind.

VII

THE WAVE THEORY OF LIGHT IS FOUNDED

'Light is probably the undulation of an elastic medium.' YOUNG

As has already been suggested in an earlier chapter, the greatest contribution which Young made to theoretical physics, and probably his greatest contribution to knowledge, was his work on the wave theory of light. In his time two theories were in conflict. One, the corpuscular theory, supposed the sensation of light to be due to a stream of minute particles or 'corpuscles' which were shot off from the source and entered the eye. Their paths were the rays of light. The other theory regarded the sensation as due to waves travelling in an impalpable medium called the ether and spreading out in all directions from the source of light, much as sound waves spread out through the air in all directions from a sounding tuning fork. Both theories could boast an ancestry of respectable antiquity and are found among the scientific speculations of the Greeks. Neither could be regarded as in any sense established, being in much the same position as two possible solutions for the same crossword clue when there is no effective cross-checking which can decide between them.

Now it is important to realize that a scientific theory is never susceptible of proof in the sense of logical demonstration. A theory is accepted as true when the known phenomena can be deduced from the theory in a simple and direct manner. The theory is an induction from the phenomena and the phenomena are deductions from the theory, confirmed by observation and experiment. Bearing this in mind, let us review the position when, at the end of the seventeenth century, Newton was trying to make the right decision between the two theories of light. What were the facts—the phenomena—that the true theory must explain?

The earliest known fact was probably the rectilinear propagation of light. Shafts of sunlight coming through cloud are always straight. Shadows show that light does not bend round corners to any very appreciable extent and an object is only visible to the eye when no obstacle is interposed. This is obviously what one would expect from streams of corpuscles, but certainly not from waves. Sound was known to be propagated by waves in the air and sound waves *do* bend round obstacles. If a source of sound could be heard when not seen, how could light and sound both be propagated by waves? Thus on this very first count the application of the corpuscular theory is direct and simple; that of the wave theory uncertain and difficult.

Taking next the phenomenon of regular reflection, we find that rays of light striking a plane surface are reflected so that the angles of incidence and reflection are equal. This phenomenon gives no advantage to either theory. If the corpuscles

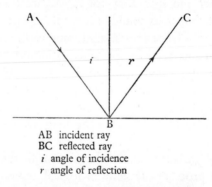

AB   incident ray
BC   reflected ray
i angle of incidence
r angle of reflection

Fig. 13. Law of Reflection

are elastic they will bounce from the surface like a billiard ball from the cushion and the angles will be equal. This same law, however, was directly deduced by Huygens from the wave theory also, where the ray is the path of a point on the wave.

These two phenomena were investigated before the history of physics came to be written. The phenomenon of refraction, however, was first studied by Ptolemy (178–100 B.C.) for light falling on a water surface. He found that the path of the ray was bent at the surface.

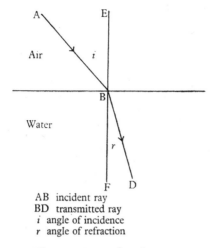

AB incident ray
BD transmitted ray
i angle of incidence
r angle of refraction

Fig. 14. Law of Refraction

He was unable to find any simple relation between the angles of incidence and refraction, and indeed the true relation was not found until Snell's Law was published in 1621. On the corpuscular theory the phenomenon was explained by assuming that as it passed through the surface of separation the corpuscle was acted upon by a force along the normal *EBF*, which increased the velocity of the corpuscle and altered the direction of its motion. This explanation introduced a force for which there was no other evidence, and involved the assumption that the velocity of light was *greater* in water than in air. On the other hand, Huygens showed that the wave theory offered a direct and simple explanation and led to Snell's Law if the velocity of light was assumed to be *less* in water than in air. This time it is the wave theory that scores, for it requires no additional hypothesis invented *ad hoc*. It seems, however, as if a decisive test between the two theories could be made by measuring the velocity of light in air and in water. No such measurement was possible at the end of the seventeenth century although Römer, the Danish astronomer, showed that light had a finite velocity and measured it for astronomical distances. When finally the velocity of light was measured in water it was found to be less than in air, thus supporting the wave theory. In any case, however, no *decisive* test of this kind is ever possible. The corpuscular theory could have been modified to fit the new discovery. Almost any theory can be made to fit almost any phenomenon if a sufficiently ingenious supplementary hypothesis, invented for the purpose, is admitted. A theory is abandoned, not because it is disproved, but because it becomes too clumsy and complicated and is rejected to make way for a rival which fits in with the phenomena more simply.

Let us note in passing that the measurement of the finite velocity of light gave a further advantage to the wave theory. The velocity of a wave might well be constant, depending as it does primarily on the medium, but why should *all* corpuscles *always* travel with the same speed?

To return to the phenomena already discussed, we must further take account of the fact that reflection and refraction occur simultaneously. When a beam of light falls on a water surface, some is transmitted and some reflected. How is this to be explained? On the wave theory it is again quite simple—the phenomenon is common to all kinds of wave. Some of the energy of the wave is transmitted and some reflected. What of the corpuscles? Why do some pass on and some come back if they are all identical? Here we have a good example of the *ad hoc* hypothesis. And it is supplied by no less a person than Newton himself. He suggested that when the corpuscles reached the boundary, some were in a 'fit of easy transmission' and some in a 'fit of easy reflection'. What happened at the surface depended on the fit of the moment. It is difficult for us to take this theory seriously, but certainly Newton did, and he even suggested waves as the predisposing cause of the fits:[1]

And in like manner, when a ray of light falls upon the surface of any pellucid Body, and is there refracted or reflected, may not waves

[1] Sir Isaac Newton, *Opticks*, (London, 1704), book III, part I, Query 17, reprint from 4th ed. (London, 1931), p. 347.

or vibrations or Tremors be there excited in the refracting or reflecting medium at the point of incidence? And do they not overtake the Rays of Light, and by overtaking them successively, do they not put them into the Fits of easy Reflexion and easy Transmission described above?

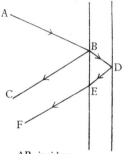

AB incident ray
BC ray reflected at first surface
EF ray reflected at second surface
BC and DF form together the 'duplicated pulse'

Fig. 15. Duplicated Pulse

To these old-established phenomena three others were added during Newton's lifetime. The first of these was a phenomenon to which Robert Hooke (1635–1703) called attention in his book *Micrographia*, published in 1665. In this work he suggests that light consists in a 'quick short vibratory motion'.[1]

Every pulse or vibration of the luminous body will generate a sphere which will continually increase and grow bigger, just after the same manner (though indefinitely swifter) as the waves or rings on the surface of water do swell into bigger and bigger circles about a point in it.

This is all rather vague and abstract, but Hooke proceeds to consider how his idea may be used to explain the colours of thin films or plates. These colours are perhaps most familiar to us when we see them produced by petrol which has been spilt on a wet road and has spread out in a thin film. Hooke called them 'fantastical colours'. He saw them in soap bubbles, in the

[1] R. Hooke, *Micrographia* (London, 1665).

film of oxide on a heated metal and in the air film between glass plates. He noticed the the colour was related to the thickness of the film and his suggested explanation is as follows: With a soap film some light is reflected at the surface of the film but some penetrates into it. Of the light that penetrates some passes through and emerges but some is reflected from the first surface and 'this compound or duplicated pulse' produces on the retina the sensation of colour. This attempt to explain the colours of thin films is not too convincing, but the only alternative was a further extension of the theory of corpuscular fits.

The second phenomenon was that of 'Diffraction'. It was discovered by Grimaldi (1616–63) and published in 1665, two years after his death. He showed that light coming through a slit diverged more widely than it ought to do if rays were straight; that the shadow of an obstacle was by no means sharp, some light bending round into the shadow; and that at the outer edge of the shadow a series of very narrow coloured bands appeared following the outline of the shadow. Thus either the edges of the obstacle or slit interfered in some way with the straight path of the corpuscles or the bending was due to the fact that light was propagated by waves.

The third new phenomenon which demanded explanation was 'Double Refraction', discovered by Bartolinus (1625–98) in the course of some experiments on Iceland Spar in 1670. If a ray of light falls on the face of a slice of this crystal, then in general it gives rise to *two* refracted rays. One of these behaves like the refracted ray in the case of water or glass and obeys the ordinary laws of refraction. The other behaves in a quite new way and does not obey the ordinary laws of refraction. It is therefore called the 'extraordinary' ray. Huygens explained this phenomenon by supposing the ether in the crystal to propagate two waves—one a spherical wave giving the ordinary ray, and one an ellipsoidal wave giving the extraordinary ray. The ellipsoidal shape of the extraordinary wave was attributed to the fact that for this wave the velocity of the wave was different in different directions. By making quite simple assump-

tions about the exact shape of the ellipsoid Huygens could
calculate for any given case the direction of the extraordinary
ray, and he showed that it agreed with experiment. Support

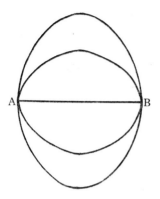

Fig. 16. Ordinary and Extraordinary Waves in a crystal of
Iceland Spar

for his theory came from the fact that the crystals which show
double refraction are not in fact 'isotropic'—i.e. their properties
vary with the direction in the crystal along which they are
measured. The conductivity for heat and the elasticity of a small
rod of crystal depends on the direction in which it has been cut.
This again gave the wave theory a slight superiority, as no
attempt to explain extraordinary refraction on the corpuscular
theory had then been made.

But if Huygens gave the wave theory a slight advantage in
explaining double refraction he provided by his experiments
another challenge to that theory, and to the corpuscular theory
as well, by discovering that both the ordinary ray and the
extraordinary ray were 'polarized'. The nature of this phenomenon can perhaps best be understood by reference to a
particular experiment. The mineral tourmaline exhibits double
refraction, but one of the two refracted rays (the ordinary) is
absorbed in traversing quite a small thickness of the crystal. If
two slices are cut from a tourmaline crystal and put one behind

the other just as they were before they were cut, then a ray of ordinary light appears to pass through them unchanged. If, however, the second slice is turned through 90°, no light passes through it. On rotation through a further 90° light passes again. Thus the light passed by the first slice has 'sides'; it is polarized.

Even more remarkable is the result if we let a ray of light fall on a crystal of Iceland Spar and then on the tourmaline slice. The Iceland Spar transmits two rays. If the tourmaline is in one position it transmits the ordinary ray and cuts off the extraordinary ray. When twisted through 90° it passes the extraordinary ray and cuts off the ordinary ray. In intermediate positions it passes some of both. Thus when double refraction takes place, both rays are polarized, and they are polarized at right angles to one another. Huygens was quite unable to offer any explanation of this curious phenomenon based on the wave theory, and no supporter of the corpuscular theory was in any better case.

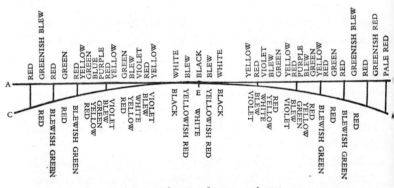

Fig. 17. Colours of Newton's Rings

Here then was the point reached when Newton surveyed the evidence. It was undoubtedly inconclusive. He himself extended the studies of Hooke on the colours of thin films and the whole of book II of his *Opticks* is devoted to an account of his measurements and the deductions he made from them. The opening section of the book is headed 'Observations Concern-

PLATE II

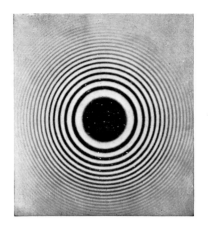

(1) NEWTON'S RINGS

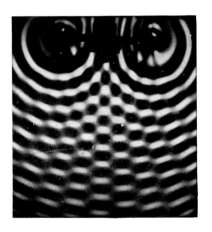

(2) INTERFERENCE FRINGES
IN WATER

ing the Reflexions, Refractions and Colours of Thin Transparent Bodies' and begins thus (p. 193):

It has been observed by others, that transparent substances, as glass, water, air, etc. when made very thin by being blown into bubbles or otherwise formed into plates, do exhibit various colours according to their various thinness, although at a greater thickness they appear very clear and colourless. In the former book I forbore to treat of these colours because they seemed of a more difficult consideration, and were not necessary for establishing the Properties of Light there discoursed of.

In order to make his study of these colours precise he lays a convex lens on a plane plate of glass so that the two enclose a film of air, symmetrical about the point of contact and such that if the curvature of the convex surface is known the thickness of the air film at any required distance from the point of contact may be calculated. Using white light and allowing it to fall normally on the air film, it is reflected to the eye as two beams of light, one reflected at the upper surface of the air film and the other at the lower surface. Newton found a series of coloured rings showing the order of colours set out in Fig. 17, which is taken from his book.[1] He found that the light which passed through the lens and plate when it was viewed from the other side also showed coloured rings and that these were complementary in colour to those reflected, as might be expected. They are indicated by the set of colour names on the left of the diagram. He found that the rings were narrow if light from the violet end of the spectrum only was used, and wide if light from the red end of the spectrum only was used; and he explained the colours seen in white light by supposing that each of the constituent colours of white light produced its own system of rings and that the colours observed were due to the overlapping of all these various systems. Far from the centre the overlapping became so great that no colours could be seen. The actual colours are shown in Fig. 17. When using light of one colour only he could measure about 30 successive rings and he found that in moving from one ring to

[1] Newton, *op. cit.* Fig. 3, p. 209.

the next the corresponding thickness of the air film always increased by the same amount. This amount was related to Newton's theory of fits. It was in fact the 'Interval of the Fits'.[1]

The returns of the disposition of any Ray to be Reflected I will call its Fits of easy Reflexion, and those of its disposition to be transmitted its Fits of easy Transmission, and the space it passes between every return and the next return, the Interval of its Fits.

Newton also studied Diffraction, or, as he called it, Inflexion, and repeated and extended the experiments of Grimaldi. But the comparatively slight bending of rays at the edge of an obstacle left him strongly prejudiced in favour of the corpuscular theory even though he had to use what amounted to a wave theory as a subsidiary hypothesis. Thus he says:[2]

Are not all hypotheses erroneous in which light is supposed to consist of a pression or motion, propagated through a fluid medium? If it consisted in pression or motion, propagated either in an instant or in time, it would bend into the shadow. For pression or motion cannot be propagated in a fluid in right lines beyond an obstacle which stops part of the motion, but will bend and spread every way into the quiescent medium which lies beyond the obstacle. The waves on the surface of stagnating water, passing by the sides of a broad obstacle which stops part of them, bend afterwards and dilate themselves gradually into the quiet water behind the obstacle. The waves, pulses or vibrations of the air, wherein sounds consist, bend manifestly though not so much as the waves of water. For a bell or a cannon may be heard beyond a hill which interrupts the sight of the sounding body; and sounds are propagated as readily through crooked pipes as straight ones. But light is never known to follow crooked passages, nor to bend into the shadow. For the fixed stars, by the interposition of any of the planets, cease to be seen, and so do the parts of the sun by the interposition of the moon, Mercury or Venus.

and again:[3]

To me, the fundamental supposition itself seems impossible, namely, that the waves or vibrations of any fluid can, like rays of light, be propagated in straight lines without a continual and very

---

[1] Newton, *l.c.* p. 281.   [2] *Ibid.* p. 362.   [3] *Phil. Trans.* 7 (1672), 5089.

extravagant spreading and bending every way into the quiescent medium where they are terminated by it. I mistake if there be not both experiment and demonstration to the contrary.

It is quite obvious that the objection was, to Newton, insuperable. His mind was not closed against the possibility of waves playing a subsidiary part in the propagation of Light, and he was not altogether satisfied with the corpuscular theory, but he felt constrained to throw the weight of his great name and reputation behind it. As a result, criticism was disarmed for a century and the theory was never seriously challenged again until Thomas Young became interested in the controversy during his time at Cambridge.

No contribution of major importance was made in the period intervening between the publication of Newton's *Opticks* and the time of Young. Euler (1707–83) had indeed written in support of the wave theory, but without adding very much to the discussion. In the paper already noticed (p. 141) on 'Sound and Light', published in 1800, Young deals with 'the analogy between light and sound' and summarizes the position as follows:[1]

Every since the publication of Sir Isaac Newton's incomparable writings, his doctrines of the emanation of particles of light from lucid substances . . . have been almost universally admitted in this country, and but little opposed in others. . . . Without pretending to decide positively on the controversy, it is conceived that some considerations may be brought forwards which may tend to diminish the weight of objections to a theory similar to the Huygenian. There are also one or two difficulties in the Newtonian system which have been little observed.

The difficulties of the corpuscular theory which he cites are those to which attention has already been called.

(*a*) That the velocity of light is the same in all circumstances.[2]

How happens it that, whether the projecting force is the slightest transmission of electricity, the friction of two pebbles, the lowest degree of visible ignition, the white heat of a wind furnace, or the

[1] *Works of Young*, vol. I, pp. 78–9.   [2] *Ibid.* p. 79.

intense heat of the sun itself, these wonderful corpuscles are always propelled with one uniform velocity?

(b) Simultaneous reflection and refraction.[1]

Why, of the same kind of rays, in every circumstance precisely similar, some should always be reflected and others transmitted, appears in this system to be wholly inexplicable.

(c) Colours of thin plates.[2]

The phenomena of the colours of thin plates require, in the Newtonian system, a very complicated supposition, of an ether, anticipating by its motion the velocity of the corpuscles of light, and thus producing the fits of transmission and reflection; and even this supposition does not much assist the explanation.

By way of meeting in some degree the objections to the wave theory he suggests that the same ether which carries the waves of light may transmit the electric shock and that it fills the interstices between the molecules of all substances, retaining its elasticity but becoming denser and so transmitting the light more slowly.

The paper is remarkable because of the statement in paragraph XI of what happens when two sounds cross. The fact that each proceeds independently from the region where they cross had led Dr Smith, the author of a work on *Harmonics*, to suggest that in crossing the two sounds acted upon different particles of the medium. In reply Young stated his principle of superposition, which afterwards became fundamental to his explanation of the phenomenon of 'interference'.[3]

It is surprising that so great a mathematician as Dr Smith could have entertained for a moment an idea that the vibrations constituting different sounds should be able to cross each other in all directions, without affecting the same individual particles of air by their joint forces: undoubtedly they cross, without disturbing each other's progress; but this can be no otherwise effected than by each particle's partaking of both motions.

He goes on to illustrate this statement and to use it to explain

---

[1] *Works of Young*, vol. I, p. 79.   [2] *Ibid.* p. 81.   [3] *Ibid.* p. 83.

the phenomenon of 'beats', in which two sounds may be combined to give an instant of silence at a given point because there the air is urged in opposite directions by the two sets of sound waves and so remains at rest. He discusses this production of beats at some length, giving the correct explanation and illustrating it by diagrams.

In this dispute Young was, of course, completely in the right although his reference to Dr Smith was, perhaps, more slighting than was altogether necessary. Unfortunately he goes on in paragraph XVI to discuss the 'Temperament of Musical Intervals', another subject with which Smith had dealt in his *Harmonics*, and finds himself betrayed into dismissing Smith with one devastating sentence. 'Dr Smith has written a large and obscure volume, which, for every purpose but for the use of an impracticable instrument, leaves the whole subject precisely where it found it.'[1]

Now the Dr Smith who receives this somewhat cavalier treatment at the hands of Young in his early paper was an authority whose work was highly regarded. He was a mathematician of note, who had been Professor of Astronomy at Cambridge and Master of Trinity. He founded the Smith's Prizes, still regarded as the highest distinction open to the younger mathematicians, and he wrote two important treatises, one on *Opticks* (1738) and the other on *Harmonics, or the Philosophy of Musical Sounds* (1749). Both were widely translated into European languages. It was not surprising then that this criticism by an unknown author who had only just graduated was not taken very well. The first comment was no more than the truth, but the second was unnecessarily disparaging.

Young was taken to task by John Gough (1757–1825), a blind Quaker botanist and mathematician who was pretty well known. But the severest strictures came from Professor John Robison of Glasgow (1739–1805), a man with a great reputation as a mathematician and physicist. In an article on 'Temperament' in the Supplement to the *Encyclopaedia Britannica* he wrote:

[1] *Ibid.* p. 93.

We are surprised to see this work of Dr Smith greatly under-valued by a most ingenious gentleman in the Philosophical Transactions for 1800, and called a large and obscure volume, which leaves the matter just as it was, and its results useless and impracticable. We are sorry to see this, because we have great expectations from the future labours of this gentleman in the field of harmonics; and his late work is rich in refined and valuable matter. We presume humbly to recommend to him attention to his own admonitions to a very young and ingenious gentleman, who he thinks, proceeded too far in animadverting on the writings of Newton, Barrow and other eminent mathematicians.

The reference here is to an essay published by Young in the same year, 1800, in the *British Magazine*, on 'Cycloidal Curves'. This essay contains nothing of outstanding merit, but the introduction is a defence of geometrical as opposed to analytical methods on the ground of their superior simplicity and clarity. In the course of this essay Young refers in very derogatory terms to a paper printed in the *Philosophical Transactions* in 1798.[1]

But when we see an author exerting all his ingenuity in order to avoid every idea that has the least tincture of geometry, when he obliges us to toil through immense volumes filled with all manner of literal characters, without a single diagram to diversify the prospect, we may observe with the less surprise that such an author appears to be confined in his conception of the most elementary doctrines, and that he fancies he has made an improvement of consequence, when, in fact, he is only viewing an old object in a new disguise.

No names are mentioned here, but later there is a reference to 'a young gentleman in Edinburgh' and to the paper in the *Philosophical Transactions*. After substantiating his view that the discoveries given in the paper are not new but only derived by a new method, Young continues:[2]

On the whole it appears that this ingenious gentleman has been somewhat unfortunate in the choice of those problems which he has selected as specimens of the elegance of the modern mode of demonstration; whether those which he has brought forward with-

---

[1] *Works*, vol. I, p. 100.   [2] *Ibid.* p. 102.

out proof would have furnished him with a more favourable opportunity for the display of neatness and accuracy, may be more easily determined whenever he may think proper to lay before the public their analysis and demonstration, at full length.

These comments were unfortunate. In substance they are fully justified, but their tone was such as to cause lasting resentment—a resentment which waited its opportunity and then took full advantage of it. The scathing reference to Smith had brought rebuke from John Gough and Professor Robison and the incident seemed closed. But the writer of the mathematical paper was no less a person than the young Henry Brougham (1778–1868), afterwards Lord Chancellor, and his bitter and virulent attacks on Young's later work certainly did much to delay the acceptance of the wave theory.

In the following year Young summarized his arguments in a 'letter to Mr Nicholson, Professor of Natural Philosophy in the Royal Institution respecting Sound and Light, and in reply to some observations of Professor Robison'. This letter, dated from 48 Welbeck Street, 13 July 1801, was published in *Nicholson's Journal*—one of the principal scientific journals of the time. The summary is very interesting as showing the evidence which we have already discussed set out succinctly in Young's own way.[1]

Light is probably the undulation of an elastic medium.

(*a*) Because its velocity in the same medium is always equal.

(*b*) Because all refractions are attended with a partial reflection.

(*c*) Because there is no reason to expect that such a vibration should diverge equally in all directions, and because it is probable that it does diverge in a small degree in every direction.

(*d*) Because the dispersion of differently coloured rays is no more incompatible with this system than with the common opinion, which only assigns for it the nominal cause of different elective attractions.

(*e*) Because refraction and reflection in general are equally explicable on both suppositions.

(*f*) Because inflection (diffraction) is as well, and it may be added, even much better explained by this theory.

[1] *Ibid.* p. 132.

(*g*) Because all the phenomena of the colours of thin plates, which are in reality totally unintelligible on the common hypothesis, admit a very complete and simple explanation by this supposition. The analogy which is here superficially indicated, will probably soon be made public more in detail; and will also be extended to the colours of thick plates, and to the fringes produced by inflection, affording from Newton's own elaborate experiments, a most convincing argument in favour of this system.

This last paragraph forecasts the publication of Young's most original and most convincing contribution to physics—the application of the principle of superposition (or interference) to the explanation of some phenomena of light already familiar and of some which he himself was to discover and expound. A few months later the first instalment was given in a Bakerian Lecture.

The rest of his letter on Sound and Light, which is the bulk of it, is a reply to Professor Robison, whose indictment of him he deals with under three heads: (1) that he had taken the liberty of giving severe advice to a young mathematician who had never asked it; (2) that this advice was equally applicable to his own presumption; and (3) that Dr Smith's treatise on *Harmonics* is a work entitled to the highest praise. On the first count he has little to say.[1]

I did, in fact, endeavour to show that the gentleman in question had overlooked the labours of some former authors relative to his subject, but I accompanied my remarks with nothing like admonition.

On the next two counts his defence is a firm one:[2]

I have read Dr Smith's work with attention, and I imag'ne, from the polite manner in which Professor Robison is pleased to speak of my essay, he will not hesitate to allow that I have understood it. I took it up with great expectations: those expectations having been completely disappointed, I thought it right to state my cool and unprejudiced opinion of its merits, in order to prevent a similar disappointment in others. It is impossible, therefore, that an 'attention' to any 'admonitions' of a general nature, wherever they may

[1] *Works*, vol. I, p. 135.   [2] *Ibid.*

be found, can influence such an opinion; and so far only as I am supposed to be an incompetent judge on the subject of harmonics can it be asserted that it was either blameable or superfluous for me to express that opinion. As a mathematician, and an optician, I value Dr Smith highly; but I must still beg leave to affirm that his whole book of harmonics contains far, far less information than either of the articles Temperament or Trumpet, in the Supplement to the Encyclopedia.

He goes on to argue his case with great ability but at quite unnecessary length. Posterity is on his side but will not entirely acquit him of a certain provocativeness in the form of his judgments. He was completely unprejudiced and never harboured any bitterness of feeling, but while very sensitive himself, he seemed unable to put himself in the place of others and to realize their reaction to his words. He had no idea of 'tempering the wind' of his criticism.

The preceding letter was written in July 1801, and Young's first Bakerian Lecture was read to the Royal Society on 12 November of that year and was printed in the *Philosophical Transactions* for 1802. He begins by setting down his purpose in the following words:[1]

Although the invention of plausible hypotheses, independent of any connexion with experimental observations, can be of very little use in the promotion of natural knowledge; yet the discovery of simple and uniform principles, by which a great number of apparently heterogeneous phenomena are reduced to coherent and universal laws, must ever be allowed to be of considerable importance towards the improvement of the human intellect.

He goes on to pay a very high tribute to the work of Newton in the field of Optics and, in the course of it, to refer to Euler 'whose system of light, as far as it is worthy of notice, either was, or might have been, wholly borrowed from Newton, Hooke, Huygens and Malebranche'.[2] He then sets out his lecture as a series of hypotheses, propositions and corollaries, being at pains in the case of each to support it with relevant quotations from Newton. In part, this arises from his genuine

---

[1] *Ibid.* p. 140.　　　　　　　　[2] *Ibid.* p. 141.

respect for Newton, in part, as he frankly admits, in order to commend by the authority of Newton such features of the wave theory as could be so commended.

The hypotheses with which the lecture opens are four in number:

(1) A luminiferous ether pervades the universe, rare and elastic in a high degree.

(2) Undulations are excited in this ether whenever a body becomes luminous.

(3) The Sensation of different Colours depends on the different frequency of Vibrations excited by Light in the Retina.

(4) All material Bodies have an Attraction for the ethereal Medium, by means of which it is accumulated within their substance, and for a small Distance around them, in a state of greater Density, but not of greater Elasticity.

This last hypothesis would account for the fact that light travels more slowly in transparent solids and liquids than in air. About this hypothesis he is rather apologetic. It is in contradiction to that of Newton 'yet it appears to be the simplest and the best of any that have occurred to me'.

Young then goes on to develop the wave theory in a series of propositions which it is unnecessary to quote in detail. Proposition III deals with the vexed question of diffraction, and here Newton's objections are stated at length and Young's reply set out. It elaborates the point, made earlier, that the wave theory does not require an equal spreading into a shadow in all directions and that in point of fact some spreading of light into a shadow is established. Various other phenomena already considered are explained and illustrated in terms of the wave theory until, in Proposition VIII, we reach the new evidence for which Young was responsible and which constitutes his main contribution. 'When two Undulations, from different origins, coincide either perfectly or very nearly in Direction, their joint effect is a Combination of the Motions belonging to each.'[1]

This new principle of interference of waves may be most

[1] *Works*, vol. I, p. 157.

clearly illustrated by borrowing an illustration from the propagation of water waves which Young himself used on a later occasion.[1]

Suppose a number of equal waves of water to move upon the surface of a stagnant lake, with a certain constant velocity, and to enter a narrow channel leading out of the lake. Suppose then another similar cause to have excited another equal series of waves, which arrive at the same channel, with the same velocity, and at the same time with the first. Neither series of waves will destroy the other, but their effects will be combined; if they enter the channel in such a manner that the elevations of one series coincide with those of the other, they must together produce a series of greater joint elevations; but if the elevations of one series are so situated as to correspond to the depressions of the other, they must exactly fill up those depressions, and the surface of the water must remain smooth: at least I can discover no alternative, either from theory or from experiment.[2]

Now I maintain that similar effects take place whenever two portions of light are thus mixed; and this I call the general law of the interference of light.

If then, in place of the two sets of waves on the lake, we think of two 'portions' of light, and instead of the channel leading out of the lake we think of a point on a screen where the two portions of light converge or of the eye of an observer which they enter together, then in either case the result may be double brightness, complete darkness or something between, according as the waves of light are exactly in step, exactly out of step, or not quite either.

Obviously, in the case of the water waves, if the two sources are vibrating together and they are equidistant from the channel, the waves will arrive with crest coinciding with crest and trough with trough, and we shall get reinforcement. Thus in Fig. 18, which is taken from Young's Royal Institution Lectures, 'two equal series of waves, diverging from centres A and B, and crossing each other in such a manner, that in the

---

[1] *Ibid.* p. 202.
[2] The experiment had been described in his Royal Institution Lectures and is illustrated in Plate XX, Fig. 276.

lines tending towards C, D, E and F, they counteract each other's effects (*interfere*) and the water remains nearly smooth, while in the intermediate spaces it is agitated (*reinforced*)'. The

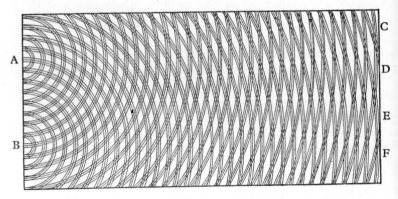

Fig. 18. Interference or Superposition for two sets of ripples

phenomenon is shown in the photograph of ripples from two sources in Pl. III. Thus the joint effect depends upon the relation of the difference of path to the wave-length; maximum reinforcement occurs when the path difference is a whole multiple of one wave-length and destructive interference when the path difference has half a wave-length over. It should be noted that in the case of white light we have a mixture of all the colours and that each colour has its own wave-length, that of the red being nearly twice that of the violet. It may, therefore, happen that, when white light is used, a point which is a point of reinforcement for one colour may be a point of destructive interference for another colour with a different wave-length. Thus, white light will appear as coloured light, some of its constituents being wholly and some partially suppressed while others are reinforced.

In Corollary I to this proposition—'Of the Colours of Striated Surfaces'—Young applies his principle quite correctly and explains these colours, for instance in the case of mother-of-pearl, as due to the light waves from successive scratches interfering with one another.

Thus in Fig. 19 let the reflected light waves start simultaneously from *A* and *B*. Then in the direction *E* the wave from *A* will

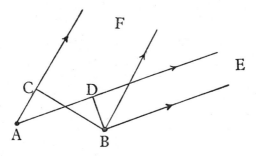

Fig. 19. Path Difference varying with angle

lag behind that from *B* by a distance *AD*. Similarly in the direction *F* the wave from *A* will lag behind that from *B* by a distance *AC*. Thus the path difference varies with the direction, so that *AD* might be a whole wave-length for red light and the two sets of red waves would be in step, while *AC* might be half a wave-length for red light and the two reflected waves of red light would be exactly out of step. Thus red light would be strongly reflected in the direction *E* and not at all in the direction *F*. This explains why the colour produced from white light varies with the direction in which the surface is viewed. Young goes on to suggest that certain iridescent colours are probably caused in this way by a striated surface, and he mentions specifically 'the integuments of some insects and of some other natural bodies'. In this he was correct—wing cases of beetles, peacock's feathers and mother-of-pearl are all illustrations which may be quoted.

In Corollary II, 'Of the Colours of Thin Plates', Young applies his principle in more detail. Light is supposed to reach an eye at *E* from a source at *A* by two different paths: *AFE* by reflection at the top face of the plate and *ABCDE* by reflection at the lower face. The difference in length of path will depend on the thickness of the plate and the angle at which the light is reflected inside the film. Thus when white light falls on the plate, an eye at E will receive light reflected from the plate with the colour for which the waves are exactly out of

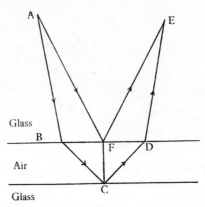

Fig. 20. Ray diagram. 'Of the colours of thin plates'

step missing, the colour for which the waves are exactly in step specially bright, and all other colours more or less reduced because to *some* extent their corresponding waves are out of step.

If the 'plate' is a film of air and is bounded by a plane glass surface below and a spherical glass surface above and if we allow light to fall on it normally, then we have the experimental arrangement used by Newton to produce 'Newton's Rings'.

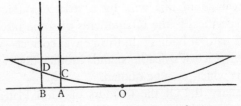

Fig. 21. Ray diagram. Normal Incidence for Newton's Rings

The thickness of the air plate is the same at all points on a circle round the point of contact O as centre. If red light shows a bright ring through A and another bright ring through B, then the two sets of waves reflected at A and C and at B and D, respectively, are exactly in step. Now the difference in length of path for light reflected at A and at C is twice the thickness AC and the difference in length of path at B and D is twice the thickness BD. And these must differ by one wave-length of red light. Using Newton's actual measurements, Young was able to calculate the wave-lengths for the seven colours of the spectrum, and these are tabulated and set out. He admits that, after having worked out the whole theory of the phenomenon, he came across in Hooke's *Micrographia* 'a passage which might have led me earlier to a similar conclusion'. To this passage reference has already been made. Young sets it out in full in its context. It contains no *explanation* of the 'duplicated pulse' and no reference to the principle of interference. Young goes on in later corollaries to apply the principle successfully to a phenomenon known as 'The Colours of thick Plates', and, with partial success, to the coloured fringes due to diffraction, or, as he and Newton called it, 'inflexion'.

In the course of some general remarks he supports the wave theory by reference to experiments of Mr Bennett,[1] in which it was demonstrated that light exerted no pressure on the surface on which it fell. It was argued that the corpuscles supposed to constitute light must, by their impact, exert a pressure, and therefore light could not be corpuscular in nature. Young was happily ignorant of the fact, only established later, that waves as well as particles exert a pressure on the surface on which they fall. The pressure of light has since been demonstrated.

Young's final proposition is that radiant light consists in undulations of the luminiferous ether and his comment on the proposition is: 'This proposition is the general conclusion from all the preceding, and it is conceived that they conspire to prove it in as satisfactory a manner as can possibly be expected from the nature of the subject.'[2] The evidence is certainly convincing, but it is indirect. The *direct* evidence for the interference of light was still wanting and Young set himself to produce it, but it was two years later before it was published.

[1] *Phil. Trans.* (1792), p. 87.   [2] Sir J. Larmor, *Collected Papers*, vol. II, p. 351.

The lecture contains another remarkable anticipation of later work in Proposition VII. In considering the passage of light through a transparent substance he assumes the particles of the substance to have their own natural frequencies of vibration. In this he was ahead of Cauchy (1789–1857) and Poisson (1781–1840). He also assumed not only an action of the light waves on the particles but a reaction of the particles on the wave, and in this he was ahead of Kelvin (1824–1907) and Stokes (1819–1903).

Meantime another paper was read to the Royal Society on 1 July 1802 and published in the *Philosophical Transactions* for that year (p. 387). This paper, 'An Account of Some Cases of the Production of Colours not hitherto described', opens with a reassertion of Young's fundamental discovery:[1]

Whatever opinion may be entertained of the theory of light and colours which I have lately had the honour of submitting to the Royal Society, it must at any rate be allowed that it has given birth to the discovery of a simple and general law, capable of explaining a number of the phenomena of coloured light, which, without this law, would remain insulated and unintelligible. The law is that wherever two portions of the same light arrive at the eye by different routes, either exactly or very nearly in the same direction, the light becomes most intense when the difference of the routes is any multiple of a certain length, and least intense in the intermediate state of the interfering portions; and this length is different for light of different colours.

The paper deals with diffraction fringes surrounding the edge of the shadow of an obstacle by treating them as due to interference between light passing the edge and light reflected from the edge, a theory which we now know to be untenable. But it gives the correct explanation of what Young calls the colours of 'mixed plates'—the colours seen when a candle is viewed through two pieces of plate glass with a little moisture between them. The most interesting contribution, however, is the explanation of the black spot seen when a *very* thin plate or film is viewed by reflected light. It can be seen in a soap

[1] *Works*, vol. I, p. 170.

film just before it bursts and at the centre of Newton's rings where the lens and plate are in contact. In these cases the difference of path is almost nil; why then do not the two sets of waves conspire to give maximum illumination? Young's reply is that the reflection for the two waves takes place under opposite conditions. In the case of Newton's rings, for instance, one reflection takes place at the upper face of the air film where the light emerges from the denser glass into the less dense air. The reflection at the lower face, on the other hand, takes place where the light is passing from the less dense air into the more dense glass. This reflection under different conditions is, Young argues, equivalent to increasing the path of one set of waves by half a wave-length and so producing destructive interference, even when the difference of path is zero. To demonstrate his theory he used between the lens and plate a film of liquid which was optically denser than the lens but less dense than the plate, so that the two reflections were under the *same* conditions, i.e. at the passage from a less dense to a more dense medium in each case. 'I have fully verified this prediction by interposing a drop of oil of sassafras between a prism of flint glass and a lens of crown-glass: the central spot seen by reflected light was *white* and surrounded by a dark ring.'[1] Young's explanation was, in fact, correct.

In 1803 Young again delivered a Bakerian Lecture. It was read on 24 November and published in the *Philosophical Transactions* for 1804. It was called 'Experiments and Calculations relative to Physical Optics'. This paper begins with what was almost the most convincing of all Young's demonstrations of interference and gave the first direct evidence of the principle. The experiments 'may be repeated with great ease whenever the sun shines, and without any other apparatus than is at hand to everyone'. As these experiments are both simple and epoch-making it is well that we should have his own account of the first of them:[2]

Exper. 1. I made a small hole in a window-shutter, and covered it with a piece of thick paper, which I perforated with a fine needle,

[1] *Ibid.* p. 175.   [2] *Ibid.* p. 179.

For greater convenience of observation I placed a small looking-glass without the window-shutter, in such a position as to reflect the sun's light, in a direction nearly horizontal, upon the opposite wall, and to cause the cone of diverging light to pass over a table on which were several little screens of card-paper. I brought into the sunbeam a slip of card, about one-thirtieth of an inch in breadth, and observed its shadow, either on the wall or on other cards held at different distances. Besides the fringes of colour on each side of the shadow, the shadow itself was divided by similar parallel fringes, of smaller dimensions, differing in number, according to the distance at which the shadow was observed, but leaving the middle of the shadow always white. Now these fringes were the joint effects of the portions of light passing on each side of the slip of card and inflected, or rather diffracted, into the shadow. For, a little screen being placed a few inches from the card, so as to receive either edge of the shadow on its margin, all the fringes which had before been observed in the shadow on the wall, immediately disappeared, although the light inflected on the other side was allowed to retain its course, and although this light must have undergone any modification that the proximity of the other edge of the slip of card might have been capable of occasioning. . . . Nor was it for want of a sufficient intensity of light that one of the two portions was incapable of producing the fringes alone; for when they were both uninterrupted, the lines appeared, even if the intensity was reduced to one-tenth or one-twentieth.

Young is able from his measurements to calculate the wave-length of light, to compare the value thus obtained with the value calculated from the colours of thin plates, and to compare his own measurements of the fringes with those of Newton. The results were such as to leave very little doubt that all the phenomena were due to interference and that light was indeed transmitted by a wave motion. The foundations of the wave theory of light had been well and truly laid.

It was at this stage, when his work on the wave theory seemed conclusive and the principle of interference established, that the storm which had been brewing since Young's early criticism of Henry Brougham broke about his head. The year 1802 had seen a new departure in journalism. A brilliant group in Edinburgh, including Sydney Smith, Francis Jeffrey and Henry Brougham, started a new magazine called *The Edinburgh Review*. The avowed aim was 'to erect a higher standard of merit, and secure bolder and purer taste in literature, and to apply philosophical principles and the maxims of truth and humanity to politics'. Lord Cockburn, in his *Life of Lord Jeffrey*, says:[1]

The effect was electrical. It was an entire and instant change of everything that the public had been accustomed to in that sort of composition. The learning of the new journal, its talent, its spirit, its writing, its independence, were all new. Its literature, its political economy and its pure science were generally admired. It was hailed as the dawn of a brighter day.

It was in the pages of this new periodical that there appeared, at intervals, three articles reviewing Young's contributions to the *Philosophical Transactions*. They were anonymous, but Young unhesitatingly traced them to Henry Brougham, and the authorship was never denied either by Brougham himself or by his friends. The articles were abusive and sarcastic, and while having all the appearance of being well informed were not really so. In the first, the writer, opening his review of the first of Young's Bakerian Lectures, says:[2]

As this paper contains nothing which deserves the name, either of experiment or of discovery, and as it is, in fact, destitute of every species of merit, we should have allowed it to pass among the multitude of those articles which must always find admittance into the collections of a Society which is pledged to publish two or three volumes every year.

He goes on to protest against the action of the Royal Society in recognizing Young's 'lucubrations' at all.

In the second article Young's paper on 'Cases of the Production of Colours' comes in for bitter criticism, and again the Royal Society is adjured not to lower its standards by the admission of Young's work. 'We cannot conclude our review

---

[1] Henry Cockburn, Lord Cockburn, *Life of Lord Jeffrey* (1852).
[2] *Edinburgh Review*, vol. I, p. 450.

of these articles without entreating, for a moment, the attention of that illustrious body, which has admitted of late years so many paltry and unsubstantial papers into its Transactions.'[1]

But it was in the third article of the series that the invective reached its height. After an attempt at a serious criticism of Young's work which had no kind of justification, Brougham continued:[2]

We now dismiss, for the present, the feeble lucubrations of this author, in which we have searched without success for some traces of learning, acuteness, and ingenuity, that might compensate his evident deficiency in the powers of solid thinking, calm and patient investigation, and successful development of the laws of Nature, by steady and modest observation of her operations. We came to this examination with no other prejudices than the very allowable pre-possession against vague hypothesis, by which all true lovers of science have for above a century and a half been swayed. We pursued it, both on the present and on a former occasion, without any feelings except those of regret at the abuse of that time and opportunity which no greater share of talents than Dr Young's are sufficient to render fruitful by mere diligence and moderation. From us, however, he cannot claim any portion of respect until he shall alter his mode of proceeding or change the subject of his lucubrations; and we feel ourselves more particularly called upon to express our disapprobation, because, as distinction has unwarily been bestowed on his labours by the most illustrious of scientific bodies, it is the more necessary that a free protest should be recorded before the more humble tribunals of literature.

There can be no doubt that these three articles stung Young to the quick. They were damaging to his reputation as a physicist, but, even more serious, they were prejudicial to his reputation as a physician as well. In addition they were un-doubtedly meant to wound and they achieved their malevolent purpose. Readers of *The Edinburgh Review* had no means of knowing that Brougham had no qualification to speak as a critic of physical theories. Nor could they know that Young was one of the most careful of men, a patient experimenter and

[1] *Edinburgh Review*, vol. i, p. 459.   [2] *Ibid.* vol. v, p. 103.

a cautious theoriser. The articles carried conviction and the damage was done.

It was natural, and indeed inevitable, that Young should attempt a reply. One could wish that he had written something dignified, concise and to the point. Instead he wrote his reply in his usual ponderous controversial manner and unfortunately couched it in terms which, while not rivalling the abuse of Brougham, were more acid than became his nature. Neither the content nor the form, however, mattered in the least, as the reply had no public circulation and Young tells us that only one copy was sold.[1]

The flowing periods of Young's opening sentences laid bare his wounds.

A man who has a proper regard for the dignity of his own character, although his sensibility may sometimes be awakened by the unjust attacks of interested malevolence, will esteem it in general more advisable to bear in silence, the temporary effects of a short-lived injury, than to suffer his own pursuits to be interrupted, in making an effort to repel the invective, and to punish the aggressor. But it is possible that art and malice may be so insidiously combined as to give to the grossest misrepresentations the semblance of justice and candour; and, especially where the subject of the discussion is of a nature little adapted to the comprehension of the generality of readers, even a man's friends may be so far misled by a garbled extract from his own works, and by the specious mixture of partial truth with essential falsehood, that they may not only be unable to defend him from the unfavourable opinion of others, but may themselves be disposed to suspect, in spite of their partiality, that he has been hasty and inconsiderate at least, if not radically weak and mistaken.

He complains that the articles are not so much criticism as 'ridicule and invective' and constitute an attack 'not only upon my writings and my literary pursuits but almost on my moral character'. He proceeds to establish the authorship of the article thus:[2]

The peculiarity of the style and tendency of this attack led me at once to suspect, that it must have been suggested by some other

[1] *Works*, vol. I, p. 192. [2] *Ibid.* p. 194.

motive than the love of truth; and I have both internal and external evidence for believing that the articles in question are either wholly, or in great measure, the productions of an individual, upon whose mathematical works I had formerly thought it necessary to make some remarks, which, though not favourable, were far from being severe; and whose optical speculations, partly confuted before, and already forgotten, appeared, to their fond parent, to be in danger of a still more complete rejection from the establishment of my opinions.

Young then proceeds to reply in detail to the charges made in the articles and does so with far more thoroughness than the articles deserve. His early assertion that the accommodation of the eye is carried out by the crystalline lens, his subsequent withdrawal of this view and his return to it later, had been quoted as evidence of his vacillation. In reply he sets out the circumstances, step by step, and goes on to show in detail how his work led him to the study of light and to the discovery of the principle of interference. He easily meets, by quotations from his own works, the charge that he underrates the genius and achievements of Newton. He restates the principle of interference, giving the illustration, quoted earlier, of two series of waves on the surface of a lake. He points out that Newton had used the principle without working out its further implications when he explained the tides in the Port of Batsha. Finally, he comes to the last link in the chain of his evidence—the experiment by which interference fringes were produced by light coming round into the shadow past opposite sides of a very narrow obstacle. Brougham had thrown doubt on the accuracy of the experiment and this draws from Young another of his purple passages:[1]

The reviewer has afforded me, in the next observation, an opportunity for a triumph as gratifying as any triumph can be where the enemy is so contemptible. Conscious of his inability to explain the experiment which I have advanced, too ungenerous to confess that inability, and too idle to repeat the experiment, he is compelled to advance the supposition that it was incorrect, and to insinuate that my hand may easily have erred through a space so narrow as one-thirtieth of an inch. But the truth is, that my hand was not con-

[1] *Works*, vol. I, p. 210.

cerned; the screen was placed on a table, and moved mechanically forwards with the utmost caution; the experiment succeeded in some circumstances where the breadth of the object was doubled or trebled; and I assert that it was as easy to me to estimate one-thirtieth of an inch, as an interval a hundred or a thousand times as great. Let him make the experiment, and then deny the result if he can.

Brougham had poured ridicule on Young's Royal Institution Lectures (in their oral form—they were not yet published) and Young concludes with a defence of his lectures and of the Institution and forecasts the early appearance of the published lectures and the bibliography. He concludes by saying:[1]

With this work my pursuit of general science will terminate; henceforwards I have resolved to confine my studies and my pen to medical subjects only. For the talents which God has not given me, I am not responsible, but those which I possess, I have hitherto cultivated and employed as diligently as my opportunities have allowed me to do; and I shall continue to apply them with assiduity, and in tranquillity, to that profession which has constantly been the ultimate object of all my labours.

This, of course, he was never able to do. For better or for worse his interests refused to be confined to one groove. They not only attached themselves to other subjects which were in some way related to what he wished to make his main interest, but they attached themselves to subjects which were completely unrelated and which made large demands on his time and energy. It is almost certainly true that in this way he made a greater contribution to the advancement of knowledge than he could have done if he had achieved his declared object of confining himself to the theory and practice of medicine.

There can be no doubt that the effect of these devastating articles was considerable and that their effect on public opinion was not adequately countered by Young's published reply. That only one copy was sold does not, of course, necessarily mean that it had no circulation. Young probably circulated it privately. Among his friends was George Ellis of Sunning Hill,

[1] *Ibid.* p. 215.

literary critic and friend of Canning and of Sir Walter Scott. Writing to Young, he says:[1]

I thought it would be more satisfactory to you to hear the opinion entertained of your reply by persons more impartial than your Sunning Hill audience, and at the same time so intelligent as to make their opinions worth procuring. Canning read it with great attention, and the impression it made on him was exactly what I could have wished, namely that the *malice and want of candour* of the Edinburgh Reviewer was fully made out, and that your explanation of your own meaning was perfectly satisfactory. He added that he thought if you had as good reasons as he supposed for feeling certain that Mr Brougham was the author of the attack, you had treated him with rather too much lenity, and that you would have been fully justified in retorting on his Dissertation concerning 'inflection' all the ridicule which he had endeavoured to fix upon your 'interference of vibrations'. With this judgment I was well pleased, as I think that your answer, as it appeared to unprejudiced persons, sufficiently full and satisfactory, is all the better for being too temperate.

According to Ellis the articles made it difficult for Young to secure a publisher for his Royal Institution Lectures. In a letter to Sir Walter Scott he says:

He had been for some time lecturer at the Royal Institution and having determined to publish his lectures, he had received from one of the booksellers the offer of £1000 for the copyright. He was actually preparing for the press, when the bookseller came to him and told him that the ridicule thrown by the Edinburgh Review on some papers of his in the Philosophical Transactions, had so frightened the whole *trade* that he must request to be released from his bargain. This consequence, it is true, could not have been foreseen by the reviewer, who, however, appears to have written from feelings of private animosity, and I still continue to think, though I greatly admire the good taste of the literary essays, and the perspicuity of the dissertations on political economy, that an apparent want of candour is too generally the character of a work which, from its independence on the interests of booksellers, might have been expected to be particularly free from this defect.

Scott rejoins:

[1] Peacock, *op. cit.* p. 184.

I am sorry for the very pitiful catastrophe of Dr Young's publication, because, although I am altogether unacquainted with the merits of the controversy, one must always regret so very serious a consequence of a diatribe. The truth is, that these gentlemen reviewers ought often to read over the fable of the boys and the frogs, and should also remember it is much more easy to destroy than to build, to criticise than to compose.[1]

In the end Young did, of course, secure a publisher at the figure indicated in the letter.

So far as the general effect of the articles is concerned, Peacock's verdict[2] agrees with that of Ellis:

Their influence, however, upon public opinion was more remarkable than could reasonably have been expected, even from the great authority of the publication in which they appeared, and the unquestionable ability with which they were written. They not only seriously damaged, for the time, the estimation of the scientific character of Dr Young, but diverted public attention from the examination of the truth of his theories, at least among his own countrymen, for nearly twenty years.

The whole subject was expanded, systematized, and set out in its proper perspective in two later publications. The first of these was Young's Royal Institution Lectures. Here there appears the most convincing of all his experimental illustrations of the interference of light—the one which has come to be called Young's Experiment. In this there are three screens, see Fig. 22. An illuminated pinhole, or slit perpendicular to the diagram, in S, acts as the source. The light from this source falls on two pinholes or parallel slits $A B$ cut very close together. The light issuing from these overlaps on the screen, and in the part where they overlap a series of dark and bright interference bands may be seen. Here is Young's account of this crucial experiment:[3]

In order that the effects of two portions of light may be thus combined, it is necessary that they be derived from the same

[1] J. G. Lockhart, *Life of Sir Walter Scott* (London, 1896), p. 119.
[2] *Works*, vol. I, p. 192.
[3] Thomas Young, *Lectures on Natural Philosophy* (London, 1807), vol. I, p. 464.

origin, and that they arrive at the same point by different paths, in directions not much deviating from each other. This deviation may be produced in one or both of the portions by diffraction, by reflection, by refraction or by any of these effects combined; but

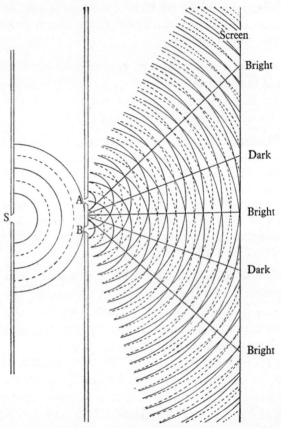

Fig. 22. Interference—Young's double slit method

the simplest case appears to be, when a beam of homogeneous light (i.e. of one colour and wave length) falls on a screen in which are two very small holes or slits, which may be considered as centres of divergence, from whence the light is diffracted in every direction. In this case, when the two newly formed beams are received on a surface placed so as to intercept them, their light is divided by dark stripes into portions nearly equal, but becoming wider as the surface is more remote from the apertures at all distances, and wider also in the same proportion as the apertures are closer to each other. The middle of the two portions is always light, and the bright stripes on each side are at such distances, that the light coming to them from one of the apertures must have passed through a longer space than that which comes from the other, by an interval which is equal to the breadth of one, two, three or more, of the supposed undulations, while the intervening dark spaces correspond to a difference of half a supposed undulation, of one and a half, of two and a half, or more.

From a comparison of various experiments, it appears that the breadth of the undulations constituting the extreme red light must be supposed to be, in air, about one 36-thousandth of an inch, and those of the extreme violet about one 60-thousandth: the mean of the whole spectrum, with respect to the intensity of light, being about one 45-thousandth.

These values agree very well with accepted measurements, but the importance of the experiment, of course, is the evidence it provides for the wave theory and not its use as an accurate method of measuring the wave-length of light.

In the same lecture Young makes cautious use of the argument that transparent substances transmit light through such great thickness that it is inconceivable that light should consist of particles. He gives reason for believing that the transparency of water is so great that it would require 'the diameter of each atom to be less than the hundred and forty thousandth part of its distance from the neighbouring particles; so that the whole space occupied by the substance must be as little filled as the whole of England would be filled by a hundred men, placed at the distance of about thirty miles from each other'.[1]

It is worth noticing that before the nature of cathode rays was understood there was a similar controversy. Opinion was divided as to whether they were particles or waves. The same argument was used by the supporters of the wave theory of cathode rays—that it was inconceivable that particles should penetrate considerable thicknesses of solid materials as cathode rays were known to do. In the end a relation between empty space and atomic nuclei not differing very greatly from that

[1] Young, *Lectures on Natural Philosophy*, p. 459.

N

imagined by Young was established by experiment and the objection to the particle theory of cathode rays was removed. The caution in Young's conclusion appears in his statement that:

This astonishing degree of porosity is not indeed absolutely inadmissible, and there are many reasons for believing the statement to agree in some measure with the actual constitution of material substances.[1]

This is a very surprising statement for 1807 and it is not easy to know what Young had in his mind. He continues:

But the Huyghenian hypothesis does not require the disproportion to be by any means so great, since the general direction, and even the intensity of an undulation, could be very little affected by the interposition of the atoms of matter, while these atoms may at the same time be supposed to assist in the transmission of the impulse by propagating it through their own substance.

In this last supposition Young was mistaken, but the rest of the passage is of considerable interest.

We may regard his treatment of the whole subject in his *Lectures* as completing the first phase of his work on the wave theory. The case for his own principle of interference was overwhelming. It was not only supported indirectly by a great variety of phenomena but it was established by the most direct experiment which could be planned. And the principle of interference, deduced from a consideration of waves, seemed inconsistent with any other type of theory. Yet there remained the phenomena of double refraction and polarization, and these could not easily be fitted into the wave theory. It is true that Huygens had explained double refraction by assuming two different waves to travel in a crystal. But why should there be two waves, and how was polarization to be explained?

[1] Young, *Lectures on Natural Philosophy*, p. 459.

VIII

THEORY OF LIGHT

*'The theory of light and colours, though it did not occupy a large
portion of my time, I conceived to be of more importance than all that
I have ever done, or ever shall do besides.'* YOUNG

So far Young's work had been a purely individual achievement. No one else had made any contribution in the spheres
of either experiment or theory. The achievement was ad-
mittedly incomplete, but even so it was a very impressive one—
one which we shall not attempt to appraise until we see how,
with the assistance of other workers in Britain and France, it
was brought to a successful conclusion.

The most difficult years for the defenders of the wave theory
were those between 1807, when Young published his Royal
Institution Lectures, and 1817, when the work of Fresnel
brought new and powerful support. In those years Young
stood almost alone. His friend and contemporary, W. H.
Wollaston, wrote in August 1801: 'I like your Bakerian
(Lecture) very much, but I cannot say that I have yet inserted
the undulatory doctrine into my creed and it may be some
time before I repeat it with fluency.'[1] In the following year
Wollaston published an account of careful measurements designed to test Huygens's theory of the extraordinary wave in
crystals. His conclusion is that his results

must be admitted to be highly favourable to the Huygenian Theory.
Since the theory by which he was guided in his enquiries affords (as
has lately been shown by Dr Young) a simple explanation of several
phenomena not yet accounted for upon any other hypothesis, it
must be admitted that it is entitled to a higher degree of consideration
than it has hitherto received.[2]

This rather cautious commendation was as far as Wollaston was

---

[1] *Works*, vol. I, p. 261.   [2] *Phil. Trans.* (1802), p. 381.

prepared to go. Against this we must place the fact that in 1807, 1809 and 1810 William Herschel, who was an acknowledged authority, communicated to the Royal Society three papers on Newton's Rings in which Young's work was not even mentioned. It is true that there was a good deal of controversy about the acceptance of these articles by the Royal Society; that his son John Herschel afterwards admitted 'that the views there taken found no concurrence on the part of later photologists';[1] and that Arago,[2] much later, gave it as his view that these papers had not contributed to the progress of the theory of these curious phenomena and that he understood from a reliable source that the great astronomer (Herschel) was of the same opinion. But they indicate the scepticism and neglect prevailing even ten years after Young's first Bakerian Lecture.

Much more dangerous was a Memoir by Laplace on 'Extraordinary Refraction' published in the *Journal de Physique* for January 1809. It deduced the laws of Double Refraction from the corpuscular theory on certain assumptions by what Larmor has described as 'a most astonishing analytical performance', and as he was one of the great names in the field of mathematical physics his support was almost as powerful as had been that of Newton at an earlier stage.

Meantime a new British review had appeared as a counterblast to the *Edinburgh* and it was in this new *Quarterly Review* for November 1809 that Young's reply to Laplace appeared. The memoir had assigned the credit of verifying Huygens's Law of Extraordinary Refraction to the French physicist Malus. Young claims this for Wollaston and then proceeds to demolish the case made by Laplace. 'Here', says Larmor,[3] 'contemplative insight asserted its mastery, as regards general ideas, over merely formal algebraic development'.

In his reply Young is again a little more pugnacious than would be regarded as proper in a scientific controversy to-day and complains, on national grounds, of an 'unjustifiable want

[1] Sir William Herschel, *Collected Scientific Papers* (London, 1912), p. viii.
[2] *Annuaire du Bureau de Longitude* (Paris, 1842), p. 598.
[3] *Nature* (London), 133 (1934), 276.

of candour' on the part of Laplace in not allotting to the observations of different authors their proper share of originality. This charge, as we shall see, was later to be turned against British physicists by Fresnel on behalf of the French, and the time was soon to come when the complaint had no longer any substance so far as Young's own work was concerned. This work was rescued from oblivion by the French astronomer Arago, and given currency both in France and in Britain.

Young goes on to support Huygens's theory that the extraordinary refraction is due to light travelling with different velocities in different directions in the crystal, and quotes some figures of Chladni's to show that in Scots pine sound travels with different velocities along the grain and at an angle to the grain, so that there is nothing unreasonable in supposing that crystals may have an analogous structure acting in a similar way for light waves.

In the year 1809 Malus discovered that light could be polarized by reflection from a glass surface at a particular angle. This raised all the old difficulties of polarization in a new form, and although Malus himself did not claim that his discovery favoured one theory more than the other, it obviously shook Young. In reviewing the work in *The Quarterly Review* for 1810 he says:[1]

This statement appears to us to be conclusive with respect to the insufficiency of the undulatory theory, in its present state, for explaining all the phenomena of light. But we are not therefore by any means persuaded of the perfect sufficiency of the projectile system: and all the satisfaction that we have derived from an attentive consideration of the accumulated evidence, which has been brought forward within the last ten years, on both sides of the question, is that of being convinced that much more evidence is still wanting before it can be positively decided.

Meantime Arago and Biot in France, and Brewster in England, were experimenting with the very beautiful and interesting colours which appeared when polarized light was

---

[1] *Quarterly Review*, III (1810), 462.

passed through a crystal slice and afterwards through a second polarizer (called the analyser). These colours may be examined for instance if ordinary light is passed first through a slice of tourmaline to polarize it, then through a slice of doubly refracting crystal and lastly through another slice of tourmaline. The resulting colour depends on the thickness of the crystal slice, and for slices of increasing thickness the resulting colour goes through the same gradations of tint as for Newton's Rings or any other example of the colours of thin plates when the thickness is increased. This led Young to attribute them to interference, and to explain them as due to the ordinary ray and the extraordinary ray traversing the crystal slice with different speeds and so emerging in a condition to interfere. This explanation was essentially sound, but was incomplete because the nature of polarization was still not known and the complete explanation involved this knowledge. In a letter to Young in 1815 Brewster[1] says of one of his own experiments: 'It appears to give very great support to your opinion, that the colours produced by the action of crystallized bodies upon polarised light are referable to your theory of periodical colours.'

Young's reply on 13 September of the same year makes it clear where he stands:[2]

With respect to my own fundamental hypotheses respecting the nature of light I become less and less fond of dwelling on them as I learn more and more facts like those which Mr Malus discovered; because, although they may not be incompatible with these facts, they certainly give us no assistance in explaining them.

By far the most complete account of the whole subject as it stood at this time is given by Young in an article on 'Chromatics' contributed to the Supplement to the *Encyclopaedia Britannica* then being published. It was written during the autumn of 1817 and opens with an attempt to put the whole controversy in perspective without in any way exaggerating the importance of his own work.[3]

But notwithstanding all that has hitherto been done, it appears to be utterly impracticable, in the present state of our knowledge, to

[1] *Works*, vol. I, p. 359.   [2] *Ibid.* p. 360.   [3] *Ibid.* p. 279.

obtain a satisfactory explanation of all the phenomena of optics, considered as mechanical operations, upon any hypothesis respecting the nature of light that has hitherto been advanced; it will, therefore, be desirable to consider the facts which have been discovered, with as little reference as possible to any general theory; at the same time, it will be absolutely necessary, as a temporary expedient, to borrow, from the undulatory system, Dr Young's law of the interference of light, as affording the only practicable mode of connecting an immense variety of facts with each other, and of enabling the memory to retain them; and this adoption will be the more unexceptionable, as many of the most strenuous advocates for the projectile theory have been disposed, especially since the experiments of Mr Arago and Mr Fresnel, to admit the truth of the results of the calculations, in which this law has been employed.

Note Young's contention that the usefulness of a theory depends on its power to co-ordinate the facts of experience, to make them easy to apprehend and easy to transmit just because they are systematized and related instead of being separate isolated facts. The article deals with the spectrum; with the colours of haloes as first explained by Mariotte and revived and extended by Young; and with the rainbow. Then follows a paragraph on interference, which is enunciated in a new form.[1]

The law is, that when two equal portions of light, in circumstances exactly similar, have been separated and coincide again, in nearly the same direction, they will either co-operate, or destroy each other, according as the difference of the times, occupied in their separate paths, is an even or an odd multiple of a certain half interval, which is different for the different colours, but constant for the same kind of light.

There follows in an extended form the explanation, using this principle, of all the types of colours to which Young had previously applied it and to some others—notably what he calls the 'Colours of double plates'. These were discovered by Nicholson on looking through two plates of nearly equal thickness. Young explained them by assuming that some light would be twice reflected internally in *A* and some in *B*. If the thicknesses of A and B are e and e' respectively and the material is the same, then the path of ray 1 is increased by $2e$ and that of 2 by $2e'$, so that the path of ray 1 is longer than that of ray 2 by

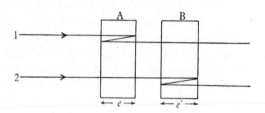

Fig 23.   Colours of Double Plates

an amount $2e-2e'$. Obviously if e is very nearly equal to e', then this difference is very small and the rays will interfere if brought to the same point.[1]

A considerable part of the article is devoted to an account of the phenomena of polarization and double refraction, and Young shows that in the case of double refraction, as the incident white light is split into two waves which traverse the crystal with different velocities, these ought, on emergence, to be in a condition to give interference colours. He successfully treats of many of the cases where those colours do appear and shows that the wave-length involved agrees with that calculated from other experiments. But often the colours do not appear and in some cases the phenomena seem to be anomalous. This leads him in the final section of the article to a summary of the whole position:[2]

Notwithstanding the acknowledged impossibility of fully explaining all the phenomena of light and colours by any imaginable hypothesis respecting their nature, it is yet practicable to illustrate them very essentially by a comparison with the known effects of

[1] These colours were used by Fabry and Perot in determining the length of the standard metre in terms of the wave-length of light, and have been used at the National Physical Laboratory for the same purpose by Sears and Barrell.

[2] *Works*, vol. I, p. 325.

certain mechanical causes, which are observed to act in circumstances somewhat analogous; and as far as a theory will enable us to connect with each other a variety of facts, it is perfectly justifiable to employ it hypothetically, as a temporary expedient for assisting the memory and the judgment until all doubts are removed respecting its actual foundation in truth and nature. Whether, therefore, light may consist merely in the projection of detached particles with a certain velocity, as some of the most celebrated philosophers of modern times assert, or whether in the undulations of a certain ethereal medium as Hooke and Huyghens maintained, or whether, as Sir Isaac Newton believed, both of these causes are concerned in the phenomena; without positively admitting or rejecting any opinion as demonstrably true or false, it is our duty to enquire what assistance can be given to our conception and recollection by the adoption of any comparison, which may be pointedly applicable even to some insulated facts only. It has, however, been thought desirable to separate this investigation as much as possible, from the relation of the facts, in order to avoid confounding the result of observation with the deduction from mere hypothesis; an error which has been committed by some of the latest and most meritorious authors in this department. It may be objected to some of the preceding sections, that this forbearance has not been exercised with respect to the general law of interference and its modifications; but it would have been impossible to give any correct statement of the facts in question without determining whether the appearances depend upon one or both of the portions of light supposed to be concerned.

This passage treats the nature of light as still quite an open question. Partly, of course, this is due to the fact that the article could not be an expression of his own personal views and had to be an account of the generally accepted views. Partly it was due to the fact that, although he had no doubt about the principle of interference and probably very little about the essential truth of the wave theory, he was still puzzled by the new facts of polarization.

The laws of interference, which have been shown to be so extensively applicable to the diversified appearances of periodical colours, point very directly to the theory of undulation; so directly, indeed, that their establishment has been considered, by many persons on the continent, as almost paramount [tantamount] to the establishment of that theory.[1]

The experiments of Mr Arago, not yet published in detail, which show that light does not interfere with light polarised in a transverse direction, lead us immediately to the consideration of the general phenomena of polarisation, which cannot be said to have been by any means explained on any hypothesis respecting the nature of light. It is certainly easier to conceive a detached particle, however minute, distinguished by its different sides, and having a particular axis turned in a particular direction, than to imagine how an undulation, resembling the motion of the air which constitutes sound, can have any different properties, with respect to the different planes which diverge from its path.[2]

This passage is important as showing what it was that blinded Young and others to the secret of polarization. If one is led to the wave theory of light, as Young was, by the analogy between sound and light, then it is the most natural thing in the world to press this analogy too far. Both are propagated by waves, but not necessarily by waves of the same type. In the sound wave the motion of the medium is to and fro along the ray— i.e. the path of any small portion of the wave. In this case no plane through the ray is distinguished from any other. If the polarized light wave is of this type, then why, when it falls on a slice of tourmaline, should it be transmitted when the crystal slice is in one position, but cut off and extinguished when the slice is turned through an angle of 90° in its own plane?

It may clarify our ideas if at this stage we anticipate a little and use an illustration later used by Young. Let us consider a stretched rubber cord held horizontally with one end fixed and the other in the hand. If we move the hand to and fro, tightening and slackening the cord, waves will be transmitted along the cord, but the motion of the waves will not be visible except to a close inspection, because the motion of each part of the cord is to and fro in the direction of the length of the cord. This type of vibration and its associated wave is called *longitudinal*. It is the type which corresponds to sound waves. The

[1] *Works*, vol. I, p. 328.   [2] *Ibid.* p. 332.

ray (represented by the rubber cord) has the same properties all round; no plane through it is distinguished from any other; polarization does not seem possible. But move the hand vertically up and down. Waves of a different kind now travel along the cord. Each point on the cord moves up and down in a vertical plane. This plane, which contains the motion, is easily distinguished from the horizontal plane in which there is no motion. This type of wave is called transverse and it provides an obvious analogy to polarization. If we have a slit in a piece of card and the cord is threaded through it, then if the card is held with the slit vertical, the waves produced by a vertical motion of the hand will pass unchanged. If, on the other hand, the slit is held horizontal, the waves cannot pass. If we think of a crystal slice as having what we may crudely regard as a grid structure and ordinary light as transmitted by transverse vibrations executed in every plane through the ray, then one tourmaline slice on which a horizontal beam of light fell might pass only vertical vibrations. If a second crystal slice was placed with its grid vertical, all the vibrations passed by the first slice would pass the second, while if the crystal slice was turned round so that its grid was horizontal, none of the light passed by the first slice would get through the second. Thus, the idea that light was propagated by a transverse vibration executed at right angles to the ray might be the key to the explanation of polarization. The paragraph quoted above shows Young adhering to the analogy of sound waves, but a later paragraph, very obscure and difficult, shows that the analogy of light with water waves where the vibration is transverse was beginning to work in his mind:[1]

In the case of a wave moving on the surface of a liquid, considering the motion of the particles at some little distance below the surface, as concerned in the propagation of an undulation in a horizontal direction, we may observe that there is actually a lateral motion, throughout the liquid, in a plane which is determined by that of gravitation: but this happens because the liquor is more at liberty to extend itself on this side than on any other, the force of gravitation

[1] *Ibid.*

tending to bring it back, with a pressure of which the operation is analogous to that of elasticity; and we cannot find a parallel for this force in the motions of an elastic medium.

Still thinking in terms of a wave motion mainly longitudinal —i.e. along the ray—he tries to think of ways in which a small amount of lateral motion might be developed. He goes on to say:[1]

It is true that all these modifications of motion would be minute beyond the power of imagination, even when compared with other motions, themselves extending to a space far too minute to be immediately perceived by the senses; and this consideration may perhaps lessen the probability of the theory as a physical explanation; but it would not destroy its utility as a mathematical representation of them, provided that such a representation could be rendered general, and reducible to calculation; and even in a physical sense, if the alternative were unavoidable, it is easier to imagine the powers of perceiving minute changes to be all but infinite than to admit the portentous complication of machinery, which must be heaped up, in order to afford a solution of the difficulties, which beset the application of the doctrine of simple projection to all the phenomena of polarisation and of colours. It is not, however, possible at present to complete such a mathematical theory, even on imaginary grounds; although a few further analogies between polarisation and transverse motion force themselves on our observation.

This passage is of great importance because it shows clearly that Young foresaw the simplification of the whole subject which would result if only a transverse vibration could be associated with the longitudinal. What he failed at this date (1817) to see was that the vibration might be wholly transverse and not at all longitudinal. Later in the article Young reverts to the idea without carrying it much further, and to see how he finally cleared his mind on the subject we must consider his later correspondence with his illustrious contemporaries.

Before the above article was actually written (in September and October 1817), Young had been made aware of the work of Fresnel in France. The rather slight reference which occurs

[1] *Works*, p. 333.

in the article fails completely to give any indication of the real value and significance of the paper which had been communicated by Fresnel to the Académie des Sciences, Paris, in October 1815[1] and published with modifications in the *Annales de Chimie* in 1816. Fresnel must be reckoned as sharing with Young the honour of establishing the wave theory on a broad and sound basis. His work was done not only independently of Young but without any knowledge of Young's work. It duplicated some of his discoveries, but it introduced a new and original treatment of the phenomena of diffraction. Fresnel's attention was first drawn to Young's published papers by Arago in November 1815, nearly fifteen years after the first Bakerian Lecture was published. On 24 May 1816 he wrote to Young in a very generous and unselfish strain. Enclosing a copy of his memoir, he says:[2]

When I submitted it to the Institute I did not know of your experiments and the deduction you drew from them, so that I presented as new explanations which you had already given long before. I have withdrawn these in the printed memoir which I now have the honour to send you and I have only left the explanation of the coloured fringes of shadows, for there I have added something to what you had already said on this phenomenon.

He concludes by saying:[3]

When one believes one has made a discovery one cannot learn without regret that one has been anticipated, and I admit frankly that this was indeed my feeling when M. Arago convinced me how few of the observations in the memoir which I presented to the Institute were really new. But if anything could console me for not having the advantage of priority, it would be having been brought into contact with a scholar who has enriched physics with so many important discoveries and has contributed not a little to increase my confidence in the theory which I had adopted.

This letter from Fresnel was followed by one from Arago, written on 13 July 1816, enclosing further copies of Fresnel's memoir. He refers to the fact that Fresnel was ignorant of

[1] Augustin Fresnel, *Oeuvres Complètes* (1866), vol. i, p. 9.
[2] *Works*, vol. i, p. 376.   [3] *Ibid.* p. 378.

Young's earlier work and points out how careful Fresnel has been to give Young his due and to recognize his claim to priority. He then goes on to refer to the work of another distinguished French physicist, Biot. Biot's experimental work was good, but he was a disciple of Poisson, and therefore a believer in the corpuscular theory. Arago describes his arguments as 'pitiable' and mentions some experiments of his own which confirm Young's theories. He concludes: 'In any case, these considerations will always have in my eyes one great value, since they have been the pretext for this letter and have supplied the occasion of presenting to you my assurance of the profound esteem which your work has for a long time inspired in me.'[1]

Later in the summer Arago visited England with Gay-Lussac and the two went down to Worthing to visit Young. For an account of this visit we are indebted to Arago, who recalled it in his Éloge to the memory of Young as one of the eight foreign members of the Paris Institute:[2]

In the year 1816 I visited England, in company with my learned friend Gay-Lussac. Fresnel had recently made his début in the career of the sciences, in the most brilliant manner, by his Memoir on Diffraction. This work, which, in our opinion, contained a capital experiment irreconcileable with the Newtonian theory of light, became naturally the first subject of our conversation with Dr Young. We were astonished at the number of restrictions which he imposed upon our commendation of it, when at last he declared that the experiment which we valued so highly was to be found, since 1807, in his Lectures on Natural Philosophy. This assertion appeared to us unfounded, and a long and very minute discussion followed. Mrs Young was present at it, without offering to take any part in it—as the fear of being designated by the ridicule implied in the sobriquet of *bas bleus* makes English ladies reserved in the presence of strangers; our neglect of propriety never struck us until the moment when Mrs Young quitted the room somewhat precipitately. We were beginning to make our apologies to her husband when we saw her return with an enormous quarto under her arm. It was the first volume of the Treatise on Natural Philosophy. She

[1] *Works*, vol. I, p. 379.   [2] Peacock, *op. cit.* p. 388.

placed it on the table, opened the book without saying a word, at page 387, and showed with her finger a figure where the Curvilinear Course of the diffracted bands, which were the subject of the discussion, is found to be established theoretically.

As Peacock points out,[1] Arago had got his numbers wrong. The page is obviously p. 467 and the figure is 445. This is one of the very few recorded incidents in which Mrs Young appears and it makes us wish there were more. Young himself was much pleased by the visit as an indication of French appreciation of his work. Writing to his sister Emily, then in Paris, he says:[2]

Do you know that I almost fancied you would have heard of me at the meeting of the Institute which you attended; for I am told that my theories of light have been the subject of some very warm discussions among the members on some public occasions. They have certainly attracted much more notice at Paris than in London; and Humboldt the traveller writes to me warmly wanting me to come there. To show how far politeness will go: I had a visit on Sunday week from Gay-Lussac, the chemist, and Arago the astronomer, who came down from town on purpose to spend an evening with me, and told me, as a motive for their visit, 'People would have laughed at us if we had returned without seeing you.' They have promised to come again a few days hence, on their return through Brighton, and I hope they will stay a longer time.

One result of this visit was a very important letter from Young to Arago dated 12 January 1817. After reproaching Arago for not paying him a second visit according to arrangement before leaving England, he proceeds to deal with one or two points that had arisen during their conversations. He then makes a slightly patronizing reference to Fresnel:[3]

I am sincerely delighted with the success which has attended Mr Fresnel's efforts, as I beg you will tell him; and I think some of his proofs and illustrations very distinctly stated; but I cannot fully adopt your expression in the letter you wrote by Mr Dupin, that his memoir may be 'considéré comme la démonstration de la doctrine des interférences'; for neither I nor any of those few who were acquainted with what I had written can find a single *new*

---

[1] *Ibid.* p. 389.   [2] *Ibid.*   [3] *Works*, vol. I, p. 381.

fact in it of the least importance: nothing certainly half so important as your experiments on the colours seen in transmitted light, or on the non-interference of light polarised in opposite directions.

Later there follows the first recorded suggestion that polarization might be explained by a transverse vibration—the suggestion to which he returns in the article on 'Chromatics' to which reference has already been made and which he wrote in September and October of this same year:[1]

I have also been reflecting on the possibility of giving an imperfect explanation of the affection of light which constitutes polarisation, without departing from the genuine doctrine of undulations. It is a principle in this theory that all undulations are simply propagated through homogeneous mediums in concentric spherical surfaces like the undulation of Sound, consisting simply in the direct retrograde motions of the particles in the direction of the radius, with their concomitant condensation and rarefactions. And yet it is possible to explain in this theory a transverse vibration, propagated also in the direction of the radius, and with equal velocity, the motions of the particles being in a certain constant direction with respect to that radius; and this is a *polarisation*. But its inconceivable minuteness suggests a doubt as to the possibility of its producing any sensible effects: in a physical sense, it is almost an evanescent quantity, although not in a mathematical one. Its foundation is this:

He then proceeds to derive the transverse vibration from the interference of longitudinal vibrations. Now this suggestion of Young's was of capital importance as fixing on transverse vibration as the only possible explanation of polarization. But he was, of course, wrong in regarding the transverse vibration as derived from the longitudinal. He was still bemused by the analogy of sound waves in air and had not yet grasped the revolutionary idea that the vibrations were *wholly* transverse. But if Young was bemused, Arago and Fresnel were even more bemused. Fresnel afterwards claimed to have discussed the possibility of transverse vibrations with Ampère a year earlier (i.e. in 1816), but as we shall see it was long before he published his idea, and even when he did publish it Arago was still unwilling to accept it.

[1] *Works*, vol. I, p. 383.

Meantime Brewster was preparing an important paper 'On the Laws of Polarization and Double Refraction in regularly Crystallized Bodies' which was read to the Royal Society on 13 January 1818 and published in the *Philosophical Transactions* for the same year.[1] On 4 October 1817 he wrote to Young:[2]

As you formerly requested me not to mention your name in connection with any of your anonymous works, I write you at present chiefly to ask if you have any objections to have your theory of the Colours produced by the action of crystals upon polarised light mentioned as your own. I have just come to that part of my paper on the laws of polarisation and double refraction, where I mean to introduce the subject. I have little doubt that it will be found to represent all the phenomena; and my paper will furnish you with the means of putting it to the most decisive test. . . . The greater number of the generalisations of Mr Biot are completely erroneous. His division of crystals into attractive and repulsive is unfounded, and his results respecting the rotation of the luminous particles are mere delusions.

Young's reply shows how hard he was struggling to prevent his potential patients from having any reason to suspect that his interests were not in his medical work. Writing on 10 October 1817, he replied:[3]

I can have no objection to your quoting the article in question, as one which *you judge*, from internal evidence, to be mine, if you feel no difficulty in hazarding such an opinion, although, for many reasons, I do not wish to be considered as avowing it *publicly* at present. . . . I have, indeed, very lately been entering into some optical subjects pretty much at large; but I do not think that I shall resume the consideration of them for a long time.

Brewster agreed to abide by Young's wishes in the matter and at the same time mentioned that Biot, Laplace and Poisson had expressed the view that 'in the present state of mathematical analysis, the simplest case of an undulation could not be calculated', and therefore a theorem which Young claimed to have proved 'was not capable of demonstration'.[4] This was a

---

[1] *Phil. Trans.* (1818), p. 199.   [2] *Works*, vol. I, p. 367.
[3] *Ibid.* p. 368.   [4] *Ibid.* p. 370.

O

very powerful trio of opponents. Laplace and Poisson were
at the height of their fame and their opposition to the wave
theory was persistent and unrelenting.

In a later letter to Young of January 1818, Brewster tells of a
distinguished follower of Laplace who

did not scruple to declare, when I saw him in Edinburgh last summer
that any experimental laws of double refraction which I had discovered *must* be erroneous, unless they agreed with those given by
Laplace; and that I ought to compare them with his before I published them. My reply was, that as my laws were deduced from
experiment, it was rather Laplace's affair to see that his theoretical
ones agreed with mine.[1]

Young could not, of course, be intimidated by authority, and
in replying to the earlier letter on 9 November 1817 gave vent
to his irritation:[2]

I conclude that Mr Biot had the candour to tell you that he had
read none of my papers whatever; he promised me that he would
attempt it in the course of the summer, but I daresay he has not
found leisure. Mr Laplace has now arrived at so happy a pre-
eminence in science, that he thinks it sufficient to assert where others
would assign their reasons; and having once asserted, he is not very
impatient to retract. He told me in July, as he had often declared
before, that the Huyghenian theory was incapable of determining
the relation of the angles of incidence and refraction; and when I
could hardly help smiling at the absurdity of the assertion and
endeavoured to prove to him, in three words, how easily and
necessarily the law was deduced from the hypothesis, he begged me
to send him a short demonstration in writing. I did so, and instead
of either admitting it, or endeavouring to point out its deficiency,
he now tells me that it is only an 'aperçu', a sketch or a presumption.
This little occurrence is certainly of some value to me, because it
spares me a great deal of labour in entering into any further controversy on such a subject with such a person. With respect to Mr
Poisson, when we know how repeatedly and how deeply he has
committed himself in praising and in imitating some of Mr Laplace's
least successful speculations, we cannot be surprised at his bearing
him out on this point.

[1] *Works*, p. 220.   [2] *Ibid.* p. 371.

The very surprising comment of Laplace to which Young refers was contained in a letter of 6 October 1817:[1]

I have received the letter which you have done me the honour to write, and in which you seek to establish that according to the wave theory of light, the sines of the angles of incidence and refraction are in a constant ratio when light passes from one medium to another. Ingenious as this reasoning is, I can only regard it as an aperçu and not as a geometrical demonstration. I persist in believing that the problem of the propagation of waves, when they traverse different media, has never been solved, and that it surpasses perhaps the existing powers of analysis.

This demonstration which Laplace regarded as beyond the powers of analysis is now, of course, to be found in every elementary textbook of physics.

During 1818 Arago, Poisson and two other French scientists were elected foreign members of the Royal Society. It fell to Young as foreign secretary of the Society to convey the fact to the recipients of the honour, and in acknowledging Young's letter Arago describes himself as 'one of the most zealous of his proselytes'.

Interest in the wave theory was now increasing in France and the Paris Academy offered a prize for a memoir on the subject of 'Diffraction', the memoir to be submitted before 1 August 1818 and the award to be at the public session in March 1819. On 29 July 1818 a memoir[2] was deposited by Fresnel and was referred to Laplace, Biot, Poisson, Arago and Gay-Lussac, who unanimously recommended it for the award.

In this memoir Fresnel combined a principle first stated by Huygens with Young's principle of interference. Huygens's principle[3] enabled Fresnel to deal with the interference arising from parts of the same wave. Using this method he gave a complete explanation of diffraction fringes, superseding Young's explanation, which, although rightly attributing them to interference, wrongly assumed one set of interfering rays to be

---

[1] *Ibid.* p. 374. [2] Fresnel, *op. cit.* p. 247.
[3] According to which the effect of a wave might be deduced by treating each point on it at any given moment as the source of a new wave.

reflected from the edge of the obstacle. He was also able completely to dispose of Newton's old difficulty about the rectilinear propagation of light and to show how to calculate the degree of spreading into the shadow for any particular case. This memoir cleared up all outstanding questions with the one exception of polarization, to which no reference was made, although, as will appear, it was in Fresnel's mind. Young saw the paper (incomplete) in the *Annales de Chimie* and at once wrote to Arago[1] (4 August 1819):

Perhaps indeed, you will suspect that I am not a little provoked to think that so immediate a consequence of the Huyghenian system, as that which Mr Fresnel has very ingeniously deduced, should have escaped myself, when I was endeavouring to apply it to the phenomena in question.

Arago must have passed this comment on to Fresnel, for on 19 September 1819 the latter pays a very generous tribute to Young in a letter:[2]

This theory, as you have well said, is only Huyghens' principle applied to the phenomena in question. Undoubtedly this great geometer would easily have deduced from it the laws of diffraction, if he had thought of the mutual influence which waves produced by an oscillatory movement must exercise on one another. But it was reserved for you to enrich science with the fruitful principle of interference, and to show by a large number of ingenious applications how useful it can be in optics.

Young's reply[3] (16 October 1819) was couched in the same generous terms and, contrary to his usual practice, was written in French. He characterizes the memoir as deserving a distinguished place among the writings which have contributed most to the progress of optics and he definitely withdraws his own explanation of the production of diffraction fringes in favour of that of Fresnel.

Fresnel was at the same time working on the interference of polarized light. This work was embodied in a series of communications to the Academy extending from October 1816 to

[1] *Works*, vol. I, p. 388.   [2] *Ibid.* p. 389.   [3] *Ibid.* p. 393.

January 1821.[1] The papers were submitted to Ampère and Arago for report, and their report[2]—for which Arago was mainly responsible—was wholly favourable to Fresnel's work and to the wave theory. It provoked very strong disagreement from Biot, whose own theory was quite irreconcilable with the conclusions reached by Fresnel and who felt that to adopt the report was to commit the Academy to one side in a controversy still *sub judice*. In these circumstances the rapporteurs made some modifications in the concluding paragraph of their report and it was agreed that the Academy should be committed only to this final paragraph. Biot then accepted the report, but strongly criticized its content in a speech published in the *Annales*.[3] To this Arago made an equally forthright rejoinder[4] and the passions aroused were so violent that a lifelong friendship between Arago and Biot was abruptly terminated.

Writing to Hudson Gurney from Paris in 1822, Young says:[5]

In my own pursuits I have found abundance of novelty to interest me; both the scientific and literary departments of the Institute happening at this moment to be particularly engaged with my investigations, and a Frenchman having in each of them been engaged in going over my own ground without being fully acquainted with what I had done, and having had to exclaim *Pereant qui ante nos nostra dixerunt*.[6] Fresnel, a young mathematician of the Civil Engineers, has really been doing some very good things in the extension and application of my theory of light.

Notice that the wave theory has now become 'my theory of light', and that Fresnel's claim to fame is 'the extension and application' of the theory. This modest rôle was one which Fresnel would not, of course, accept, and Young admitted in his better moments that it was very much an understatement.

After a gap in the correspondence between Young and Fresnel of nearly four years, three letters from Fresnel to Young occur in fairly quick succession. In the first, of 18 February 1823, he gives an account of his work in the meantime and

[1] Fresnel, *op. cit.* p. 568.   [2] *Ibid.* p. 553.   [3] *Ibid.* p. 569.
[4] *Ibid.* p. 591.   [5] Peacock, *op. cit.* p. 251.
[6] 'Perish those who have anticipated us.'

complains that all his memoirs have been insufficient to open to him the membership of the Académie des Sciences. M. Dulong has been preferred to him: 'You see, Monsieur, that the wave theory has brought me no good fortune; but this does not disgust me; and I console myself for my bad fortune by working at Optics with a new ardour.'[1] The second[2] (27 March 1823) sends copies of his latest memoir for Wollaston, Dalton, Herschel, Brewster and Leslie. The third[3] (16 September 1823) explains how fully he is occupied with service duties and in particular with his work on lighthouses.

In 1824 Young transmitted to Fresnel a request that he should do an article on 'Light' for the Supplement to the *Encyclopaedia Britannica*. Fresnel accepts[4] (16 October 1824), but complains of overwork and ends by saying that he is 'overwhelmed with fatigue and with want of sleep'. This letter brought a further one from Young on 17 November 1824, which has not been preserved. Fresnel's reply,[5] written in some bitterness of spirit on 26 November 1824, is of great importance as indicating his view of the relative importance of his own work and is worth quoting at length. He explains that grave illness prevents him from undertaking any work and that he hardly has the strength to write. He goes on to complain of the neglect of his work in England—a complaint which was probably thoroughly justified.

If I succeed in demonstrating to M. Herschel and M. Wollaston and to the other English physicists attached to the system of Newton, that the wave theory is to be preferred, they will not fail to say that it is solely to your works that we owe the overthrow of the emission theory and the progress of the wave theory. If, disabusing your scientists in the matter of movable polarisation, I induce them to accept the explanation which I have given of the colours of thin crystalline plates and these methods generally by means of which we may calculate the tints in all crystals for which we know the double refraction for each kind of ray, they would still say that the explanation of these phenomena belongs to you; they would equally attribute to you the phenomena complicated by diffraction.

---

[1] *Works*, vol. i, p. 395.   [2] *Ibid.* p. 396.   [3] *Ibid.* p. 397.
[4] *Ibid.* p. 399.   [5] *Ibid.* p. 400.

It seems to me, however (perhaps my amour propre blinds me), that what you left me to do in those parts of optics was as difficult as what you yourself had done. You had gathered the flowers, may I say with English modesty, and I have dug painfully to discover the roots.

I am far from laying claim to what belongs to you, Monsieur, as you have seen in the Supplement to the French translation of Thomson's Chemistry, as you will see also in the article I have just prepared for the European Review. I have declared with sufficiently good grace before the public, on several occasions, the priority of your discoveries, your observations and even your hypotheses. However, between ourselves, I am not persuaded of the justice of the remark in which you would compare yourself to a tree and me to the apple which the tree has produced; I am personally convinced that the apple would have appeared without the tree, for the first explanations which occurred to me of the phenomena of diffraction and of the coloured rings, of the laws of reflection and of refraction, I have drawn from my own resources, without having read either your work or that of Huyghens. I noticed for myself also that the difference of path of the ordinary and extra-ordinary rays on emerging from a crystal plate was equal to that of the rays reflected at the first and second surfaces of a film of air which gives the same tint in the coloured rings. It was when I communicated this observation to M. Arago that he spoke to me for the first time of the note which you had published two years before on the same subject and to which, until then, he had not paid much attention. This does not, of course, entitle me to share with you Monsieur, the merit of these discoveries, which belong to you exclusively by priority: also I have thought it useless to inform the public of those things which I discovered independently but after you; and if I speak of them to you, it is only to justify my paradoxical proposition, *that the apple would have come without the tree.* For a long time, Monsieur, I have wanted to open my heart to you on this subject, and to show you exactly the extent of my claims.

Let us admit that my amour propre is too exacting and that I have received justice in your country (for I am perhaps one of the Frenchmen who have least to complain of at the hands of your countrymen), I am not the less astonished, I would almost say revolted, by what is so often reported to me of the shocking partiality with which your scientific journals exalt the most insignificant English discoveries over the most remarkable French ones. Certainly I should be the last to minimise your undeniable superiorities, especially in the realm of politics; but you will allow at least that we are far ahead in impartiality and love of justice.

This letter will perhaps appear to you, Monsieur, the outpouring of a sick man tormented by bile, and whose amour propre has been wounded by the neglect of his work in your country. I am far from denying the value which I would attach to the praise of English scientists and from pretending that such praise would not have been agreeable. But, for a long time this sensitiveness or this vanity which is called love of fame has been much blunted in me; I work far less to impress the public than to obtain that self approval which has always been the sweetest reward of my efforts. Without doubt I have often needed the spur of vanity to stimulate me to pursue my researches in moments of disgust or discouragement; but all the compliments which I have been able to receive from MM. Arago, Laplace, or Biot have never given me as much pleasure as the discovery of one theoretical truth and the confirmation of my calculations by experiment. The smallness of the effort I have made to secure the publication of my memoirs, of which only extracts have appeared, shows that I am not tormented by a thirst for fame, and that I have enough philosophy to prevent me from attaching too much importance to the enjoyment of vanity. But it is useless for me to spread myself further on this subject in writing to one who is himself too superior to be a stranger to this philosophy and who will readily understand me.

The next letter[1] extant is dated two months later (19 January 1825) and is again from Fresnel to Young, apologizing for his earlier letter. He had put down his ideas to relieve his mind and ought to have left it at that. He ought not to have sent the letter and he hopes Young will burn it. He promises the article for the *Encyclopaedia*, but explains that he has had a long illness, is not yet recovered and is much in arrears with necessary work. Finally he restates quite clearly the division of labour between himself and Young in the matter of colours in polarized light:[2]

You were the first to remark and to demonstrate that the colours

---

[1] *Works*, vol. I, p. 403.   [2] *Ibid.* p. 405.

originated in the difference of path in the crystal slice for the ordinary and extraordinary waves; but it remained to establish the direction of polarisation of the waves in the crystal; it was necessary to explain why their interference only produced colours when the emergent light was passed through a polariser; and why it was necessary that the original incident light should be polarised. I believe I am the first to have given rigorous general methods of calculating the tints that polarisation develops in thin crystal slices. Excuse, Monsieur, the abrupt frankness of this claim.

No reply from Young to these two letters has been discovered, but in 'An Account of some Recent Discoveries in Hieroglyphical Literature'[1] this passage occurs in connection with a visit to Paris:

I had first the pleasure of hearing at a meeting of the Academy of Science, an Optical paper read by Mr Fresnel, who, though he appears to have rediscovered, by his own efforts, the laws of the interference of light, and though he has applied them, by some refined calculations, to cases which I had almost despaired of being able to explain by them, has, on all occasions, and particularly in a very luminous statement of the theory, lately inserted in a translation of Thomson's Chemistry, acknowledged ,with the most scrupulous justice, and the most liberal candour, the indisputable priority of my investigations.

One more letter[2] from Fresnel was written on 4 September 1825, and in it he announces that in a memoir inserted in the *Bulletin of the Sciences* of the Société Philomathique for October 1824 and published about the middle of the winter he had shown that the vibrations constituting light were *exclusively* transverse. This was the discovery required to complete the wave theory and it is interesting to glance at its history. The idea of transverse vibrations was first recorded in Young's letter to Arago of January 1817 and the idea was developed further in his article on 'Chromatics' written in the autumn of the same year. But, as we have seen, he thought in terms of transverse vibrations auxiliary to the longitudinal vibrations.

[1] *Works*, vol. III, p. 287. [2] *Works*, vol. I, p. 407.

He saw clearly that transverse vibrations would explain polarization, but he was too heavily committed in his thinking to the analogy with sound waves to discard the longitudinal vibration altogether. Fresnel claims to have mentioned the possibility of transverse vibrations to Ampère in 1816, but he went no further with it at the time. Whewell says that

Arago was wont to relate, that when he and Fresnel had obtained their joint experimental results of the non-interference of oppositely polarised pencils, and when Fresnel had pointed out that transverse vibrations were the only possible translation of this fact into the undulatory theory, he himself protested that he had not the courage to publish such a conception; and accordingly, the second part of the Memoir was published in Fresnel's name alone. What renders this more remarkable is, that it occurred when Arago had in his possession the very letter of Young, in which he proposed the same suggestion.[1]

The letter to which this refers is not the letter of January 1817 but a later letter of 29 April 1818, which is now missing. In an article by Fresnel[2] published after his death he says:

A remark in a letter of Dr Young, dated on the 29th April, 1818, which M. Arago communicated to me, helped to raise in my mind a doubt of the existence of longitudinal vibrations. Dr Young inferred from the optical properties of crystals of two axes, discovered by Sir David Brewster, that the vibrations of the ether might probably resemble those of a stretched cord of indefinite length, and be propagated in the same manner. There is undoubtedly a great analogy between this definition of luminous waves and that which I have given above, but I do not believe that Dr Young has shown in what manner to reconcile such a mutual dependence on the molecules of the ether with its fluidity, and to conceive the production in it of such vibrations to the exclusion of vibrations in the direction of propagation. Now, it was this difficulty which had embarrassed me up to the present time, and hindered me from resting satisfied with my first idea. I ought, nevertheless, to acknowledge, though he may not have given this explanation, that Dr Young is the first who has announced positively the possibility of

---

[1] W. Whewell, *History of the Inductive Sciences* (London, 1837), vol. II, p. 418.
[2] *Ann. de Chimie*, 17 (1831), 184.

such a property of an elastic fluid. I am ignorant whether this learned philosopher has published his views on this subject, or whether they have assumed a definite form in his mind, but I have thought that the publicity about, I hope, to be given to them. cannot be disagreeable to him.

As a matter of fact Young had no clear idea how this transverse vibration arose, as is shown by his comment on Fresnel's hypothesis, made in an addition to Arago's 'Treatise on the Polarization of Light'.[1]

This hypothesis of Mr Fresnel is at least very ingenious, and may lead us to some satisfactory computations: but it is attended by one circumstance which is perfectly *appalling* in its consequences. The substances on which Mr Savart made his experiments were *solids* only; and it is only to solids that such a *lateral* resistance has ever been attributed: so that if we adopted the distinctions laid down by the reviver of the undulatory system himself [Young] in his Lectures, it might be inferred that the luminiferous ether, pervading all space, and penetrating almost all substances, is not only highly elastic, but absolutely solid!!!

It was, of course, in this form—the elastic solid theory of the ether—that the wave theory of light survived through most of the nineteenth century.

And now any feeling of neglect which Fresnel might once have harboured against British physicists was completely dissipated, first by his election as a corresponding member of the Royal Society in 1825 and then by the award of the Society's Rumford Medal in 1827. The first announcement was made to Arago by Young on 29 March 1827, and the medal and prize money were sent to Fresnel by Young on 18 June 1827 for 'the application of the undulatory theory of light to the phenomenon of polarization'. Young suggests that he himself might also claim some right to participate in the compliment, but admits that as it is more than a quarter of a century since his principal experiments were made he can only feel it 'a sort of anticipation of posthumous fame, which I have never particularly coveted'.

A reciprocal honour came to Young in the same year in the

[1] *Works*, vol. I, p. 415.

shape of his election as one of the eight foreign associates of the
Paris Academy. The letter of Arago (6 August 1827) which
conveys the news announces also the tragic death of Fresnel at
the early ago of thirty-nine. 'The poor Fresnel was already
dying when I sent him your medals.'[1] Young's reply shows
how deeply he appreciated the honour he received. Unfortunately, two years later he too passed away at the comparatively
early age of fifty-six. →1 →(1773 - 1829)

The wave theory of light was probably the greatest achievement of early nineteenth-century theoretical science. It won
its way slowly, but after the work of Young and Fresnel its
victory was inevitable. John Herschel was not an easy convert
and until 1827 found it hard to give a complete acceptance. He
was in the end convinced, however, and described the theory
in terms which carried wide support. After discussing the
corpuscular theory he goes on to say:[2]

But the unpursued speculations of Newton, and the 'aperçus' of
Hooke, however distinct, must not be put in competition, and,
indeed, ought not to be mentioned, with the elegant, simple, and
comprehensive theory of Young—a theory which, if not founded
in Nature, is certainly one of the happiest fictions that the genius of
man ever invented to grasp together natural phenomena, which, at
their first discovery, seemed in irreconcilable opposition to it; it is,
in fact, with all its applications and details, a succession of felicities,
insomuch that we may be almost induced to say, if it be not true,
it deserves to be so.

Of the relative claims of Young and Fresnel he says:[3]

Such is the beautiful theory of Fresnel and Young; for we must
not, in our regard for one great name, forget the justice which is
due to the other; and to separate them and assign to each his share
would be as impracticable as invidious, so intimately are they
blended together throughout every part of this system—early, acute
and pregnant suggestion characterising the one; and maturity of
thought, fullness of systematic development and decisive experimental illustration, equally distinguishing the other.

[1] *Works*, vol. I, p. 410.
[2] J. F. W. Herschel, *Encyclopaedia Metropolitana*, vol. II, p. 456.
[3] Peacock, *op. cit.* p. 397.

Young quoted this judgment with approval in a letter[1] to his sister, Mrs Earle (November 1827), admitting that 'acute suggestion was always more in the line of my ambition than experimental illustration'. Young's early judgment made in 1802 in a letter to Dalzel had come true: 'The theory of light and colours, though it did not occupy a large portion of my time, I conceive to be of more importance than all that I have ever done, or ever shall do besides.'[2]

[1] *Ibid.* p. 397.   [2] Dalzel, *Memoir*, p. 212.

IX

THE ROSETTA STONE

'It is around this wonderful document that all the interest in the decipherment of the Egyptian hieroglyphics clings.'   BUDGE

ONE of the most famous archaeological treasures of the British Museum is the Rosetta Stone. It was discovered in August 1799 by French troops in the course of some excavations near a little town called Rashid, or Rosetta, in the Nile Delta near the mouth of the western branch of the river. The French officer in charge, noticing that the stone was covered with writing, handed it over to the French General. A cursory examination showed that the writing was in three different scripts, one of which was hieroglyphic, one was an Egyptian running script, while the third was Greek.

The potential value of this discovery was at once obvious. If, as seemed probable, the subject-matter of all three inscriptions was the same, then the Greek, when translated, might give the key to the interpretation of the Egyptian hieroglyphics and of the Egyptian popular script. As all knowledge of hieroglyphics had been lost soon after the end of the fourth century A.D., and the Coptic language—a late phase in the development of modern Egyptian, which used an alphabet of Greek letters supplemented by native symbols—became extinct as a spoken language in the sixteenth century A.D., it will be seen how much depended on the possibility of interpreting the two Egyptian scripts of the Rosetta Stone.

The stone, a photograph of which is shown in Pl. III, was unfortunately found to be severely damaged. It is a slab of black basalt about 3 ft. 9 in. long by 2 ft. $4\frac{1}{2}$ in. wide and about 11 in. thick. The damage is most serious in the case of the

PLATE III

THE ROSETTA STONE

hieroglyphic script. Not one line is complete and we now know that about half of the entire inscription has disappeared. The middle text contains thirty-two lines, of which fourteen are incomplete, and the Greek fifty-four lines, of which twenty-six are mutilated at the ends. An intensive search failed to reveal any trace of the missing fragments.

Impressions of the whole inscription were made in ink, and these were circulated to scholars all over Europe, two of them going to the Institut National at Paris. Meantime the French in Egypt surrendered to the British, and early in 1801 the Rosetta Stone and other antiquities were ceded to the British by treaty. The stone was shipped to this country and landed at Deptford in February 1802, transferred to the headquarters of the Society of Antiquaries for a time, and then removed to the British Museum, where it has remained ever since. The first published description of it was issued in Paris shortly after the arrival there of the first impressions of the inscriptions.

The earliest translation of the Greek was made by the Rev. Stephen Weston and communicated to the Society of Antiquaries in April 1802. Later translations by Porson and by Heyne included conjectural substitutions for the missing portions and were sufficient to establish the content of the proclamation with reasonable accuracy and certainty. The subject-matter proved to be the edict of an assembly of the priests of all the Gods of Upper and Lower Egypt held at Memphis. The object of the assembly was to do honour to the boy king Ptolemy V, to record his good deeds and to decree the honours to be paid to him in return. It was ordained that a copy of the edict in Greek, together with translations into the 'writing of the speech of the God', and into the 'writing of the books', cut on a basalt slab, 'shall be set up in the temples of the first, second and third orders'. The decree is dated 27 March 196 B.C. in modern reckoning.

These facts established the importance of the stone. Here was an opportunity of reopening the closed treasure-houses of Egyptian literature and history by interpreting the picture-writing used from the earliest dynasties in all monumental inscriptions and in tomb decoration as well as on tombstones and in many religious papyri, and also the script in general use for literary and commercial purposes at the time of Ptolemy. The secrets of an ancient civilization would stand revealed.

After the Greek had been translated the middle inscription was the next attempted. Young subsequently called this script 'enchorial', the name used in the Greek inscription and meaning simply 'of the country'. Champollion, afterwards a rival claimant to priority in the interpretation of the hieroglyphic script, called it 'demotic' (i.e. 'of the people') after Herodotus, and this name is still used. The first attempt to read it was made by a French archaeologist, Silvestre de Sacy, who in 1802 identified the names of Ptolemy, Alexander and Alexandria and made an unsuccessful attempt to establish an alphabet. This work was carried a little further by J. D. Åkerblad, a Swedish diplomat and a good classical and Coptic scholar. He identified sixteen other names and words and continued de Sacy's attempt to establish an alphabet. In this he had some success in the matter of the proper names, but found it impossible to apply his results to the rest of the inscription.

Young's interest in Egyptology and in the Rosetta Stone was first aroused during the writing of an article on the *Mithridates* of Adelung,[1] in which he found a reference by the editor to the unknown language of the Rosetta Stone. This interest lay dormant, however, until his friend Sir W. Rouse Boughton purchased a papyrus at Luxor in 1814. It was written in running Egyptian characters and had been found in a mummy case in a tomb near Thebes. The papyrus had been badly damaged in transit and the fragments were submitted to Young, presumably because of his known interest in languages. Boughton published a 'Letter respecting Egyptian Antiquities', and Young wrote a short article on the fragments which was published in *Archaeologia* in 1817. This paper, however, 'Remarks on the Ancient Egyptian Manuscripts', had in fact been

---

[1] J. C. Adelung, *Mithridates, or a General History of Languages* (Berlin), vol. I, 1806; vol. II, continued by Prof. Vater, 1809; vol. III, part I, 1812.

read on 19 May 1814 and published in the *Museum Criticum*.[1]

The Rosetta Stone had by this time been discovered for fifteen years and had been in England for twelve years, but Young had so far given it no consideration. In the summer of 1814, however, his interest having been roused, he took a copy of the inscription with him on his annual visit to Worthing, together with the published results of de Sacy and Åkerblad, and settled down to work at the enchorial script. He has given the following account of his method of attack:[2]

The second inscription, which it will be safest to distinguish by the Greek name *enchorial*, signifying merely 'of the country', notwithstanding its deficiencies near the beginning, is still sufficiently perfect to allow us to compare its different parts with each other and with the Greek by the same method that we should employ if it were entire. Thus, if we examine the parts corresponding, in their relative situation, to two passages of the Greek inscription in which *Alexander* and *Alexandria* occur, we soon recognise two well marked groups of characters resembling each other, which we may therefore consider as representing these names; a remark which was first made by Mr de Sacy, in his letter relating to this inscription. A small group of characters occurring very often in almost every line, might be either some termination or some very common particle; it must, therefore, be reserved till it is found in some decisive situation, after some other words have been identified and it will then easily be shown to mean *and*. The next remarkable collection of characters is repeated twenty-nine or thirty times in the enchorial inscription; and we find nothing that occurs so often in the Greek, except the word *king*, with its compounds, which is found about thirty-seven times. A fourth assemblage of characters is found fourteen times in the enchorial inscription, agreeing sufficiently well with the name of *Ptolemy*, which occurs eleven times in the Greek and generally in passages corresponding to those of the enchorial text in their relative situation: and, by a similar comparison the name Egypt is identified, although it occurs much more frequently in the enchorial inscription than in the Greek, which often substitutes for it *country* only, or omits it entirely. Having thus obtained a sufficient number of common points of subdivision we may next proceed to write in the Greek

[1] Part VI (1815), p. 15.
[2] Article on 'Egypt', Supplement to 4th ed. of *Encyclopaedia Britannica*, 1819.

P

text over the enchorial, in such a manner that the passages ascertained may all coincide as nearly as possible; and it is obvious that the intermediate parts of each inscription will then stand very near to the corresponding passages of the other.

It is clear that the two main difficulties encountered were (1) that the inscription was incomplete; and (2) that it was obviously neither a literal translation of the Greek nor the original of a literal translation into Greek, otherwise the proper names would occur the same number of times in the two scripts. Progress was slow and, to Young, disappointing. He seems not to have realized that experts with much better equipment for this kind of work had been busy on the inscription for twelve years with the most meagre results. Writing in August 1814 to Hudson Gurney, who had heard of his new interest, he says:[1]

You tell me that I shall astonish the world if I make out the inscription. I think it on the contrary astonishing that it should not have been made out already, and that I should find the task so difficult as it appears to be. Certainly the labour of a few days would be sufficient for the comparison of an equal number of lines in any ordinary unknown language, aided by a literal translation, so as to identify pretty satisfactorily all the words that occurred more than once, and to ascertain their meaning; but I have been a month upon this, and have still several passages that occur more than once which I cannot completely identify, or at least understand. But by far the greater part of the words I have ascertained with tolerable certainty, and some of the most interesting without the shadow of a doubt; but I can read very few of them alphabetically, except the proper names which Åkerblad has read before and this is the more intolerably provoking as there was so much reason to expect a very general coincidence with the Coptic, the names of the three months mentioned in the Greek agreeing very correctly with the Coptic names.

I have certainly deciphered much more of the Egyptian inscription than Åkerblad had done when he published his Essay ten years ago, and as he professed his intention of pursuing the subject, I think he must have done something more; and as he had undoubtedly begun right, I am very desirious of knowing what has prevented his

[1] Peacock, *op. cit.* p. 261.

completing the task, and of comparing our ideas, as possibly one may have succeeded where the other has failed.

This anxiety of Young to discover what was being done by others was extremely natural. He knew that de Sacy and Åkerblad had had a long start, yet neither of them had published anything for some twelve years. In a memorandum dated 13 July 1814 Young notes this fact and continues:

Under these circumstances it seems most eligible to consider Mr Åkerblad's attempt as having altogether failed and to begin the process anew, without any regard to the partial interpretation which his labours have afforded and without having his remarks at hand to consult.

With this view, having provided myself with the Dictionary and Grammar of Scholtz and Lacroze, and with Wilkin's edition of the Coptic Testament, I have read in the course of the spring the greater part of the Gospels in this version.

Writing to de Sacy in August 1814, he inquires about Åkerblad and expresses a doubt whether Åkerblad's alphabet is likely to be of any further utility than in the deciphering of proper names. Åkerblad and de Sacy had worked on the assumption that the demotic script was alphabetical, and this first expression of a doubt about the matter by Young is important.

To this letter de Sacy replies on 23 September 1814:[1]

M. Åkerblad has been at Rome for several years and although I have been in correspondence with him and have often pressed him to make his results public he has never been willing to defer to my wishes. When he was in Paris he was not any more willing to communicate his work to me. . . . I will not conceal from you that in spite of the qualified approval which I gave to the system of M. Åkerblad I have always entertained grave doubts of the validity of the alphabet which he has made. . . . I ought to add that M. Åkerblad is not the only one who flatters himself that he has read the Egyptian text of the Rosetta inscription. M. Champollion, who has just published two volumes[2] on the ancient geography of Egypt

[1] *Works*, vol. III, p. 17.   [2] *L'Égypte sous les Pharaons.*

and who is active in the study of the Coptic language claims also to have read the inscription.

This letter is an important document because it shows that between 1802 and 1814 neither de Sacy nor Åkerblad had made any progress worth publishing. It is important also as giving de Sacy's estimate of Åkerblad. And it introduces Young to Champollion, a new and formidable rival in this field of study.

A reference to the same book by Gurney in a letter to Young about the same time excited his interest and apprehension and he wrote:[1]

Your first letter disturbed my rest with impatience to see Champollion's work; soon afterwards, however, I had a few lines from Silvestre de Sacy, mentioning that author, but merely as *pretending*[2] to understand the inscription and not as having published his interpretation. . . . Of the Egyptian de Sacy has made out three proper names and Åkerblad nine more and five or six Coptic words. I have detected fifty or sixty Coptic words, ten or twelve of them without doubt, but this makes little more than one tenth of the whole inscription, and I doubt if it will ever be possible to reduce much more of it to Coptic. . . . The difficulties have been far greater than there was any reason to expect, and I am almost surprised that the labour I have bestowed on them has effected so little in comparison of what it might have happened to effect; at the same time, in point of public interest, the result is sufficiently striking.

The final result of Young's few months' work was a complete translation of the enchorial inscription. This was added as a note, dated 9 November 1814, to the 'Remarks on the Ancient Egyptian Manuscripts' communicated by Sir W. E. Rouse Boughton to the Society of Antiquaries,[3] and it was also sent to de Sacy on 3 October 1814.[4] The translation, of course, consisted merely of an attempt to identify the words of the enchorial inscription which corresponded to known words in the Greek. It contained much that was conjectural and much that was in error, but in the few summer months he

---

[1] Peacock, *op. cit.* p. 262.

[2] Young here translates de Sacy's word *prétend* as if it bore the meaning of the similar English word. It is more properly translated 'claiming'.

[3] *Works*, vol. III, p. 3.   [4] *Ibid.* p. 18.

had devoted to this study Young had undoubtedly overtaken and passed both de Sacy and Åkerblad. He had read Åkerblad's work before making his own attempt, had then worked independently and had checked his final result against that of Åkerblad. The relation of the two 'translations' is made clear in Young's letter to de Sacy. After remarking on his agreement with Åkerblad's results he goes on to say: 'I must, however, confess that it relates only to a few of the first steps of the investigation; and that the greatest and the most difficult part of the translation still remains unsupported by the authority of any external evidence of this kind.'

The view that Åkerblad had shot his bolt is confirmed by a letter[1] written by him to Young in January 1815. In this he pleads guilty to having been 'engaged in less unproductive studies'. He admits that he has always felt that his researches on the monument are 'deficient in that sort of evidence which carries full conviction'. He encloses his translation of the first five lines of the inscription, but can promise nothing more than 'a statement of my doubts and uncertainties together with a few more plausible conjectures'.

Young, while working on the enchorial inscription, was impressed with the occurrence of characters which bore a strong resemblance to the characters of the hieroglyphic inscription. Closer examination tended to confirm him in the view that the two scripts were related and that the enchorial was in fact derived from the hieroglyphic. This important conclusion was first indicated in a letter to de Sacy.[2]

Two days after the date of my last letter I was fortunate enough to satisfy myself respecting the sense of some of the hieroglyphic characters. . . . After having completed this analysis of the hieroglyphic inscription, I observed that the epistolographic characters of the Egyptian inscription, which expressed the words God, Immortal, Vulcan, Priests, Diadem, Thirty, and some others, had a striking resemblance to the corresponding hieroglyphics; and since none of these characters could be reconciled, without inconceivable violence,

[1] *Miscellaneous Works of Thomas Young*, vol. III, Hieroglyphical Essays and Correspondence; ed. John Leitch (London, 1855), p. 30.   [2] *Works*, vol. III, p. 52.

to the forms of any imaginable alphabet, I could scarcely doubt, that they were imitations of the hieroglyphics, adopted as monograms or verbal characters, and mixed with the letters of the alphabet.

This discovery, that at least some of the demotic characters were derived from the hieroglyphic and that the demotic was therefore probably in part symbolic and not, as had been thought, entirely alphabetical, was a very important step in the interpretation of the script. It was much too important to be broadcast without confirmatory evidence, and so we find Young collecting all the available material and subjecting it to careful scrutiny from this point of view. Henry Salt, who had already acquired some reputation as an orientalist, had been appointed Consul-General in Egypt, and Young not only obtained his personal interest but persuaded the British Government to authorize him to transmit to this country any specimens of inscriptions likely to be useful.

I met Hamilton at Sir Joseph Banks's on Sunday last, and attacked him on Egyptian affairs; he told me that everything had been done at the Foreign Office which I wished; that Salt had full powers to hunt for all the fragments of which I had shown the importance, and credit for a specific sum to cover his expenses.[1]

Among the inscriptions studied by Young were those reproduced in the *Description de l'Égypte*. This very important French serial work was then just being published, and made available to scholars an immense amount of new material. In addition to inscriptions on temples and other buildings, it reproduced the script of numerous 'funeral rolls' taken from the wrapping of mummies. Unfortunately the reproduction of detail in the publication was not good and Young's studies did not make very rapid progress. His earlier discoveries had been prepared for publication in the *Museum Criticum*, but nothing had appeared, and writing to Hudson Gurney early in 1816 Young says:[2]

The printers at Cambridge are models of slow and dignified

[1] Letter from Young to Mrs Chambers, 7 Dec. 1815 (Peacock, *op. cit.* p. 269).
[2] Peacock, *op. cit.* p. 277.

deliberation. I made it a condition in August last that my paper should be immediately printed. It was accepted, and now, in January, the three sheets are not yet worked off; but it is of little consequence, or rather of none at all. I have had the great Description de l'Égypte for some time on my table through W. Hamilton's kindness, and I have been copying out some of the hieroglyphics for future use, but I have not attempted to decypher any of them, meaning to wait for further assistance from Egypt: I much fear, however, I have made out much less than I thought must almost certainly have been intelligible, and on the whole, I have no confidence in being able to do much more than fully to illustrate the inscription of Rosetta, and to trace the nature and origin of several of the characters contained in it. All the inscriptions on temples, and the generality of the manuscripts found with the mummies, appear to relate to their ridiculous rites and ceremonies: I see nothing that looks like history: the obeliscs seem to be the only kind of monument likely to be worth reading, even if one could make out the characters, and there are too few to afford us much of importance.

In October 1817 he writes to Gurney:

With the hieroglyphics I have done little or nothing since I saw you—but I could never get to *the end* of them, as long as any materials exist unexamined and uncompared: I suppose they might furnish employment for an academy of forty members for half a century, and it will be enough for me to have discovered a mine by which others may enrich themselves. But I do mean to try to make out more—and in a year or two I shall publish what I have done—still anonymously as far as the form goes.

Shortly after this the last number of the series of the *Description de l'Égypte* appeared, and contained much more accurate facsimiles. Many of these referred to the 'funeral rolls' already mentioned, one of them being a particularly good specimen which Young calls the Codex Ritualis; Champollion found a similar papyrus in the Museum of Turin. These papyri contain drawings representing various incidents in the passage of the deceased through the underworld and the prayers addressed to the various divinities to whom he was presented.

The Codex Ritualis, the most impressive of the funeral rolls discovered up to that time, contained more than 500 columns

of hieroglyphics with brilliantly coloured drawings. Young
soon discovered that these funeral rolls had many sections in
common with one another and with the master text of this
Codex Ritualis, and he proceeded to a careful collation.

The first detailed account of his discovery and the method
by which he had arrived at it was given in a letter[1] to the
Archduke John of Austria, 2 August 1816, subsequently published in the *Museum Criticum*. It was at once printed and
widely circulated at home and abroad among interested scholars,
although the actual publication of the number of the *Museum
Criticum* was delayed till 1821. In this letter Young writes:

> I had already ascertained, as I have mentioned in one of my letters
> to Mr de Sacy, that the enchorial inscription of Rosetta contained a
> number of individual characters, resembling the corresponding
> hieroglyphics, and I was not disposed to place any great reliance on
> the alphabetical interpretation of any considerable part of the
> inscription. I have now fully demonstrated the hieroglyphical origin
> of the running hand, in which the manuscripts on papyrus, found
> with the mummies, are commonly written, and which is obviously
> of the same kind with the enchorial characters of the Stone of
> Rosetta, as Mr Åkerblad, and his disciple Mr Champollion, have
> both justly observed. In the great Description de l'Égypte there are
> several engravings of manuscripts on papyrus; one of them contains
> more than five hundred columns of well delineated hieroglyphics,
> consisting, according to Mr Jomard, of about thirty thousand
> characters, arranged under a series of vignettes, which run along the
> greater part of the margin. I was first struck with the evident
> relation of some of the figures in the margin to the text below; and
> having observed the same figures in the margins of several other
> manuscripts written in the running hand, I was led to examine with
> attention the corresponding texts and I found at last a similar agree-
> ment in almost all of them. I then made copies of the respective
> passages in continuous lines, and I found that the characters agreed
> throughout with each other, in such a manner as completely to put
> an end to the idea of the alphabetical nature of any of them. In this
> manner I obtained a duplicate, and sometimes a triplicate and
> quadruplicate copy of almost half of the great hieroglyphical manu-
> script, although not without some variation in particular passages:

[1] *Works*, vol. III, p. 74.

and in a manuscript of which Denon, if I mistake not, has published the first column, and of which an engraving has been obligingly sent me by Mr de Sacy, I have identified a few other passages of the great hieroglyphic manuscript, not found in either of the others contained in the Description de l'Égypte.

He goes on to indicate the hope he had at first held that this relationship of the scripts would enable him to translate back the

whole of the running hand of the Stone of Rosetta into distinct hieroglyphics, and thus to compare it with a multiplicity of other monuments; for since the enchorial inscription has been preserved nearly entire, and the sense of all its parts has been determined with sufficient certainty, and since it has been proved that these characters are truly hieroglyphics, though in a corrupted and degraded form, it is evident that we only want a sufficient number of connecting links to enable us to apply the whole inscription to the interpretation of the genuine sacred characters.

This hope he was forced to abandon because 'unfortunately the degradation is too great and the connecting links too few'.

In a letter to Åkerblad ten days later he further substantiates his discovery and gives references to the parts of the inscription on the Rosetta Stone which illustrate it. This letter, with the earlier one to the Archduke, was at once printed and distributed. The full and reasoned statement of his discovery was later given in the article on 'Egypt' which he wrote for the *Encyclopaedia Britannica* two years later.

From the second inscription Young turned his attention to the first. Here he had nothing but conjecture on the part of his predecessors to guide him. No successful step in the direction of interpreting the hieroglyphic script of Egypt had been taken, and although it was now about fifteen years since the Rosetta Stone had been discovered, none of the scholars who had worked on it had even made a start with the interpretation of it. It had indeed been suggested that the hieroglyphics on the portico of the great temple of Dendera gave a translation of the hundredth psalm of David, and conversely that all the psalms of David were merely Hebrew translations of the Egyptian rolls of papyrus. But reliable indications there were none, and the darkness which shrouded the hieroglyphs was penetrated by no ray of light. Here Young's method seems to have been to make a careful comparison of the first and second inscriptions, using the similarities of the two to identify certain landmarks in the first inscription. In this way he discovered how very imperfect this inscription is and what a considerable portion of it is missing. In spite of this fact he was able to identify the name of Ptolemy. This consists of a group of characters surrounded by an oval ring or cartouche, and Young had come to the conclusion that groups of characters enclosed in this way represented proper names. The same idea had occurred to two earlier workers,[1] but neither was able to follow it up. Young seems not to have known that any such conjecture had previously been made. It is one of the particular points which he claims as his own discovery and he says: 'As far as I have ever heard or read, *not one* of these particulars had ever been established and placed on record by *any other* person, dead or alive.'[2] This particular discovery had certainly never been *established* before, and as the whole field was an unfamiliar one to Young it is unlikely that he had even read of the conjecture.

He now proceeded a step further. It was quite clear that the hieroglyphic script had originated as picture-writing. Many of the characters were easily recognizable and obviously represented objects or ideas associated with the objects. The idea that some hieroglyphic signs might be used alphabetically and might represent speech sounds had not been taken seriously by any of the principal workers in the subject. About 1815–16, however, Young came to the conclusion that if a foreign conqueror of a country caused inscriptions commemorating his conquest to be drawn up in the native language of that country and that language was written with pictorial characters, the scribes would, in writing the conqueror's name, make use of the phonetic values of a number of pictorial characters as pictures. In this conjecture also he had been anticipated, but again the original authors of the suggestion had been unable to do anything with it and it seems very unlikely that Young had

---

[1] Barthélemy and Zöega.   [2] *Works*, vol. III, p. 274.

even heard of it. He was guided to some extent by an analogy borrowed from the Chinese language. Here also we have a script which is ideographic and not phonetic, but the characters may be given phonetic significance by a special sign. Assuming that the cartouche enclosing hieroglyphs was indeed such a sign, Young worked on the name he had identified as that of Ptolemy. This name, which is the only one surviving in the hieroglyphic inscription on the Rosetta Stone, occurs twice in a short cartouche and twice in a long one. The hieroglyphs which begin the name in the long cartouche are identical with those which occur in the same order in the short cartouche. From this Young deduced that the long cartouche included not only the name of Ptolemy but certain titles as well, while the short cartouche contained the name only. He then proceeded to identify the hieroglyphs as follows:

□	P
◠	T
𓆑	'sometimes omitted and not essential'
𓂝	OLE
⌒	MA 'or simply M'
𓏭	I
𓏤	OSH or OS

Putting these together, we have PTOLEMAIOS. We now know (a) that the sign disregarded as inessential is U or O; (b) that the lion is simply L; and (c) that the last sign is S, so that the name reads PTOLMIS or PTULMIS. This effort of Young's was the first successful attempt to decipher any Egyptian hieroglyphic inscription, and we see that four letters were correct and two nearly so.

On the ceiling of a temple at Karnak there was a Greek inscription containing the name of Ptolemy Soter and in hieroglyphs a cartouche which Young recognized as that of Ptolemy, associated with another cartouche terminated by the semicircle and oval which he knew to be the mark of a female. He concluded that this cartouche contained the name of Ptolemy's queen, Berenice, and attempted to apply to it his method of interpretation. Unfortunately the only symbol in this cartouche which also occurred in that of Ptolemy was the double reed for I. Young's interpretation was as follows:

♉	BIR
◯	E
∿	N
𓏥	I
𓎡	'seems to be superfluous'
𓄿	KE or KEN

giving BIRENIKE or BIRENIKEN. Properly interpreted, the name reads BRNKIS.

The interpretations were not, of course, mere guess-work. Thus the first hieroglyph was taken to be a basket, for which the Coptic word was 'Bir'. The bird was taken to be a goose when it was really meant to be a vulture, and the letters KE or KEN occur, according to Young, in the word given by Kircher[1] for goose.

We may sum up his work on these two proper names by saying that out of a total of thirteen signs he gave correct values to six, partly correct values to three and wrong values to four. This will be seen from the following table:

SYMBOL	YOUNG		CORRECT
—	P		P
◠	T		T
ꟼ	not essential		O
🐆	OLE		L
⟅	MA or M		M
𓏥	I		I
𓊪	OSH		S
♉	BIR		B
◯	E		R
∿	N		N
𓎡	not essential		K
𓄿	KEN		S
𓇯	Female sign		Female sign
	Correct	6	
	Partially correct	3	
	Erroneous	4	

[1] Athanasius Kircher (1601–80), German oriental scholar and mathematician.

To this list Young subsequently added the horned snake used for the letter F and a number of others.

Proceeding to the longer cartouches for the name of Ptolemy, Young identified additional hieroglyphs representing the titles 'Beloved of Ptah' and 'Ever-Living'.

And now, before attempting to assess Young's work on hieroglyphs, we must look at his most complete account of the whole subject. In spite of the anonymity behind which he sheltered—rather like an ostrich, it must be confessed—his interest was sufficiently well known and he was invited to contribute an article on 'Egypt' to the Supplement to the fourth edition of the *Encyclopaedia Britannica*. The article was written in 1818 and published in 1819. It was the first piece of work of its kind in English. It gave a comprehensive account of the state of knowledge based on extensive reading of the available authorities and was divided into eight sections. These dealt with (1) Recent publications on Egypt; (2) The Pantheon of Egypt; (3) The Historiography of Egypt; (4) The Egyptian Calendar; (5) Manners and Customs; (6) Analysis of the Triple Inscription on the Rosetta Stone; (7) Rudiments of a Hieroglyphic Vocabulary; and (8) The General Characters and Subject of the Egyptian Monuments. The article covers thirty-eight quarto pages and contains five plates, a list of 218 enchorial words, a 'supposed' enchorial alphabet and about 200 hieroglyphic signs with interpretations.

In the first five sections we have the fruit of very extensive reading, going back to classical times. In Section VI we reach Young's original contributions. This section has already been quoted. It describes his work on the enchorial inscription, the identification of the name of Ptolemy in this script and hence in the 'sacred characters', and finally gives the evidence for his discovery that the enchorial script is derived from the hieroglyphic.

We cannot altogether acquit Young of a certain smugness in the veiled account of his own work on the Rosetta Stone,[1]

a monument which has already enabled us to obtain a general

[1] *Works*, vol. III, p. 102.

idea of the nature and subject of any given hieroglyphical inscription, by pursuing the investigations already carried to an unexpected extent by an anonymous author, whose interpretation was communicated to the Antiquarian Society by Mr Rouse Boughton. . . . Mr de Sacy, and more especially Mr Åkerblad, had made some progress in identifying the sense of the several parts of the second inscription of the stone; but it was left to British industry to convert to permanent profit a monument, which had before been a useless, though a glorious trophy of British valour.

It is typical of Young that he regards his work as a tribute to British industry rather than to British genius. He emphasizes the fact that although the enchorial is derived from the hieroglyphic it had admitted all the variations of the popular dialect and bore but a faint resemblance to its original prototype. Had it been otherwise there would, of course, have been no point in duplicating the inscription on the Rosetta Stone. Young saw the first beginnings of the adaptation of the hieroglyphics in what he called the *hieratic script* but what Champollion and succeeding writers have more properly called *linear hieroglyphics*. This script was simply the inevitable modification of hieroglyphic which resulted from writing the signs with a pen—the equivalent of our 'lettering'. A further step towards a cursive script based on the hieroglyphs produced hieratic which bore more or less the same relationship to hieroglyphic as a modern fast running hand to a printed text. Hieratic must have come into use as soon as hieroglyphic writing became a practical medium of communication, but the earliest surviving examples date from the middle of the third millennium. It was employed in all the ordinary transactions of life—correspondence, accounts memoranda—as well as for literary documents, until superseded by the 'enchorial' or demotic in about the ninth century, though it survived to the second century A.D. in certain religious books. Hieratic passed through at least three clearly defined stages, each of which in turn took it further from its hieroglyphic original, till it reached an extremely cursive form out of which demotic developed. The language similarly passed through three main stages before the period of demotic writing;

so that by that time the ordinary language of the day, which in writing was expressed by the demotic script, was at least as far from the conservative language of formal and religious inscriptions expressed in hieroglyphics as our newspapers are from Chaucer.

Young perhaps stated his conclusion too broadly. He would have been less open to criticism if he had said that a sufficient number of characters in the demotic were derived from the hieroglyphic to show that it could not be alphabetical in the ordinary sense of the word, and that the kind of search for an all-sufficient limited alphabet which had occupied de Sacy and Åkerblad could be abandoned.

Section VII gives us the 'Rudiments of a Hieroglyphic Vocabulary'. Among the signs interpreted are the names of a number of gods and goddesses, kings, etc. Although there are numerous errors, it is clear that Young had discovered the notation of the numerals 1 to 9 and also 10, 100 and 1000; he had recognized the ordinal sign; and he had correctly interpreted many names and other words, although he could not transliterate them. The section includes his identification and transliterations of the names of Ptolemy and Berenice.

Peacock[1] had access to the material on which Young's article was based and gives a description of it in some detail. It consisted of an impressive series of his manuscripts covering every available inscription. The 200 hieroglyphic signs given in Section VII are each

subjected to a critical examination, special references to the Rosetta Stone and the ritual manuscripts being made with a view to the determination of the probable meaning when used singly or in combination, as well as of its equivalent signs, whether phonetic or otherwise, whenever such were discoverable.

It is impossible to form a just estimate either of the vast extent to which Dr Young had carried his hieroglyphical investigations, or of the real progress which he had made in them, without an inspection of these manuscripts. They would appear to have been prepared between the years 1814 and 1818, and to have been the result of

[1] Peacock, *op. cit.* p. 280.

labours which, though frequently interrupted by other publications and inquiries, were never entirely lost sight of.[1]

The article was described in *The Edinburgh Review* as 'the greatest effort of scholarship and ingenuity of which modern literature can boast'.[2] Budge assesses it as follows:

The results of his studies at this period were published in his Article 'Egypt'. . . . It was accompanied by five plates, containing inter alia a hieroglyphic vocabulary of 218 words, a 'supposed enchorial, i.e. demotic alphabet' and 'specimens of phrases'. The VIIth Section of the letterpress contained the 'Rudiments of a Hieroglyphic Vocabulary' and thus Young became the father of English compilers of Egyptian Vocabularies. In this article, which formed a most important and epoch-making contribution to Egyptology, Young gave a list containing a number of alphabetic Egyptian characters to which, in most cases, he assigned correct phonetic values—i.e. values which are accepted by Egyptologists today.[3]

Elsewhere he describes the article as 'practically the foundation of the science of Egyptology'.[4]

Taking up the study as a sideline twelve years after the work on the Rosetta Stone had been begun, Young outdistanced all competitors and in four years, at the time this article was written, undoubtedly led the field. His discoveries paved the way for competitors and successors and his discovery of the phonetic principle as applied to the hieroglyphs has been rightly described by Chabas as the 'Fiat Lux' of the subject.

As early as 1817[5] Young formed a project which he announced in a letter to Hudson Gurney as follows:

I intend to set about establishing something between a Society and a Subscription, for getting all the hieroglyphic inscriptions in existence copied and published, with any explanation that may be proposed in a separate series and perhaps for employing some poor Italian or Maltese to scramble over Egypt in search of more—and all

[1] These manuscripts are now in the Manuscript Room of the British Museum (MSS. 27281–5).   [2] Vol. XLV, p. 144.
[3] Sir E. A. Wallis Budge, *Egyptian Hieroglyphic Dictionary* (London, 1920), p. vi.
[4] Sir E. A. Wallis Budge, *The Rosetta Stone* (London, 1929), p. 207.
[5] 21 Oct. 1817.

this might be done very well, under the name of an Egyptian Society, without becoming too prominent individually.

When the project finally took shape there were about fifty members, each of whom paid £1 1s. to join and were to pay £2 2s. for each volume received. Unfortunately, in spite of the fact that some of the subscribers ordered more than one copy, the number of subscribers was not sufficient to carry the publication. The advertisement to the first fasciculus, which appeared early in 1819, says that the support was not sufficient to justify the publication of more than fifteen plates but that 200 copies had been printed and more subscribers were hoped for. In a letter[1] to Gurney Young says:

My youngest child has been a little expensive to me. I have advanced £160 to bring him into the world—and I am not likely at present to recover above £60 or £70 from my subscribers: I shall not, however, give myself any more trouble unless I find more contributors.

The following year he worked on the second fasciculus, and this contained the Rosetta Stone inscription with translations and a selection of other inscriptions collected by W. J. Bankes. This finally appeared in 1823 and the two fasciculi were bound as one volume. The advertisement announces the suspension of the production owing to lack of support, the number of subscriptions being less than 100.

Young explained the suspension to Gell in a letter of 13 September 1823:[2]

You will have observed that it (the second fasciculus) professes to be the last of the collection for the present. It had cost me about £100 a number beyond the receipts, and though one of my friends[3] chose to pay one hundred and now offers to pay the other, I do not think the public has a right to the more than gratuitous services of me and my friends in any extra-professional capacity: besides that, as the second fasciculus contains the Rosetta inscription and everything else that is really valuable in the investigation, I could not expect to be able to produce anything else that would be of sufficient

---

[1] 26 Oct. 1819.   [2] *Works*, vol. III, p. 369.   [3] Probably Hudson Gurney.

Q

importance to continue the series: and in the third place Champollion is doing so much that he will not suffer anything of material consequence to be lost. For these reasons I have now considered my Egyptian studies as concluded. . . . But since the appearance of my second fasciculus, I have had some negotiations with the Royal Society of Literature through their President the Bishop of St David's respecting a continuation of the collection, which would afford an object highly desirable to be incorporated with the hitherto undefined pursuits of this nascent Society; and I believe they would be very ready to undertake the pecuniary cost of the thing if I would undertake to direct the work as I have hitherto done. . . . I think it probable that I may offer to do enough to induce them to take up the work.

Gell's rejoinder is a protest against the wickedness of allowing the Egyptian Society to lapse and an appeal to Young either to set it afoot again or to stir up his 'Royal Literaries'.

The idea of inducing the newly formed Royal Society of Literature to take over the publication of further work had been in Young's mind in 1820 and in that year he had approached Colonel Leake, a Fellow of the Society. But not till the suspension was announced in 1823 did any move come from the R.S.L. In July 1823 the Bishop of St David's approached Young privately, and later in the same month officially in his capacity as President. Negotiations proceeded on the basis of the responsibility for further publication being assumed by the R.S.L., who were to clear the deficit of the Egyptian Society by a payment of £100 and take over the remaining copies of the first volume. Young on his part undertook to give advice about the continuation of the work. In 1826 Young was actively preparing the third fasciculus and writes to Gurney (10 January) to say that he has had 'a number of new characters in the running hand, which I am more and more anxious to investigate as affording the only perfectly firm foundation for approaching the older hieroglyphics'. The third fasciculus appeared in 1827 and the second volume in 1828. The two volumes were subsequently bound in one.

X

RIVAL CLAIMS OF YOUNG AND CHAMPOLLION

'He first penetrated the obscurity which had veiled for ages the hieroglyphics of Egypt.'   Memorial Tablet to Young

AND now we must turn to consider the work of Young's great rival Champollion and the relations between these two pioneers in the study of Egyptology. The rivalry between their supporters assumed at one time an international character, and although the echoes of the controversy have now died away there seems of late to have been a tendency to underrate the importance of the work Young did.

Jean François Champollion—Champollion le jeune, as he was called to distinguish him from Champollion-Figeac, his brother—was born in 1790 and died in 1832. He was admitted to the School of Oriental Languages in Paris in 1805 at the age of fifteen and began to study the inscription on the Rosetta Stone in the same year—i.e. nine years before Young was attracted to the subject. In 1812 he became Professor of Ancient History at Grenoble and soon planned an encyclopaedic work on Egypt. It was the first part of this work—two volumes on *L'Égypte sous les Pharaons*—which appeared in 1814 and which was brought to the notice of Young by Hudson Gurney. In the preface Champollion, referring to the inscription of Rosetta, writes: 'I have had the happiness to see my efforts crowned with an almost complete success; several passages in the Egyptian text are quoted in the two volumes which I now publish.'[1] On this Budge[2] comments: 'The reader who will take the trouble to examine the references to the demotic text on the Rosetta Stone which are given by Champollion in this

---

[1] J. F. Champollion, *L'Égypte sous les Pharaons* (Grenoble, 1814), p. xvii.
[2] Budge, *op. cit.* p. 218.

work will find that his knowledge of the text was not in advance of that of Åkerblad and De Sacy, a fact which need not surprise us.'

In a letter[1] already quoted, de Sacy, after referring to Champollion as having claimed to have read the inscription, goes on to say: 'I place assuredly greater confidence in the gifts and the judgment of M. Åkerblad than in those of M. Champollion, but until they have published some results of their work, it is well to suspend judgment.'

Young's first direct contact with Champollion came as a result of his tenure of the office of foreign secretary of the Royal Society. In November 1814, at the end of Young's first six months' work on the Stone, Champollion addressed a letter to the President of the Royal Society conveying to the Society as a gift the two volumes of his book on *L'Égypte sous les Pharaons*. He indicates that these volumes deal mainly with the geography of Egypt and that the language will come later. In referring to his work on the Rosetta Stone he writes:[2] 'The efforts which I have made on this have not been, if I may say so, without success; and the results which I believe I have obtained after constant and persevering study give me hope for still greater things.' He complains that his work is made more difficult by the imperfections of the copies on which he is working. One of these is 'the facsimile that your Society has engraved' and the other is the French Government copy as published in the *Description de l'Égypte*. Finally he asks that some passages which he transcribes, in which the two copies seem to be at variance, may be compared with the Stone itself.

This letter is acknowledged by Young in his official capacity as foreign secretary of the Royal Society, with a request to know whether Champollion's letter is meant for that Society or for the Society of Antiquaries, which was the body responsible for the facsimile to which he refers. Evidently, however, Young had made the comparisons asked for, because he writes of the two copies:[3]

In general that of the Society of Antiquaries seems to me to be

[1] *Works*, vol. III, p. 17.   [2] *Ibid.* p. 63.   [3] *Ibid.* p. 64.

almost perfect; sometimes, however, the French copy is the more exact; but in most of the places which you have cited there is some uncertainty in the original markings which are a little confused and worn and it is only in comparing the various parts of the Stone that one can be assured of the correct reading. As far as I can distinguish the marks on a day which was not very favourable they read thus. . . .

Young then gives an indication of what he has himself accomplished. He maintains that in spite of all uncertainties both copies are sufficiently exact to establish the sense of most of the words (of the demotic). He wonders if by chance de Sacy has referred in correspondence to his (Young's) conjectural translation of the demotic and his explanation of the last lines of the hieroglyphics: 'I have already sent him the translation of the Egyptian inscription at the beginning of last October. I only succeeded with the hieroglyphics at the end of the same month.'

Champollion's reply (9 May 1815) contains a warm acknowledgment of Young's help. He says that M. de Sacy had not informed him of Young's work and he gladly accepts Young's offer to send him a copy of his memoir, asking that it be addressed c/o his brother at Paris. He makes no claims for his own work and ends up by saying 'I dare to hope also that I may be allowed to continue a correspondence of which the whole advantage will most certainly be on my side.' Making all allowance for French courtesy, it does not seem unfair to conclude that at this date Champollion was not in a position to stake out a claim for any considerable piece of work on either of the inscriptions, even after ten years' work.

On 20 July 1815, de Sacy writes to Young to say that he has sent to Champollion-Figeac (the brother of Champollion) the English translation of the demotic inscription for his brother's use. Later in the same letter he writes:[1]

I think, Sir, that you are more advanced today, and that you read a great part at least of the Egyptian text. If I have a counsel to give it is that you should not too much communicate your discoveries to M. Champollion. He would be able then to pretend afterwards to priority. He seeks in several places in his work to create the belief

[1] *Ibid.* p. 49.

that he has discovered many words of the Egyptian inscription of Rosetta. I fear that this is nothing but charlatanism; I would even add that I have strong reasons for thinking so. . . . In addition I cannot persuade myself that if M. Åkerblad, Etienne Quartemere or Champollion had made real progress in the reading of the Egyptian text they would not have hastened to make their discovery public. It would be a very rare modesty and one of which not one of them seems to me to be capable.

This passage sounds somewhat biased, but the sentence about priority was certainly prophetic. When Young published his correspondence on the Rosetta inscription in the *Museum Criticum*,[1] he of course omitted this and all other disparaging references to Champollion.

By 1818 Young had completed his earlier and more important work and, as we have seen, it was published in his article on 'Egypt' in 1819. Champollion had, till this time, published practically nothing on the demotic inscription and nothing at all on the hieroglyphic. His first published work specifically on the scripts did not appear until 1821, two years later. It was called *De l'Écriture hiératique des Anciens Égyptiens* and represented sixteen years' work, although, of course, he was still only thirty-one, being seventeen years Young's junior.

The letterpress is very brief, but there are several large plates. Referring to the funeral rolls, he says:[2]

Some students regard the writing of the funeral rolls as being the Egyptian Hieratic writing, others as the epistolographic or popular writing mentioned by the Greek authors; but all agree on the important point, that the writing of these Egyptian manuscripts is alphabetic, that is to say that it is composed of signs meant to recall the sounds of the spoken language. A long study, and above all, an attentive comparison of the hieroglyphic texts with those of the second kind regarded as alphabetic, have led us to a contrary conclusion. It follows indeed from our collation (1) that the writing of the Egyptian manuscripts of the second kind (hieratic) is certainly not [n'est point] alphabetic (2) that the second system is only a simple modification of the hieroglyphic, and differs from it solely in

[1] No. VI (1815).

[2] J. F. Champollion, *De l'Écriture hiératique* (Grenoble, 1821).

the form of the signs (3) that this second kind of writing is the hieratic of the Greek authors, and ought to be regarded as a hieroglyphic shorthand and (4) that finally the hieratic characters are signs of *things and not of sounds.*

In any consideration of priority in the discovery of the interpretation of the hieroglyphs this publication is of crucial importance. It shows that two years after Young had published his interpretation of the signs in the names of Ptolemy and Berenice on the assumption that they represented the sounds of the Greek letters of the names, Champollion was writing a definite and complete repudiation of this assumption. It will be seen also that five years after Young had announced the derivation of the hieratic script from the hieroglyphic and two years after the evidence had been fully set out in his article on 'Egypt', Champollion announces the same conclusion without any acknowledgment.

In 1822 Young paid a visit to Paris, where he met Champollion, and writes to his friend Hudson Gurney as follows:[1]

And Champollion . . . has been working still harder upon the Egyptian characters. He devotes his whole time to the pursuit and he has been wonderfully successful in some of the documents that he has obtained—but he appears to me to go too fast—and he makes up his mind in many cases where I should think it safer to doubt. But it is better to do too much than to do nothing at all, and others may separate the wheat from the chaff when his harvest is complete. How far he will acknowledge everything which he has either borrowed or might have borrowed from me I am not quite confident, but the world will be sure to remark *que c'est le premier pas qui coûte*, though the proverb is less true in this case than in most others, for here every step is laborious.

Here Young voices a suspicion—whether based on de Sacy's letter or his own personal contact we do not know.

Writing to Sir William Hamilton, F.R.S.,[2] about the same time (Paris, 29 September 1822), Young expresses himself in much the same terms, giving generous praise to Champollion, whose steps in Egyptian literature appear to be 'gigantic':[3]

[1] Peacock, *op. cit.* p. 322.
[2] H.M. Minister Plenipotentiary at the Court of Naples.   [3] *Works*, vol. III, p. 220.

If he did borrow an English key, the lock was so dreadfully rusty, that no common arm would have had strength enough to turn it. . . . Beginning with the few hieroglyphics to which I had assigned a phonetic signification, he found reason to conclude that, in the days of the Greeks and Romans at least, a considerable number of different characters were employed for expressing hieroglyphically the letters composing a foreign proper name. . . . Besides the names of Ptolemy and Berenice, which he reads as I have done, though with some slight alterations, and with several varieties of form, he makes out with more or less latitude those of [here follows a list of seventeen names].

He proceeds:

You will easily believe that were I ever so much the victim of the bad passions, I should feel nothing but exultation at Mr Champollion's success; my life seems indeed to be lengthened by the accession of a junior coadjutor in my researches, and of a person too, who is so much more versed in the different dialects of the Egyptian language than myself. I sincerely wish that his merits may be as highly appreciated by his countrymen and by their government as they ought: and I do not see how he can fail of being considered as possessing an undeniable claim to an early admission into any literary Society, that may have a place vacant for his reception. I have promised him every assistance in his researches that I can procure him in England, and I hope in return to obtain from him an early communication of all his future observations.

In that same year, 1822, Champollion published in Paris a 'Lettre à M. Dacier', giving an account of his researches agreeing very closely with the account given by Young in the preceding correspondence. This letter does not withdraw the views expressed in his publication of 1821—on the contrary it makes no reference to it whatever—but baldly states an opposite conclusion. Without any acknowledgment it gives in a footnote Young's interpretation of the names of Ptolemy and Berenice, only to emphasize that his method was wrong in interpreting characters as syllables. It does admit that Young correctly interpreted four letters, but implies that his own results were obtained independently and by another method.

According to Peacock,[1] the earlier publication was suppressed by the author in order to conceal the fact that up till 1821 he had made no progress with the study of the hieroglyphics and that 'so successful were his efforts to withdraw it from circulation and public notice, that, important as this document is in the chronology of the history of these discoveries, it has been passed over entirely without notice by every author who has written on the subject'. This is borne out by a reference to a pamphlet called 'Aperçu sur les Hiéroglyphes d'Égypte' which appeared in Paris in 1827. Referring to Champollion's pamphlet of 1821, the preface says:[2]

This little volume has become extremely rare; it is said that the author has done everything possible to withdraw copies of it from the public gaze by stopping sales and taking out of the hands of friends those which had already been distributed.[3]. . . It is permissible to think that the true motive which weighed with Champollion in suppressing the book has been to avoid giving too precise an indication of the progress made up till 1821, one year before his letter to M. Dacier. This indication resides in the assertion that the hieroglyphic signs are signs of things and not signs of sounds. Certainly he who for ten years previously had worked on the hieroglyphs without deciphering them, and had, in 1821 published such an axiom, had great need, in his new discoveries of 1822, of the guidance of the discoveries of Dr Young, published in December 1819, in the Supplement to the Encyclopaedia Britannica.

The plates of the 1821 book were circulated without the letterpress and undated, and a copy was sent to Young, who was quite unaware that it had been published as late as 1821.

In his 'Lettre à M. Dacier' Champollion gives a hieroglyphic alphabet which includes the signs Young had already interpreted, deduced from the same names, and adds to them others which Champollion had himself discovered.

By an ingenious line of argument W. J. Bankes concluded that two figures occurring on the propylaeum at Diospolis Parva were those of Ptolemy and Cleopatra. He compared

---

[1] Peacock, *op. cit.* p. 286.   [2] *Works*, vol. III, pp. 158–9.
[3] This was denied by J. J. Champollion-Figeac, 'Lettre au Directeur de la Revue Britannique' (Paris, 1857).

the hieroglyphics over the male figure with those Young had given him as the name Ptolemy and found exact agreement. He inferred that those over the female figure gave the name of Cleopatra. He found the same cartouche on an obelisk which he was removing from Philae in 1818 and which he knew to be a memorial to a Ptolemy and his two Cleopatras. The result was communicated by Bankes to Salt and to Young and noted in pencil in the margin of the copies of the print of the obelisk which were widely distributed. One of these marked copies[1] was sent to M. Denon for the French Institute. Without any acknowledgment to Bankes or to Young, this print was used by Champollion for the identification of the name Cleopatra, although it could not have been so identified with certainty at that time without the chain of reasoning followed by these two scholars. In the letter to M. Dacier, Champollion uses the signs from the names Ptolemy and Berenice to identify the additional signs in Cleopatra.

In the case of Ptolemaios there were ten Greek letters and seven hieroglyphic symbols; in the case of Berenike, eight letters and six symbols. In the case of Kleopatra, however, there were nine letters and nine symbols, and of these two were identical, three occurred in Ptolemy and one in Berenice. This fact illustrates well the increasing ease with which an alphabet can be extended when once a start has been made.

Writing to Bankes on 21 October 1822 from Calais, Young says:[2]

I cannot more effectually lighten the heavy hours that I am compelled to pass in waiting for the winds and waves than by employing
them in giving you an account of the advantage that has already
been derived, to the cause of Egyptian Literature, from the study of
the drawings of your great obelisc of Philae, combined most
ingeniously, by Mr Champollion, with the fortunate discovery of a
manuscript among the papyri of Casati, which is written exactly in
the enchorial character of the Stone of Rosetta. . . . By setting out
from the comparison of this name with the Cleopatra of your

[1] Henry Salt, *On the Phonetic System of Hieroglyphics* (London, 1825), p. 10. The date when the copy was sent is not given.   [2] *Works*, vol. III, p. 234.

obelisc, Mr Champollion has fully confirmed, and considerably extended the system of phonetic hieroglyphics, which I had conjecturally proposed from the examination of those of Ptolemy and Berenice.

Generally speaking, Champollion follows Young in (*a*) referring to the Chinese analogy for the use of signs as alphabetic symbols; (*b*) taking the cartouche to indicate that the enclosed characters have a phonetic value whether the enclosed name be royal or private, domestic or foreign; and (*c*) regarding the phonetic power of the character to be derived from the initial letter or syllable of the name of the object represented. Unlike Young, Champollion regarded the syllabic use in general as infrequent and only occurring with a short vowel.

On 12 November 1822, Champollion writes to Young[1] enclosing two copies of 'my Lettre à M. Dacier in which I give, very rapidly, the theory of, and some applications of, *my* alphabet or Syllabary of Phonetic Hieroglyphics.' The letter is couched in quite cordial terms:

It is unnecessary to say with what interest I shall receive all the communications which you may wish to send to me, either corroborating by new applications the phonetic alphabet or amending and purifying it by other observations. I place the greatest value on maintaining and drawing closer the relationship which your two short stays in Paris has allowed me to establish.

Even in a letter[2] written later (23 November 1822) this cordial tone is maintained. He thanks Young for references to himself in letters to Hamilton and to Bankes (published by Young). He refers to the help he has derived from Young's 'precious' notes and syllabary. He discusses numerous points of interest and concludes by promising another letter soon. On 16 December 1822 and 9 January 1823 there are two other letters[3] equally cordial. These letters accompany material sent to Young and contain requests for material from him in exchange—particularly inscriptions discovered by Bankes of which he has heard—and he encloses a letter to Bankes which Young is asked to forward and support. This request was

---

[1] *Ibid.* p. 238.   [2] *Ibid.* p. 243.   [3] *Ibid.* pp. 247–9.

ignored by Bankes because of the poor opinion he entertained of Champollion as a man.[1]

The place occupied by Young in the estimation of French Egyptologists at that time is made clear in two letters written to him early in March 1823. Letronne sends him a copy of a new book and hopes to be pardoned for the liberty of placing Young's name on the title-page. He emphasizes the importance of dissociating estimates of literary and scientific achievement from national considerations: 'The liberty which I have taken in speaking of a certain charlatan of our country, monopolist of Egypt, does not please everyone; but this disturbs me little.'[2] The hard word used here for Champollion is the same as that previously used by de Sacy. But it is unjust. Champollion was no charlatan. Von Humboldt writes:

M. Waddington has announced to me the great work which you are going to publish. It is you who have put the others on the way, and you ought to enjoy, more than anyone, the rapid progress made by the interpretation of these mysterious writings. I beg you to send me one of the first copies of your new work.[3]

In the first number of *The Quarterly Review* for 1823 there appeared a review of Champollion's 'Lettre à M. Dacier'.[4] This article attributes to de Sacy the discovery of the relationship of the hieratic writing to the hieroglyphic and to Åkerblad the discovery of the beginnings of the hieroglyphic alphabet. Champollion's alphabet was—rightly, as it would seem—treated as a development of Young's.

In due course this number of *The Quarterly Review* found its way into the hands of Champollion and produced an immediate and violent reaction. He at once wrote to Young[5] complaining that *his* (Champollion's) discoveries had been attributed to de Sacy and Åkerblad, and claims that his alphabet 'is the true key of this whole system'. He continues:

I find in the same journal the announcement of a volume which you are about to publish and of which the title promises to indicate

---

[1] *Works*, vol. III, p. 371.   [2] *Ibid.* p. 252.   [3] *Ibid.* p. 253.
[4] Vol. XXVIII (1822–3), p. 188.   [5] *Works*, vol. III, p. 255.

the author of an alphabet which I have done nothing but extend. I shall never consent to recognise any other original alphabet than my own, where it is a matter of the hieroglyphic alphabet properly so called; and the unanimous opinion of scholars on this point will be more and more confirmed by the public examination of any other claim. I am about to reply to the anonymous author of the foregoing article. . . . I await with impatience what you have to say on this matter; I must know in order to give to my reply the tone appropriate to the interests of truth—yours as well as mine.

It is very difficult indeed to reconcile this letter with the incontrovertible facts. Young's interpretations of the hieroglyphic names of Ptolemy and Berenice, forming the first examples of a hieroglyphic alphabet, were published in 1819. Champollion's memoir of 1821 showed that he did not then suspect the existence of the phonetic principle and assumed that in general Egyptian writing was ideographic. His 'Lettre à M. Dacier', published in 1822 after he had met Young and discussed his work with him (see p. 232) and had had three years to study his article, gave Young's examples together with others which Champollion had himself interpreted. Unfortunately Young's reply to Champollion's letter has not been preserved, but his claims are fully set out in the work referred to by Champollion,[1] which appeared in 1823. It is called 'An Account of Some Recent Discoveries in Hieroglyphical Literature and Egyptian Antiquities including the Author's original alphabet as extended by M. Champollion'. He begins his preface:[2]

A complete confirmation of the principal results which I had some years since deduced, from an examination of the hieroglyphical monuments of ancient Egypt, having been very unexpectedly derived from the ulterior researches of Mr Champollion, and from the singular good fortune of Mr George Grey, I cannot resist the natural inclination, to make a public claim to whatever credit may be my due, for the labour that I have bestowed, on an attempt to unveil the mystery, in which Egyptian literature has been involved for nearly twenty centuries.

[1] *Ibid.* p. 259.   [2] *Ibid.* p. 261.

He goes on to explain why he is now abandoning his anonymity:[1]

My explanation is, that I consider myself as having already produced to the public more than sufficient 'evidence' of my claim to 'medical confidence'; and that, having now acquired the right to celebrate a year of jubilee, I think myself fully justified in endeavouring, without further regard to the strict etiquette of my profession, to obtain, while I have yet a few more years to live and to learn, whatever respect may be thought due to the discoveries, which have constituted the amusement of a few of my leisure hours.

This memoir is dedicated to Baron von Humboldt. In the course of the work Young reviews the early history of the subject and recounts the history of his own interest in it. He then proceeds to claim seven discoveries as his own:

(1) that many signs represent simple objects pictorially;
(2) that many signs represent objects but are used symbolically;
(3) the method of representing plurality;
(4) the representation of numbers;
(5) the direction in which hieroglyphic inscriptions have to be read;
(6) proper names are enclosed in a cartouche;
(7) identification of the name of Ptolemy (presumably this includes the phonetic principle).

He adds, as has already been quoted on p. 218: 'And as far as I have ever heard or read, *not one* of these particulars had ever been established and placed on record, by *any other* person, dead or alive.'[2] It will be noted that he refers to discoveries *established and placed on record*.

He then recapitulates his evidence for the derivation of hieratic writing from hieroglyphic and reiterates his statement that the letters in which the discovery was announced were printed in 1816 and 'immediately sent to Paris, and to other parts of the Continent'. He admits that Champollion has already corrected some errors in his (Young's) first list of gods

[1] *Works*, vol. III, p. 263.   [2] *Ibid.* p. 274.

and kings and quotes a letter from Salt to Hamilton confirming his work from inscriptions at Dakkeh in Nubia.[1]

Much of the rest of the memoir is occupied with the demotic or enchorial script—partly because of an extraordinary chance which had happened to Young. G. F. Grey, of University College, Oxford, had bought some manuscripts from an Arab at Thebes in 1820 and put them at Young's disposal. Young had previously had from Champollion a copy of some parts of a very important papyrus from which the name of Cleopatra had been identified. It was a document signed by witnesses and Champollion had repeated to Young the names of some of these. Young recognized the same names on the Greek manuscript which had come to him from Grey and identified it as the Greek translation of the enchorial manuscript referred to.

I could not, therefore, but conclude that a most extraordinary chance had brought into my possession a document which was not very likely in the first place ever to have existed, still less to have been preserved uninjured, for my information, through a period of near two thousand years: but that this very translation should have been brought safely to Europe, to England and to me, at the very moment when it was most of all desirable to possess it, as the illustration of an original which I was then studying, but without any other reasonable hope of being able fully to comprehend it; this combination would, in other times, have been considered as affording ample evidence of my having become an Egyptian sorcerer.[2]

The translation of the Greek manuscript showed that it referred to the sale of a portion of the Collections and Offerings made from time to time on account, or for the benefit, of a certain number of Mummies of persons described at length, in very bad Greek, with their children and all their households. The comparison with the enchorial led to the identification of more than thirty proper names and further study convinced Young that the alphabetical element in the enchorial writing was more extensive than he had thought. The memoir finishes with an appendix containing the Greek version of the papyri and specimens of hieroglyphics (about 200).

[1] *Ibid.* p. 284.   [2] *Ibid.* p. 289.

In his references to Champollion he is studiously fair. Referring to the 'Lettre à M. Dacier', he says:[1]

I must, however, at once beg to be understood, that I fully and sincerely acquit Mr Champollion of any intentions actually dishonourable; and if I have hinted, that I have received an impression of something like a want of liberality in his conduct, I have only thrown out this intimation, as an apology for being obliged to plead my own cause, and not as having any right to complain of his silence, or as having any desire or occasion to profit by his indulgence; at the same time I am far from wishing to renounce his friendship, or to forego the pleasure and advantage of his future correspondence. . . . Whether he made this discovery (of the derivation of demotic from hieroglyphic) before I had printed my letters in the Museum Criticum I have no means of ascertaining. . . . It may not be strictly just, to say that a man has no right to claim any discovery as his own, till he has printed and published it; but the rule is at least a very useful one. It is always easy to publish such an account of a discovery, as to establish the right of originality, without affording much facility to the pursuits of a competitor; although it is generally true that not only honesty, but even liberality, is the best policy.

He makes a detailed reply to the charge of Champollion that his (Young's) interpretations involve the idea that hieroglyphs represent syllables and that he was ignorant of the fact that several symbols might have the same alphabetic value, and his defence is incontrovertible. He points out that Champollion himself allows him the discovery of four letters—P, T, M and I. He claims nine others (p. 295). As for the charge that his alphabet was really a syllabary, he says:

I allow that I suspected the B, the L and the S to be sometimes used syllabically: but the analogy of these characters with the enchorial alphabet was so well marked, that my attempt to refine upon it could not easily have embarrassed anyone in making the application.

Again:

With respect to the Diversity of characters representing the same letter, it will be observed that I have marked three forms of the M,

[1] *Ibid.* p. 291.

three of the N, with a fourth suggested to me by Mr Bankes, two of the P or Ph, and two of the S.

It is unfortunate that Young missed the additions made possible by applying his method to the name Cleopatra. Why he failed is made clear in the following sentence:

It so happens that in the lithographical sketch of the obelisc of Philae, which had been put into my hands by its adventurous and liberal possessor, the artist has expressed the first letter of the name of Cleopatra by a T instead of a K, and, as I had not leisure at the time to enter into a very minute comparison of the name with other authorities, I suffered myself to be discouraged with respect to the application of my alphabet to its analysis, and contented myself with observing that if the steps of the formation of an alphabet were not exactly such as I had pointed out, they must at least have been very nearly of the same nature.

In the same year there appeared a publication by Young's Egyptian Society which consisted of a collection of hieroglyphics. He sent a copy to Champollion, who acknowledged it on 21 August and took the occasion of reasserting his claim to priority.[1] Commenting on Young's comparison of the three texts of the Rosetta Stone, he expresses his agreement with Young's results on many points, but his disagreement on others. He also announces his decision not to publish his own results until he can place under each demotic group of signs the reading in Coptic and under each hieroglyph the pronunciation, if it is phonetic, and the idea if it is not:

I persist more than ever in believing, or rather I am now certain, that a great part of the signs employed in the inscriptions, both hieratic and hieroglyphic, are nothing but signs of *sound*, as well as the great part of the demotic or enchorial text.

He claims that he has established these conclusions in a Memoir communicated to the Academy and that when this is published in book form he will send a copy to Young:

I have discussed in the first chapter of this book your system of reading the proper names of Ptolemy and Berenice and that which

---

[1] *Works*, vol. III, p. 366.

I have presented myself. I have wished to avoid 'proprietary' discussions, which matter very little to the public who only ask for light without bothering about the question of from whom this light comes to them.

Champollion sends a copy of his new 'Egyptian Pantheon' but reiterates his claim to read phonetically by means of the hieroglyphic alphabet of which he had given the foundation in his 'Letter to M. Dacier'.

Young, writing to Sir William Gell, 13 September 1823,[1] makes his position with respect to Champollion crystal-clear. He claims that the article on 'Egypt' was an extension, but the real solution of the problem was contained in the paper printed in *Archaeologia*,[2] and it was 'sent at the time to Champollion and he acknowledged the receipt of it'.

To have placed more emphasis on the precise dates than I have done, would have been to display more parade than the thing required, or to have shown too much hostility to Champollion, to whom I would rather give up something that is my right than take from him anything that ought to be his.

In 1824 Champollion's great work appeared. It was entitled *Précis du Système Hiéroglyphique*. This showed that Champollion, in addition to the alphabet derived from the names of Ptolemy, Berenice and Cleopatra, had made great progress, and that with every step he made the progress became more rapid and more certain. He refers summarily to Young's work and repeats the claim that without any knowledge of the opinions of Dr Young he had arrived at nearly the same results. This in spite of the testimony of de Sacy that he had himself transmitted Young's enchorial translation to Champollion and that Young's articles in the *Museum Criticum*, his letter to the Archduke John, and the plates illustrating his article on 'Egypt' were freely distributed at Paris and elsewhere in 1818, while the article itself was published in 1819, three years before Champollion's first published attempt at the interpretation of hieroglyphics.

Meanwhile the controversy began to take on an international

---

[1] *Works*, vol. III, p. 369.   [2] Vol. XVIII (1815).

character. De Sacy swung round to the side of Champollion, Chevalier de Bunsen espoused his cause, and even Arago, who had done so much to establish Young's claims in relation to the wave theory of light, went over to the enemy!

Young, in an endeavour to persuade the owner and custodian of an inscription to allow him to have a cast of it, had said in 1821 that he was 'the only person living that could fully appreciate the value of the object in question'. This was made the basis of an attack on him for 'presumption' by M. Peyron. Young's defence is a restatement of his claims:[1]

Åkerblad was dead; Champollion had not *then* done anything worth mentioning on the subject of hieroglyphics. I had published, *seven years* before, and had sent directly to Champollion, a literal translation of the two inscriptions on the Pillar of Rosetta: I had sent the name of Ptolemy and the interpretation of many other characters to the English travellers in Egypt; it was *after* my return from Italy that Champollion received the name of Cleopatra, as ascertained in Egypt by Mr Bankes from my letters; it is hence that he himself dates the origin of his system: Ergo opera illius mea sunt! And I willingly add, of this new Achilles, 'fortemque in fortia misi!'

However this may be, it was late in 1822 that Champollion published his letter to M. Dacier, and I shall be very much surprised if M. Peyron can produce a single page in any work that I could have seen in 1821, which could have convinced me that I was mistaken in the grounds of my presumption.

It was a great grief to Young that his friend Arago sided with Champollion, and in July 1828 he made an attempt to convince Arago of the justice of his claims by letter. Arago seems to have accepted the contention of Champollion that his *method* of interpretation was different from that of Young and that the difference lay in the fact that while Young interpreted the hieroglyphs as syllables, Champollion, more correctly, interpreted them as letters. He was also impressed by the fact that Young had read the name 'Caesaris' as 'Arsinoe'. This seemed to him a sufficient refutation of the 'system'. On this point Young remarks that the name was read on external evidence

[1] *Works*, vol. III, p. 399.

and not by applying any system, and for the rest he restates his case along the familiar lines. Arago remained unconvinced and in his funeral oration on Young disparaged his claims in this field.

But even in France opinion was divided. Chevalier de Paravey, who was a correspondent of Young's, in sending to Peacock one of Young's letters to him, enclosed it with a covering letter in which he wrote in the third person:[1]

M. de Paravey thought, and continues to think, that Young was the first to arrive in a convincing and sure way at the interpretation of the hieroglyphics, furnishing thus to M. Champollion a key without which the latter could never have been able to arrive at the important and curious results which he has since obtained. M. de Paravey does not overlook that MM. Silvestre de Sacy and Arago have since wished to revindicate for M. Champollion alone the discovery of phonetic hieroglyphics, but, in France at least, M. de Paravey, who has been occupied with these high questions since 1815, believes himself as competent as anyone in these matters, and he agrees entirely with the Scottish scholar M. Browne, who, at Edinburgh, in a periodical review, has given a very good analysis of all these discoveries in hieroglyphics, and has established the right of Dr Young to priority—a right which M. de Paravey could establish by other facts hitherto unpublished.

The articles referred to by M. de Paravey appear to have been written by James Browne, an Edinburgh advocate who expressed his satisfaction at paying his tribute of respect to the *real* author of the late discoveries in hieroglyphics in the pages of that Journal which, in a fit of wantonness and presumption, had once treated him with injustice.

These articles from *The Edinburgh Review*[2] were translated into several European languages—French among others—and this last translation was the subject of bitter protest by the *Review*.[3]

The translation of our first and fullest article in hieroglyphical literature inserted in the 'Revue Britannique' which was published at Paris, is generally attributed, we believe correctly, to his (Cham-

[1] *Works*, vol. III, p. 405.   [2] Vol. XLV (1826–7), pp. 95, 528.
[3] Vol. LVII, p. 465.

pollion's) pen; and never, certainly, was any literary production more grossly maltreated in a translation. Many pages are wholly expunged, especially from the historical part of the article; others are altered so as to suit the views of the translator, and attribute to us opinions diametrically at variance with those which we had actually expressed, and all the facts and dates tending to establish Dr Young's discovery are carefully cancelled.

In Germany the importance of Young's work was recognized, and on 28 July 1824 Kosegarten writes a letter asking for information and material, which opens with a tribute:[1]

I have read with great interest and admiration the writings you have published relative to the explanation of the ancient Egyptian writings—i.e., your letters in the Museum Criticum and your Account of some recent Discoveries, etc. It is certainly to you that Europe owes the first certain information on this subject, as new as it is interesting: and it is above all in your 'Account' that you have communicated important fragments of this kind of literature.

The final short summary of Young's most important discoveries occurs in a letter to one of his distinguished Italian supporters—Chevalier San Quintino of Turin (24 November 1827). Referring to the suggestion that the cartouches might contain proper names, he says:[2]

The demonstration was published for the first time in Archaeologia for 1814. This was the first great step after the discovery of the Rosetta Stone. The second was the identification of the different kinds of characters in 1816; the third, the identification of Ptolemy and Berenice; the fourth Bankes' Cleopatra, sent to Paris; and on these grounds is certainly founded *all* that is at present known of Egyptian literature for a very considerable portion of which we are unquestionably indebted to M. Champollion.

In 1827 Young made a definite decision to abandon his work on hieroglyphics in favour of further work on the demotic. In a letter to Gell, 10 April 1827 he writes:[3] 'I am determined to confine myself as much as possible to the enchorial literature'; and in a letter to M. Peyron he says:[4]

[1] *Works*, vol. III, p. 381.
[3] *Ibid.* p. 415.

[2] *Ibid.* p. 451.
[4] *Ibid.* p. 425.

I send you herewith the few results that I have obtained by means of the manuscript which you have published. I fear I cannot comply with your exhortations to continue the study with any great chance of benefit . . . but I am endeavouring to methodise at least, and to preserve whatever I have made out in the Enchorial character leaving Champollion for the present to wander alone as he pleases through the pure hieroglyphics.

This turning-point in his work seems to have been due to a variety of causes. His failure to interpret the name of Cleopatra no doubt contributed, and he was undoubtedly disappointed with his progress with hieroglyphs after his early brilliant discoveries. Champollion, on the other hand, was going from strength to strength and it gave Young 'both the gout and the spleen to see others running so fast when I can scarcely hobble a step or two on'.[1] It seems too that he regarded his work on the enchorial script as the more valuable and wished to make the beginnings of a dictionary. Finally, although his intellectual powers showed no sign of failing (he was now within two years of his death), it may be that his capacity to maintain his astounding versatility was not quite so great and that his work on the *Nautical Almanac* and on life assurance and his duties as foreign secretary of the Royal Society made prohibitive claims on his time and energy.

Be that as it may, when Young heard that Dr Tattam was preparing to publish a Coptic grammar, he at once suggested that it should carry the 'Rudiments of an Egyptian Dictionary', which he himself was preparing as an appendix. The offer was gladly accepted by Tattam and Young redoubled his efforts to obtain copies of demotic inscriptions.

I have received nothing from France or from Germany for these four years past: even what is published seems by some fatality to have been withheld from me; and the booksellers send no answer to my commissions.[2]

Like the dog in the manger, these people neither eat their hay nor let me nibble at it. I cannot get a single line of all the demotic contracts on papyrus which I know to exist all over Europe.[3]

[1] Letter to Gell, *Works*, vol. III, p. 426.   [2] *Works*, vol. III, p. 441.
[3] *Ibid.* p. 442.

In December 1827 Young writes to Tattam suggesting that his work should be designated as 'With an appendix consisting of the Rudiments of a Dictionary of the Ancient Egyptian Language in the Enchorial Character by Thomas Young, M.D., F.R.S.'

A visit to Paris and Geneva in the summer of 1828 considerably delayed his work on the Dictionary, but at the same time provided him with fresh material. He took his seat as one of the eight foreign Associates of the Académie des Sciences and was received with extraordinary honours. He met Champollion, and his relations with him were a curious mixture of cordiality and correctness.[1]

My principal object, however, was Champollion, and with him I have been completely successful so far as I wanted his assistance: for to say the truth our conferences have not been very gratifying to my *vanity*: he has done so much more and so much better than I had any reason to believe he would or could have done: and as he feels his importance more, he feels less occasion to be tenacious to any trifling claims which may justly be denied him: and in this spirit he has borne my criticisms with perfect good humour, though Arago had charged me with some degree of undue severity and wanted to pass the matter over as not having been published as mine: but to this I could not submit, and supposing that Champollion might have been unacquainted with the remarks, I thought it a matter of conscience to carry them to him this morning, before I allowed him to continue his profuse liberality in furnishing me with more than I want: but he still continues his good offices: and in fact he has shown me far more attention than I ever showed or could show, to any living being: he devoted *seven* whole hours at once to looking over with me his papers and the magnificent collection which is committed to his care, and which beats every other museum in the world beyond all comparison, though it has cost but £20,000. I daresay he felt a pleasure in the display, but he must be so much accustomed to admiration and to more than I gave him that I am certainly not the less obliged to him on that score.

Champollion is going to Egypt in a few weeks at the King's expense with a party of a dozen artists and savants, he is to let me have the use in the meantime of all his collections and his notes

[1] Peacock, *op. cit.* p. 341.

relating to the enchorial character that I may make what use I please of them, and he is to employ a cheap artist to copy at my expense all the manuscripts on papyrus that I want, and to give me permission to publish any or all of them; if you see Colonel Leake, pray tell him that the Council of the R.S.L. must not retard my proceedings from their economy, for that their honour will be pledged in the production of what is really of importance.

The second letter,[1] written to Arago from Geneva just after he left Paris, says of Champollion:

I am most ready to admit that the more I see of his researches the more I admire his ingenuity as well as his industry; and I must be eager to bear witness on every occasion to the kindness and liberality which he has shown me in either giving or procuring for me copies of everything that I have asked of him, out of the treasures entrusted to his care by the magnificent liberality of a government, which far outshines the richest of its rivals, in the encouragement of literature and science and art. I have obtained in this manner a most extensive collection of enchorial documents, many of which are accompanied by Mr Champollion's own interpretations of particular passages which amply demonstrate how unjustly he has been supposed to have neglected this department of the great field, which he has cultivated with such unparalleled success.

One may be pardoned for wondering whether Champollion's behaviour was in part due to some qualms of conscience at withholding from Young the recognition of his *priority*, which was then the only point at issue.

On his return from Paris his work on the Egyptian Dictionary was resumed, and on 17 December 1828 he writes:[2]

I have just finished the fair copy of my little Egyptian Dictionary except that I must copy it all over again as the lithography goes on, which will be the work of two or three months for the fingers and the eyes, but little or nothing for the head. It contains little or nothing striking, but it preserves from oblivion all that I have made out of the running hand, which is nowhere methodically stated.

Writing again on 17 December 1828, he says:[3]

My dictionary is getting into the hands of the lithographist. I

---

[1] *Works*, vol. III, p. 469.   [2] To Hudson Gurney.   [3] *Ibid.*

give no *Hieroglyphics* except as illustrations of the running hand where they are well identified: partly to avoid discussion, and partly, because there is more difficulty in preserving Enchorial words without some such work than the distinct characters, which would lead one too far.

The advertisement for the Dictionary contains at once an apology for the limited content and a generous tribute to Champollion.

If, on the one hand, the meagreness of this catalogue should be considered as somewhat humiliating, it must be remembered, on the other, that thirty years ago, not a single article of the list existed, even in the imagination of the wildest enthusiast.[1]

The reference to Champollion says:[2]

The correct interpretation of the Enchorial dates depends almost entirely on the ingenious and successful investigations of the justly-celebrated Jean François Champollion, applied to the manuscripts which he had the good fortune to discover at Paris and at Turin . . .; and he has been equally happy in illustrating the characters denoting the months. . . .

During the spring of 1829 his work on the Dictionary was a race against time in circumstances of increasing physical weakness, and death overtook him before his task was finished. Hudson Gurney has described him at work on his deathbed, fully alive to his condition, but anxious to employ every moment usefully. Kosegarten, writing after his death, says:[3]

The work with which the excellent Young closed his literary career as well as his existence contains a valuable and well arranged collection of all the most important enchorial groups of characters hitherto deciphered. He obtained this collection from the enchorial texts published by himself, Champollion and me, and also made use of some materials communicated to him by Champollion from unpublished papyri at Paris. On his deathbed, and when writing had become difficult to him, he conducted the printing and correction of this work, in which he took great interest, and which forms, as it were, his legacy in Egyptian Philology. When he had reached

---

[1] *Works*, vol. III, p. 475.　　　　　　[2] *Works*, vol. III, p. 474.
[3] *Jahrbücher für wissenschaftliche Kritik* (1831), p. 771.

the ninety-sixth page of the proofs he was overtaken by death, so that the correction of the last pages, as well as the Indexes, were attended to by Dr Tattam.

Before we attempt to assess Young's contribution to Egyptology let us recapitulate the material dates:

1805: Champollion admitted to the School of Oriental Studies in Paris at age fifteen.

1812: Champollion, having worked at Coptic Language and on Rosetta Stone, is appointed Professor of Ancient History at Grenoble.

1814: Champollion publishes *Égypte sous les Pharaons* but makes no contribution to the language study (see p. 228).

Young's attention first attracted to Rosetta Stone and conjectural translation of demotic inscription communicated to Society of Antiquaries. Correspondence between Young and Champollion initiated.

1815: Young's translation published in *Museum Criticum*. De Sacy acknowledges receipt of Young's demotic translation and says he has forwarded to Champollion-Figeac for his brother Jean François.

1818: Young writes his article for Supplement to *Encyclopaedia Britannica*, reviewing the whole subject.

1819: Young's article published.

1821: Champollion publishes his *De l'Écriture des Anciens Égyptiens*, denying categorically the phonetic principle and giving no instance of hieroglyphic interpretation.

1822: Young meets Champollion in Paris and they discuss their work (see p. 231).

Champollion publishes his 'Lettre à M. Dacier', in which without reference to his previous work he accepts and uses the phonetic principle to obtain the letters already published by Young three years earlier and adds others of his own.

In face of these facts it is difficult to accept the judgment of a critic like Jean Sainte Fare Garnot[1] who accuses the earlier workers in the field of the hieroglyphs of not suspecting the existence of phonetic signs, and the later ones (Åkerblad, de

[1] *Annales de l'Université de Paris*, no. 1 (1848), p. 8.

Sacy and Young) of not recognizing any others. He goes on to say:

Champollion, first, had the idea that it was necessary to draw partly from both theories: the doctrine of symbolism and that of the phonetic notation, to correct the one by the other and to fix, according to exact rules, their conditions of application.

Yet Champollion had summarized his results with reference to the hieratic script in 1821 in the categorical statement that the characters were 'signs of *things* and not signs of sounds'. Nor had Young's work in his *Encyclopaedia* article in 1819 differed in principle from that given by Champollion in 1824. A large number of hieroglyphic characters were interpreted symbolically and only one paragraph was devoted to 'Sounds'.[1] Even Garnot admits[2] that:

In comparing the cartouches of the Rosetta Stone and the Royal names of its Greek text, Young *first*, Champollion *later*, identified the Egyptian transcription of Ptolemy, analysed out its elements and obtained a rudimentary alphabet.

This admission of the priority of Young having been made— an admission which Champollion obstinately refrained from making—Garnot goes on to claim that 'the rôle of Young was ended' at this point and to repeat the error made by him in substituting the name Arsinoe for Caesar. While this concedes the essential point, it gravely underestimates Young's earlier and later work.

Even more unjustified is the depreciation of his work in later editions of the *Encyclopaedia Britannica*—the very publication where his discoveries first appeared. In the eighth edition (1853–60) is an article on 'Hieroglyphics', covering sixty pages, by R.S.P.[3] In this article, appearing nearly forty years after Young's, the whole of the section of the previous article on 'Egypt' which deals with the Rosetta Stone was reprinted in full 'for it has been judged right to maintain this document intact, both in justice to the author and on account of its own importance'. By 1929 a great change has come over the scene.

---

[1] *Works*, vol. III, p. 182.   [2] *Op. cit.* p. 10.   [3] Probably R. S. Poole.

In the article on 'Egypt'[1] we find: 'Then in modern times the decipherment of the hieroglyphics begun by Young and Champollion in 1821 and put on the basis of firm knowledge by the latter', etc. Why select the date 1821? Young's work had been published two years before and Champollion had just published in that year the conclusions which he afterwards abandoned.

In the article 'Hieroglyphs'[2] we find: 'The discovery by Champollion (q.v.) of the key to Egyptian writing in 1822 brought about the first effective entry of historical research into a vast ancient world of monuments before the age of Greece and Rome.' This at least gets Champollion's date right, but completely ignores Young. And to complete the injustice there is an article on Champollion[3] in which it is said that he is 'now universally acknowledged to have been the founder of Egyptology', while again Young is not mentioned. Surely Young might be named as having at least cleared the site. Nor is there any article on Young. We find Arthur Young, Edward Young, even Brigham Young, but no Thomas!

A more favourable verdict is given by Budge:[4]

During the next three or four years he [Young] made striking progress in the decipherment of both demotic and hieroglyphic characters. The results of his studies at this period were published in his Article 'Egypt', which appeared . . . in 1819. It was accompanied by five plates, containing inter alia a hieroglyphic vocabulary of 218 words, a 'supposed enchorial, i.e. demotic alphabet' and 'specimens of phrases'. The VIIth Section of the letterpress contained the 'Rudiments of a Hieroglyphical Vocabulary' and thus Young became the 'Father of English compilers of Egyptian Vocabularies'. In this Article, which formed a most important and epoch-making contribution to Egyptology, Young gave a list containing a number of alphabetic Egyptian characters, to which, in most cases, he assigned correct phonetic values—i.e. values which are accepted by Egyptologists at the present day. In fact he showed that he had rightly grasped the idea of a phonetic principle in the reading of

---

[1] *Encyclopaedia Britannica*, 14th ed. (1929), vol. VIII, p. 41.
[2] *Ibid.* vol. XI, p. 545.   [3] *Ibid.* vol. V, p. 219.
[4] Sir E. A. Wallis Budge, *Egyptian Hieroglyphic Dictionary* (London, 1920), p. vi.

Egyptian hieroglyphs, the existence of which had been assumed and practically proved by Barthélemy and Zöega, and applied it *for the first time* in the decipherment of Egyptian hieroglyphs. This seems to me to be an indisputable fact which can easily be verified by anyone who will take the trouble to read Young's Article, Egypt, in the 'Supplement' to the Encyclopaedia Britannica and study his correspondence and papers which John Leitch reprinted in the third volume of the Miscellaneous Works of the late Thomas Young, M.D., F.R.S., London, 1855. Those whom such evidence will not satisfy may consult the five volumes of his papers that are preserved in the British Museum (Additional MSS. 27,281–27,285). In the first volume (Add. 27,281) are all the principal documents dealing with his work on the Rosetta Stone, and in the second (Add. 27,282) will be found his copies of a series of short vocabularies of Egyptian words.

The great value and importance of Young's application of the phonetic principle to Egyptian hieroglyphs has been summed up with characteristic French terseness and accuracy by Chabas, the distinguished Egyptologist, who wrote, 'Cette idée fut, dans la réalité, le *Fiat Lux* de la Science'.[1]

In his observations on the hieroglyphic and enchorial alphabets (*Coptic Grammar*, p. ix), Tattam describes briefly and accurately the various steps in the early history of Egyptian decipherment. He shows that Young was the first to read correctly the names of Ptolemy and Berenice, that Bankes, with the help of Young, discovered the name of Cleopatra, and says that the system of letters thus discovered was 'taken up, and extended, by M. Champollion and afterwards by Mr Salt'. He then gives the hieroglyphic alphabet as constructed from the researches of Young, Bankes, Champollion and Salt.

No one who reads the evidence will suggest that Young rivalled Champollion as a scholar of Egyptology or that his work in his famous article compares with the later contributions of that illustrious French savant. What seems to me indisputable is that he led the way to the decipherment of the Egyptian hieroglyphs at a time when Champollion was right off the track.

[1] *Inscription de Rosette*, p. 5 (Chalon S/S, 1867), p. xii.

Champollion was a specialist whose life interest was in this field and who had equipped himself by a study of Coptic for this particular work. Young was an amateur with a good general knowledge of languages and some slight knowledge of Coptic who had taken up the study at the age of forty-one and had many other interests. Peyron complains of this in a letter to Young:[1]

You write that from time to time you will publish new material which will increase our knowledge of Egyptian matters. I am very glad to hear this and I urge you to keep your word. For, as Champollion will witness, and other friends to whom I have mentioned your name, I have always felt and so do many others, that you are a man of rare and superhuman genius with a quick and penetrating vision, and you have the power to surpass not only myself but all the philologists of Europe, so that there is universal regret that your versatility is so widely engaged in the sciences—medicine, astronomy, analysis, etc. etc. that you are unable to press on with your discoveries and bring them to that pitch of perfection which we have the right to expect from a man of your conspicuous talents; for you are constantly being drawn from one science to another, you have to turn your attention from mathematics to Greek philosophy and from that to medicine etc. The result is that there are some mistakes in your books which you yourself might well have corrected.

Whether it would have been better for the progress of knowledge if Young had stuck to one subject is a matter for rather unfruitful speculation. He seemed to have a genius for breaking through into new territory which he was unable, or lacked the will, to consolidate. In his Thomas Young Oration to the Optical Society of America Tscherning[2] says:

If you take Young as the first man in the question of the theory of light, the name of the second man is Fresnel; in the question of the anomalies of refraction of the human eye, the name of the second man is Donders; in the question of colour sense, you can call the second man Clerk Maxwell or Helmholtz; in the question of hieroglyphics the name of the second man is Champollion; in the question of terrestrial radiant heat the name of the second man is

---

[1] *Works*, vol. III, p. 422.
[2] *Trans. Optical Soc. America*, vol. XXIII (1921–2), p. 2.

Wells, and I have not yet finished the list. For his own reputation it would certainly have been better if Young had completely developed but one of his ideas. But for the advancement of science it was better that he did as he did. For, if the second man is not frequently met with, the first one is extremely rare.

Be that as it may, we must judge Young by what he did and not by what he might have done. It will, I think, be admitted that in the relations of Young and Champollion the former showed a generosity to which the latter failed to respond even with bare justice; but this does not affect their reputations as *scholars*. We can, I think, do justice to Young without in any way impairing the great reputation of Champollion. We need not claim that Young's work rivals or even approaches in importance that of Champollion. But we do less than justice to Young if we do not claim for him substantial contributions to the study of Egyptology while that subject was still in its infancy—contributions which, in all the circumstances were remarkable—and if we do not reiterate the claim made for him on the tablet to his memory in Westminster Abbey that 'he first penetrated the obscurity which had veiled for ages the hieroglyphics of Egypt'.

XI

THE *ENCYCLOPAEDIA BRITANNICA* (1817–25)

*'I could probably furnish you with some articles which you would
scarcely obtain from other quarters and I should not refuse to do my
best upon any subject of science or even of literature for which you
might be at a loss to provide elsewhere.'* YOUNG

IN 1771 a new publishing enterprise was initiated by a 'Society
of gentlemen in Scotland'. This was the first edition of the
Encyclopaedia Britannica, which has since had such a long and
chequered history. It met an important need and the immediate
demand for an expansion of its subject-matter and for periodical
revision to keep pace with advances of knowledge involved the
publication of new editions. Between the first edition of 1771
and the fourth edition of 1810 the number of volumes increased
from three to twenty. The publication rights of the fourth
edition passed to the Edinburgh publisher, Constable, and he at
once set on foot the necessary preparations for a Supplement.
An able and energetic editor was found in Professor McVey
Napier, who in 1814 began to collect a team of distinguished
scholars to contribute to the work. It would seem to be just
the kind of enterprise to appeal to Young and indeed he was
one of the first to be approached. Having no personal link
with Young, Napier approached him through Professor Leslie,
one of his team. Young refused his help, but Napier, unwilling
to take no for an answer, wrote to Young and received the
following reply in a letter[1] written from Worthing on 9
August 1814.

I have to thank you for your very obliging letter; but, as I had
before told a friend of Professor Leslie in London, I am sorry that
it is not in my power at present to comply in any degree with a
proposal, which, under other circumstances, would have been far

---

[1] Brit. Mus. Add. MSS. 34611, f. 105.

from disagreeable to me; but I feel it a necessity to abstain as much as possible from appearing before the public as an author in any department of science not immediately medical; and even if this objection were removed, I am not sure that I can find time to execute any task of importance in such a way as would be satisfactory to myself—I have therefore only to wish you all possible success in your laudable undertaking, etc.

His refusal need not surprise us. It does not imply any lack of interest in the proposal. The date of his letter shows that the request must have reached him in the very middle of the summer season of 1814, when he was engrossed in his work on the Rosetta Stone. The appeal which the proposal made to him is indicated by the fact that only two years later, while still heavily committed to his work on the Egyptian scripts and in other directions, he decided to withdraw his refusal and wrote to Napier agreeing to co-operate.

I must, however, make one condition which I fear will create some difficulty; I could not at present allow my name to be published as a contributor to the work; on the other hand, I could probably furnish you with some articles which you would scarcely obtain from other quarters; I should not refuse to do my best upon any subject of science, or even of literature, for which you might be at a loss to provide elsewhere; and I would consent to acknowledge all my contributions at the end of ten years from the present time.[1]

In view of this anonymity on which he insists he offers to take a lower rate of remuneration, and ends by suggesting the following list of possible articles: Alphabet, Annuities, Attraction, Capillary Action, Cohesion, Colour, Dew, Egypt, Eye, Focus, Friction, Halo, Hieroglyphic, Hydraulics, Motion, Resistance, Ship, Sound, Strength, Tides, Waves, and anything medical. This is an imposing list of subjects covering an immense range, but, as we have seen, he was already master of several of the subjects named, and even this list is not more comprehensive than the collection of articles which he did in fact contribute.

Many of the subjects which he suggested either duplicated

---

[1] Brit. Mus. Add. MSS. 34611, f. 339.

or overlapped with those which had already been allocated to others. He was, however, given Cohesion, Chromatics, Egypt, Hydraulics and Tides, and was subsequently asked to write on Annuities, Bathing, Bridge, Carpentry, Fluents (Integrals), Herculaneum, Languages, Life Preservers, Roadmaking, Steam Engine, and Weights and Measures, besides sharing with Arago responsibility for Double Refraction. In addition to all this he did forty-five biographical articles, making a total of sixty-one articles covering in all about 380 quarto pages.

Even so Napier was not satisfied and was continually trying to foist on to Young subjects which he was unwilling to tackle, or really felt himself incapable of tackling. Thus we find him writing to Napier in February 1816: 'Baths I cannot refuse though I do not foresee anything very amusing in it. Craniology too I must accept though I am almost ashamed to be employed in such trash.'[1] And again, in refusing Blasting and Boring he writes: 'For the last ten years I have paid no attention to the mechanical arts in any form—nor do I wish to renew my acquaintance with them—preferring general investigations to particular applications.'[2]

The same kind of issue cropped up again later when, at the suggestion of Rennie, Young was approached by Napier for articles on Mining and Stone Cutting. Young's reply, dated 30 January 1821, was as follows:[3]

I am not unmindful of the original engagement into which I entered with you, to do my best in performing any part which you, as manager, might bestow on me, and to be a double for any of my colleagues in case of exigency.

I am sure you do not mean to understand this engagement quite in a literal sense. I had at that time much more leisure than I have at present, or than I am likely to have, and I know you will exercise your authority with discretion.

There was a time in my life when I should have considered myself qualified to say something on Mining but I have so totally changed my pursuits that I should be at a loss at present to know where to

[1] Brit. Mus. Add. MSS. f. 379.   [2] Ibid. f. 407.
[3] Brit. Mus. Add. MSS. 34612, f. 412.

begin, and it would require the study of some years to enable me to write a tolerable Article of a few pages on it. Of Stone Cutting I never knew anything and have still less idea what is to be known than of Mining.

His article on Bathing is a very comprehensive account of the subject with a strong medical bias, but his first really important article was Bridge, for which Napier had asked. Writing on 22 April 1816, Young says:[1]

Respecting Bridge I hesitate. I could do something good on the theory, but the details of the actual operations of architects are a little out of my way.

and again on 31 December 1816:[2]

The next is Bridge which will require considerable labour. There is much to be said . . . both theoretical and practical. I shall probably be able to give an elevation of the new Strand Bridge, and perhaps of some other new ones. . . . The historical part will chiefly relate to the Port of London, but it will also involve a number of theoretical remarks on the discordant answers of various mathematicians who were consulted on that subject and will, I trust, tend to remove the greater part of the difficulties which still embarrass it.

This refers to the fact that Young, in common with a number of other mathematicians and natural philosophers, had been consulted by the authorities in connection with a proposal for a new iron bridge over the Thames. The questions circulated came to be known as 'the bridge-builders' catechism'.

Later Young is able to report that he has procured a large plate of the Strand Bridge (unpublished) and also one of Vauxhall Bridge. Mr Rennie has promised him the use of all the materials in his possession though he does not know for 'what work I am writing'. He hopes to get from Rennie an elevation of the intended iron bridge now being built near London Bridge.

The article was finished in May 1817. It appeared in volume II, p. 497, and was accompanied by two plates carrying in all 21 figures. It contained a good deal of original work and

[1] Brit. Mus. Add. MSS. 34611, f. 379.   [2] *Ibid.* 34611, f. 463.

created much interest and some curiosity. Napier writes to Young in August 1817 and says:[1]

I have been amused with two or three conjectures as to the writer of this remarkable article. Rennie has been sadly puzzled by the signature O.R.[2] which, when separated, stands for two other contributors in the list, but whose combined strength, as he rightly says, could not have produced Bridge.

In acknowledging Young's help when the curtain of anonymity was lifted, Napier says[3] of the article:

To the head of Mechanics, may be referred the valuable article Bridge, by Dr Young, and that on Weights and Measures by the same author; both containing the substance of all the more recent discussions in regard to the principles involved in their respective subjects.

This did not altogether please Young, and in the course of a letter to Napier he says[4] the article 'is much more original than compiled'.

In point of fact Young had deduced some important general principles on the Statics of a Masonry Arch.[5] His answers to the twenty-one questions issued in relation to the proposed 600-feet span of the cast iron bridge by Telford are very incisive and his conclusions are in general accurate. Commenting on his achievement, a modern authority on the subject, Sir Charles Inglis, formerly Professor of Mechanical Sciences at Cambridge University, while admitting a certain clumsiness of treatment, says:

I was surprised to find how far his investigations had taken him and the accuracy of his conclusions. . . . As a result of reading Young's article 'Bridge' I have realized that he had a mentality of the highest quality.

The other major article in volume II for which Young was

---

[1] Brit. Mus. Add. MSS. 34612, f. 142.
[2] Young's articles were signed O.R.
[3] *Encyclopaedia Britannica* Supplement, p. xvi.
[4] Brit. Mus. Add. MSS. 34613, f. 243.
[5] For instance that if the loading is uniform the form of the arch should be parabolic, and that if the arch is circular the load distribution must be a cubic curve.

responsible was that on Carpentry. The earlier part was his own; the later part was an article on the same subject by Professor Robison of Edinburgh, reprinted from the third edition of the *Encyclopaedia* and annotated by Young. Two other articles by Robison appearing in the fourth edition are cited. Young says of his own work in the article:

> The Introductory Observations . . . may be considered as a retrospective summary of the doctrine of Passive Strength (Elasticity) accompanied by some of the most useful propositions respecting the resistance of elastic substances, derived from the principles which have already been laid down in our article Bridge; and subjoining a few notes, on such passages as may appear to require further illustration or correction. Some of the demonstrations will be partly borrowed from a work which has been published since the death of Professor Robison, the able author of these three articles; but others will be more completely original: and of the remarks the most important will probably be those which relate to the form and direction of the abutments of rafters; a subject which seems to have been very incorrectly treated by former writers on Carpentry.

The first two sections of the article were based on Young's Royal Institution Lectures and dealt with strength of materials and flexure of beams.

In volume III Young's main contributions were the two articles Chromatics and Cohesion. Both have already been the subject of comment. Chromatics was largely original and contained a rather condensed account of the evidence for the wave theory of light as applied to colour phenomena. Napier complained that the article was not sufficiently popular and suggested that it might be expanded. To this Young replied:[1]

> I agree with you that Chromatics is not a very popular article. But is it not already rather long? If it had been twice as long nobody would have had the patience to read it. The subject is still liable to much dispute, and while any branch of Natural Philosophy is undecided, a simple and popular illustration of it might do more harm than good. . . . Mathematical subjects must ever remain more or less intricate.

[1] Brit. Mus. Add. MSS. 34612, f. 167.

This last remark is true, but it is also true that even mathematical subjects need not be so intricate as Young's unconventional treatment and antiquated notation often made them.

This, of course, also applied to the article on Cohesion, in which Young summarized his work on that subject, including the original attack on the problems of capillarity, in which he reached the same conclusions as Laplace, independently, and obtained his estimate of molecular size.

There followed in volume IV his article on Egypt, the longest and perhaps the most important of all his contributions. It was written mainly in 1817. By the end of that year he was arguing with Napier about the plates, and on the ground of the immense pains he had taken with the drawings was asking that they might be engraved in London by the Royal Society printers instead of being sent to Edinburgh. With respect to reprints of the article he writes:[1]

Now I shall in this case put your indulgence respecting separate copies to a severe test, for I imagine it would be in vain to attempt to conceal from my friends that I am the author of it and I shall wish to have as many copies both of the plates and text as you will allow me.

In August 1818 Napier acknowledges the plates to be a 'great accession to the work'.

Recognizing the value of the article and also the unreality of Young's anonymity, Napier makes a further appeal to Young for his name: 'All the world will recognise you as the author of the Article "Egypt". Can you not therefore allow me to announce you as the author of this Article?' To this appeal, however, Young remained obdurate.

Napier next asked Young for an article on Herculaneum. The remains of this city had been discovered about the middle of the eighteenth century, and among the treasures found were some papyrus rolls on which work was actually being done when the article was suggested. Why Young should have been asked to write the article is a question which can only be answered by a digression dealing with his work as a classical

[1] Brit. Mus. Add. MSS. 34612, f. 170.

scholar and this we shall take up in the next chapter; in that connection also we shall consider the article on Language which he himself proposed to Napier, and which proved in the end a remarkable contribution.

In the early months of 1823 Young's further articles were agreed. He accepted the suggestion that he should undertake Roadmaking and, still more gladly, that he should do Weights and Measures. But he was particularly anxious to do Tides, and this subject, after a preliminary discussion with him some time before, Napier had overlooked. As the available space was now strictly limited and many articles were being ruthlessly cut, this was a considerable embarrassment to the editor. In the end it was agreed that Young should have twelve pages for Tides, twelve for Weights and Measures, and twelve in all for five biographies agreed at the same time. It was also conceded, to Napier's great satisfaction, that Young's name should be appended to his articles in this volume and his work in the earlier volumes acknowledged.

Concerning the article on Roadmaking Napier writes (27 April 1823): 'No subject comes amiss to you and I beg therefore to propose Roadmaking, hoping that you will do me the honour to undertake it and to treat it within the limits of a sheet.' Young replies on 30 April 1823: 'I shall not even object to following Hannibal and Bonaparte in their Roadmaking.' In acknowledging Young's willingness, Napier writes on 5 May 1823:

I was a little afraid of your refusing Roadmaking for I had no means of ascertaining whether you had attended to Mr McAdam's improvements, and the other discussions on that subject. This made your compliance the more pleasing.

The article is an interesting one—thorough and comprehensive, although not original. It opens with a section on the mechanical theory of the motion of wheel carriages, dealing with the frictional and other resistances which they have to overcome. This is followed by a section on methods of construction leading up in the end to a discussion of McAdam's improvements:

But all these improvements, whether real or imaginary, have of late been in great measure superseded by the ingenuity and success of Mr Loudon McAdam, a gentleman whose practice is in general principally to be applauded for its obvious simplicity and economy.

The third and last section is historical and deals with 'Roads of different Ages and Countries', beginning with the Roman roads. The arrangement of this article is typical of Young's method of exposition. Instead of starting with the history, which is now probably the customary practice, he believed in finishing with it.

To the article on Tides we have already referred. It made an original contribution to the subject and carried the elucidation of the problems some way forward, but it did not have the value which Young attributed to it. The other major article contributed by him was on Weights and Measures. It discusses the history of standards of length, capacity, mass, etc. and summarizes at some length the work of the Commission set up by Parliament in 1818 to deal with the situation in this country as it existed at that date. As Young played an important part in the work of this Commission it seems better to defer further consideration of it to a later chapter.

Tucked away at the very end of volume VI is a long article on 'Refraction, Double'. It is heralded in an earlier volume under 'Polarisation (see Refraction, Double)', but in spite of this early anticipation it fails to appear under R. The story of the article has considerable intrinsic interest and it throws a good deal of light on the personalities of Young, Napier, Arago and Fresnel, and on their relationships. Friendships were strained, publication was delayed and the finance of the whole scheme was jeopardized. For these reasons it seems worth while giving in the Appendix at p. 332 a summary of the relevant correspondence,[1] with extracts.

Young comes out of the correspondence well. He might have been a little more sympathetic with Napier and he was

---

[1] Some of the letters have been published in either the *Life and Works of Young* or the *Oeuvres Complètes* of Fresnel. Some unpublished letters are in the British Museum Library and the Library of the Royal Society.

foolishly optimistic about Arago, but one cannot help admiring his loyalty to Arago. Napier shows admirable restraint under almost intolerable provocation. Fresnel was working against continual ill-health and was of course carried off in his prime about two years later. It is difficult to excuse Arago. The correspondence covers almost three years and at some points the remaining sheets were offered in a few days! He was fortunate in having so loyal and stout a champion. It is unfortunate that no letters from Young to Arago seem to have survived. Perhaps the most extraordinary feature of the whole matter is that the correspondence contains no hint of the reason for the delay given in the editorial note appended to the article:

This article has been obligingly furnished by M. Arago and has been translated, with some additions, by a distinguished friend, already well known to our readers. The state of the author's health will, it is hoped, be received as an apology for the very great and unexpected delay which has taken place in the completion of his undertaking.—Ed.

Probably the most important original investigation Young wrote for the *Encyclopaedia Britannica* was his essay on Tides. Of it, in writing to Napier, he says:[1]

I must however remind you of an article which I think important and which we long ago agreed upon—that is Tides; upon which I have even commenced my operations. I think it will be the best physico-mathematical investigation that I have ever attempted. My Tides will be rather long. How much space can you give for it?

The subject is first dealt with by Young in his *Lectures*.[2] It was extended in an article contributed anonymously in 1813 to Nicholson's *Journal* and later formed part of the Supplement to the *Encyclopaedia Britannica*. By this time he had read the works of Laplace on this subject and was able to give to his investigations a more complete development.

Previous workers on the subject, particularly Newton, had simplified the problem by assuming the earth to be a solid sphere at rest covered with water. The gravitational attractions

[1] Brit. Mus. Add. MSS. 34613, f. 139.   [2] Lecture 47, p. 576.

of the moon and sun would then account for the elevation or depression of the water, i.e. the tide. It was further assumed that the same effects would follow if the earth revolved on its axis and the earth and moon in their orbits and that no effect was produced by the oscillations of the sea. The merit of the theory was its striking success in accounting for the principal movements of the tides. It is possible to divide the types of waves in the theory of the tides into two groups, firstly the great ocean waves due to the action of the moon and sun which are naturally periodic in resonance with their causes, and secondly those which follow the laws of oscillation of water. The two types are usually considered as 'forced' and 'natural' vibrations respectively. Now Young was probably the greatest exponent of his day in problems concerning pendulums and it was natural for him to apply the theory which he had developed so successfully in this field to the analogous case of the tides. It will be recalled that scientists were eager to use the seconds pendulum as a standard of length, and this accounted for the excellent practical investigations carried out by Captain Kater. A description of Kater's pendulum and its possible use as a standard of length, will be found in the next chapter (p. 291). In the present instance Young's chief interest was to determine the magnitude of the errors in experiments involving such pendulums. Some of these may be errors of observation; others may be due to the form the pendulum takes. In investigating the various sources of error in the experiment Young worked out the effect of the curvature of the knife edges;[1] he also showed how to allow for the resistance of the air to the motion of the pendulum.[2] Another investigation he made concerned the effect of a movable support on the time of swing of a pendulum.

In applying these effects to the tides Young considers:[3]

two pendulums one of which naturally vibrates in the period of the forces, whether of the sun or moon, and the other in that of the

[1] *Works*, vol. II, p. 1, and *Phil. Trans.* (1818).
[2] Brande's *Quarterly Journal*, vol. XV (1823), p. 351.
[3] Peacock, *op. cit.* p. 441.

spontaneous oscillations of the sea; let the first pendulum be supposed to vibrate round a fixed centre and let its extremity carry the second; then whatever be the initial condition of the pendulums, they will sooner or later arrive at a state of permanence and the period of vibration of the second pendulum with a movable centre of suspension will become identical with that of the first, but its motion will be in the same or in opposite directions to that of its centre, according as the time of this compulsory vibration is greater or less than that of its natural oscillations. . . . It will follow, therefore, generally that the time of *high* water will coincide with the passage of the luminary over the meridian in the first case and with that of *low* water in the second. Peacock continues:

The theorem for determining the laws of vibration of a pendulum with a movable centre of suspension in a medium, whether absolutely non-resisting or where the resistance varies according to the simple power of the velocity or its square were investigated by Young in his first published Essay on the Tides, partly by the aid of simple and elegant geometrical constructions, and partly by other expedients, *which display in an extraordinary degree his great resources in dealing with problems which were beyond the legitimate powers of the machinery which was brought to bear upon them; it was like the capture of a fortified town by open assault without resorting to the more regular and slow, but therefore more certain approaches which the rules of war prescribe.*[1]

Another important problem solved by Young at this time was that of the tidal effects in canals and narrow seas making any angle with the meridian. Unfortunately Young's work was hardly read and his immediate successor in the field of study, Sir G. B. Airy, states that when writing his own article on Waves and Tides for the *Encyclopaedia Metropolitana* he was ignorant of its existence. In a letter to Peacock, Airy writes 'You ask my opinion of Dr Young's Researches on Tides. As far as they go they are capital; when I was writing my article, I totally forgot Dr Young, although I well knew that in writing on *any* physical subject it is but ordinary prudence to look at him first.'

In the light of present-day investigation in this difficult

---

[1] Author's italics.

subject the opinion of Rollin A. Harris—in Part I of the United States Coast Guard Survey Report for 1897—is apposite. Of Young's work he writes:

He was the first to suggest the extensive system of co-tidal lines. He also complains that the observations recorded are inadequate for the purpose of tracing contemporary high water and that he cannot deduce the time of it, from the hypotheses of Newton and Laplace, without some direct observations.

Somewhat after the manner of Euler he first treats the tidal problem by the equilibrium theory using the horizontal component of the tidal force. He does not fail to notice the necessity of taking into account the attraction due to high water regions when the density of the high water is considerable. He states as theorems that the horizontal disturbing force of a body varies as the sine of twice its altitude; that an oblong spheroid with its axis passing through the disturbing body is a form of equilibrium; that the tide will be propagated with a velocity equal to the velocity of a body falling through half the depth of fluid (Lagrange's rule); that the oscillations of the sea and lakes constituting the tides, are subject to laws exactly similar to those of pendulums.

Besides these he states theorems relating to the disturbing attraction of the meniscus of water, to the reflection of waves, and to certain differential equations.

He introduces fluid friction into his equations, generally regarding it as proportional to the square of the velocity. The arbitrary constants entering into his solution being assumed at pleasure give possible explanations of phenomena observed in various places; such as unusually large or small tides; also whether high-water or low-water should occur at the time of transition.

He finds that the 'age' of the tide may be explained either by the difference of the velocities of sun and moon, or by the resistance due to friction. In fact, he was the first to mention the latter explanation. His equations refer to a simple oscillating particle without reference to the ocean as a whole, and so their solution must be regarded as giving results analogous to nature, but not as being a complete solution of the tidal problem. The manner of treating the subject, while open to criticism from the theoretical point of view, is in line with most working hypotheses, especially that underlying the harmonic analysis. In further anticipation of the analysis it may be noted that he gives some developments of tidal forces, and that he makes the following significant statement:

There is indeed little doubt that if we were provided with a sufficiently correct series of minutely accurate observations on the tides, made, not merely with a view to the times of low and high water, but rather to the heights at the intermediate times, we might by degrees, with the assistance of the theory contained in this article, form almost as perfect a set of tables for the motions of the ocean as we have already obtained for those of the celestial bodies which are the more immediate objects of the attention of the practical astronomer. There is some reason to hope that a system of such observations will speedily be set on foot by a public authority; and it will be necessary, in pursuing the calculation, on the other hand, to extend the formula for the forces to the case of the sea performing its principal oscillation in a direction oblique to the meridian, as stated in the beginning of this section.

I[1] am indebted to Professor J. Proudman of the Department of Oceanography, Liverpool University, for the following opinion of Dr Young's work:

There could not be a greater authority on the soundness of dynamics than the late Sir Horace Lamb, who was an admirer of Young. Some of the general features of the forced tides in a closed basin were given by Young in 1813, who made much use of the analogy with a pendulum. He also examined the effect on the tides of friction varying as various powers of the speed, including the second power, and he gave the mathematical method given in my Adams Prize Essay on Tides (1923), but I did not then know that it had been given by Young. I rate his work very highly.

In addition to the subject-articles which we have already considered, Young did no fewer than forty-four biographical articles. Most of these are short, occupying three pages or less, and refer to individuals whose names have hardly survived. The longer articles are ten in number and refer to Cavendish,

[1] F.O.

Coulomb, Fourcroy, Guyton de Morveau, Lagrange, Lalande, Porson, Robison, Thompson (Count Rumford) and Tooke. In every case, even in the shorter biographies, an admirable summary of the life is given and a careful and detailed bibliography. This latter not only enumerates the published papers of each author but summarizes their contents.

Reference is made to this by Napier in the Preface:

Of these articles, a large proportion of such as relate to men of science has been contributed by Dr Young. Valuable in many respects, as accounts of such men, written by one so deeply versed in all that they have done and taught, could not fail to be, they are recommended in a particular manner for the purposes of a work of reference by their accurate bibliographical notices and lists of even the smallest pieces written by the persons whom they commemorate.

Young's two most outstanding biographies are probably those of the French mathematician Lagrange and of the Cambridge classical scholar Porson. Writing to Napier of the first of these Young says:[1]

Lagrange will be an arduous task but I must not flinch from it; I cannot promise it till Christmas; it cannot but be long, probably longer than any of my biographical articles; but the labour will be much more than in proportion to its length.

The article includes references (sometimes summaries) to over one hundred of Lagrange's original papers, all of which he must have read.

The biography of Porson is also an important piece of work. Napier congratulates him on 'a very valuable and interesting account of that extraordinary person'.[2] Young replies: 'I am glad you distinguish Porson from the rest of my contributions, as it was the only one I did con amore.'[3] Of these biographical articles Young writes to Hudson Gurney:

The biographical articles seldom *amuse* me much in writing; there is too little invention to occupy the mind sufficiently: I like a deep and difficult investigation when I happen to have made it easy to myself if not to all others—and there is a spirit of gambling in this,

---

[1] Brit. Mus. Add. MSS. 34612, f. 387.   [2] *Ibid.* 34613, f. 137.   [3] *Ibid.* f. 139.

whether as by the cast of a die, a calculation *à perte de vue* shall bring out a beautiful and simple result, or shall be wholly thrown away. Scientific investigations are a sort of warfare, carried on in the closet or on the couch against all one's contemporaries and predecessors; I have often gained a signal victory when I have been half asleep, but more frequently found, on being thoroughly awake, that the enemy had still the advantage of me when I thought I had him fast in a corner—and all this, you see, keeps one alive.

Generous acknowledgment is made in the Editorial Preface of the work of 'Dr Thomas Young; to whose profound and accurate knowledge, rare erudition, and other various attainments, this work is largely indebted in almost every department which it embraces'. Nothing could more naturally and obviously illustrate Young's versatility and 'encyclopaedic' knowledge than the work described in this chapter, which occupied a great deal of his leisure time over the period 1817–24.

XII

HERCULANEUM AND LANGUAGES

'In making some last experiments on the Herculaneum manuscripts, I hoped they might be made a little more translateable by passing them through the fire.'
'I have a long article on ancient languages already printed for the next Quarterly Review; it has no great interest or originality but looks respectable enough.'   YOUNG

WE have not so far referred to Young's work in languages except during his early years. It may not be out of place to make a digression here by way of indicating how his interest in the Classics was maintained in later life and how he came to be regarded as a suitable author for articles in the *Encyclopaedia Britannica* on Herculaneum and on Languages. We have already seen how, at the home of David Barclay at Youngsbury, Young came into contact with John Hodgkin, who had been brought in to act as tutor to him and to Hudson Gurney, whose studies he shared. Although Hodgkin was greatly impressed with Young's classical scholarship, he was himself a 'Grecian' of no mean attainments. It was probably during his time as classical tutor at Youngsbury that he conceived the idea of preparing a book on the Greek script and enlisted the help of Young in the project. The book appeared in 1794 under the title *Calligraphia Graeca* and contained very beautiful specimens of Greek lettering. The style and contents of the volume are perhaps sufficiently indicated in the following translations, in which Young's assistance is acknowledged in the warmest possible terms. In the preface to Part I we have:[1]

John Hodgkin to the Reader—Greetings.

You owe this little book to the kindness of that most learned man

[1] I am indebted for this and other translations from the Latin to my daughter Eleanor.—A.W.

to whom it is dedicated [Thomas Young]; for at a time when my affairs prevented me from pursuing this subject as I had intended, he provided all the necessary material for the book. I consider his friendship as one of the most delightful things which fortune has granted to me, for he combines amazing industry with great talent. And besides his outstanding knowledge of other branches of learning, he has achieved such skill in the Greek language as few others have done, and such elegance in forming Greek characters as scarcely any other man up till now. I would not willingly alter even a punctuation mark in the writings of such a man; therefore receive in his own words the preface which he has so kindly sent me for use in this book. Farewell.

1 October, 1794.

Thomas Young to John Hodgkin—Greetings.

When you first revealed to me your plan for preparing and publishing examples of Greek characters, I realized immediately that it was a project whose achievement could bring delight to the learned, and also be most useful to pupils and teachers, so I enthusiastically urged you to proceed with the undertaking, and I promised that, as far as I could, amid other pursuits, I would give you my help, such as it is. Now therefore accept what I have collected for this purpose, and adorn it with your clever pen. I am sending you an example of the three different types of Greek characters; if there is any beauty in them, you will very soon be able to reach that standard, or even to surpass it. I have selected from Menander, Euripides, Philemon, Phocylides, Theognis, Hesiod and others, some iambics and hexameters which I consider most suitable for your purpose, according to the type of Greek character. Since I could easily collect these, as my studies offered me opportunity, I thought it would be pleasanter for you than that you yourself should struggle on with your collection as you had been doing. I have also added some lines of poetry—and would that they were better—which you will remember that I once composed at the request of that most eloquent of orators, Edmund Burke. There follows something which, if it were fuller, could be of great use to those who read manuscripts, particularly those written in a Greek hand, that is, a catalogue of certain contractions and examples of the different forms of the same character.

The letter is dated 13 December 1793, when Young was twenty

years of age. It concludes with a list of his authorities, explanations of the three different types of character, instructions for cutting and holding the pen, and for forming the characters, which are listed according to the way in which they are formed.

There was considerable delay in the appearance of the book and at the end of Part II is printed another greeting to Young and some explanation of the delay.

John Hodgkin to Thomas Young, Doctor of Medicine, Fellow of the Royal Society and of the Linnaean Society—warmest greetings.

Behold at long last, most learned friend, your book on Greek calligraphy. The fact that you have not received it sooner is due, I will not say to the negligence but rather to the excessive business of the engraver; and as he is by far the most skilful man of his craft I wanted him to finish the work he had begun.

Hodgkin then acknowledges the help of Richard Porson and Charles Burney, and concludes:

Farewell most learned friend, and enjoy such profit from your medical skill as you may well hope for, in view of your talents, your industry, and your knowledge of all the great arts.

The date is 22 July 1807.

The work had very influential support, the list of subscribers containing among others the names of Sir George Baker, Edmund Burke, Charles Burney, Andrew Dalzel, Richard Farmer, William Heberden, John Hunter, Frederick North, Richard Porson and William Windham.

It was said that Porson considered that in some respects his handwriting was surpassed by that of Young. In Young's biographical article on Porson[1] we find the following reference to this:

Mr Weston, in speaking of his 'matchless penmanship', has observed, not very intelligibly that 'here, indeed, he thought himself surpassed by another person, not in the stroke, but the sweep of his letters': what Porson really said on this subject was, that, with respect to 'command of hand', that person had the advantage, but he preferred the *model* on which his own hand was formed. His

[1] *Encyclopaedia Britannica*, Supplement to 4th ed. (1824), vol. VI, p. 335.

writing was, in fact, more like that of a scholar, while the method explained in Mr Hodgkin's Calligraphia exhibits more the appearance of the work of a writing-master; holding, however, a middle place between the neatness of Porson, and the wonderful accuracy of the country-schoolmaster, who made the fac-simile of the Oxford Pindar in the British Museum.

After he had left Youngsbury and settled in London, Young's interest in the Classics was strongly maintained and, according to Peacock, his journal for this period shows that from time to time he took part at his uncle's house in discussions on equal terms with the great masters of Greek scholarship at that time. Peacock quotes[1] from Young's diary an account of the evening of 12 December 1791, when 'Murphy read Johnson's Latin poem on the completion of his dictionary' and Dr Lawrence, Sir George Baker, Porson and Young took part in the subsequent discussion. On the same authority we find that on several occasions he discussed disputed points with Dr Burney.

Young was described[2] as 'the friend and sometimes the boon companion of Porson' and the same authority goes on to say that after Porson's death it was 'only Dr Parr and very few others who could rank above Dr Young as Greek scholars'.

When Young went to Edinburgh University his interest in the Classics at once brought him into touch with that outstanding teacher of Greek, Andrew Dalzel. The friendship thus started was maintained long after Young left Edinburgh and resulted in his giving the same kind of help to Dalzel that he had given earlier to John Hodgkin.

Dalzel had a very high opinion of Young's scholarship. Writing to Professor Young of Glasgow,[3] he describes him as a 'great Grecian'; and in a letter of introduction to Professor John Hunter of St Andrews he describes him as 'a most admirable classical scholar' who 'has made surprising progress in the Greek'.

Young's correspondence with Dalzel while he was at Göttingen is concerned with the state of classical knowledge in

[1] Peacock, *op. cit.* p. 23. [2] E. H. Barker, *op. cit.* p. 54.
[3] Memoir of Dalzel, p. 16.

Germany and in particular with Heyne, Dalzel's opposite number at Göttingen, and reinforces the complaint to which attention has already been drawn that Heyne, like other German Professors, was an Olympian with whom close personal relations were impossible.

In 1785 Dalzel had published the first edition of the first volume of his *Collectanea Graeca*—a collection of passages from Greek authors. It met with considerable success and its third edition was published in 1797 simultaneously with a second volume of extracts from Greek poets. This contains an acknowledgment of the help which Young had given. It is clear that, although Young was only twenty-four when this work appeared, Dalzel had considerable confidence in his scholarship and taste. In the preface he says:[1]

The poems set forth here are culled from Brunck's Anthology by Thomas Young, a great scholar who, while yet a young man, was considered worthy to be elected to the Royal Society of London. While he was lately pursuing his studies at this University, everyone who was acquainted with him thought very highly of his brilliant intelligence and the breadth of his learning, while I myself in particular admired the integrity of his life and his astonishing familiarity with Greek literature. Since I was involved in various University affairs and had insufficient leisure, I asked him to choose, from what he had read in Brunck's collection, such epigrams as were best suited for the selection of poems that I was intending to make. Out of his goodwill towards me, this learned young man, who has a profound knowledge of the Greek poets, acceded to my request. He very kindly chose the majority of the poems included in this book; moreover he even wrote them out in his own most elegant script and handed over to me the beautiful 'Garland' that he had woven from the variegated flowers of poetry.

The author of the Memoir on Dalzel says:

He [Young] continued in the busiest of lives amid the claims of most exciting pursuits to revise and amend and furnish notes to successive editions of the Analecta as long as the author lived. Many sheets of his quotations are now before me, written so carefully that not a letter, or numeral, or accent is doubtful.

[1] Peacock, *op. cit.* p. 56.

But although Young may have given sporadic help later, one of his own letters to Dalzel shows that the strain imposed on him by the preparation of his Royal Institution Lectures made any continuous work at other subjects impossible at that time. Writing on 11 May 1802 he says:[1]

I am much flattered by the approbation you are pleased to bestow on the fragments that I sent you, and I shall be truly gratified if they be deemed an addition of any consequence to your useful work; they will be, for a long time at least, the last of my philological amusements, for I assure you that you are perfectly correct in supposing my professorship to be no sinecure—it involves my whole time and attention—and an immediate repetition of the labour and anxiety that I have undergone for the last twelve months, would at least make me an invalid for life.

On receipt of the new edition of the work in 1802 Young expresses the view that he 'has little or no hopes of resuming his philological studies' and it was indeed some time before he did in fact do so.

His return to the field of classical scholarship was not made till after 1810 and was connected with the discovery of the papyri found in the site of the ruined city of Herculaneum. The ruins themselves were discovered in 1753 and during the excavations which followed the diggers came upon a collection of what looked like cylindrical pieces of blackened wood. One of these was accidentally dropped and broke into fragments. It was at once noticed that letters could be seen where the fracture had taken place and that these were really papyrus rolls with the surfaces completely stuck together. The immense difficulties of unrolling were not at first foreseen and the wildest hopes were entertained. Who could say what treasure of classical authorship hitherto undiscovered might not be included in the find!

But disillusionment soon set in. Every conceivable method of unrolling was tried and many papyri were completely destroyed before an elaborate and laborious scheme attempted by a certain Father Antonio Piaggi yielded some results with the

[1] Dalzel Memoir, pp. 213–14.

easiest cases. About 1793, after forty years' work had produced the translation of one papyrus of little interest, the Academicians of Portici, a neighbouring town, who were responsible for the work, abandoned the project.

About ten years later the Prince of Wales, afterwards George IV, became interested and offered to put in hand further work at his own expense. This offer was accepted by the Government of Naples, who were the custodians, and hope sprang to life again. In 1802 the Rev. John Hayter was sent out as one of the directors of the undertaking and he at once began a new series of attempts. Heat, liquids and various mechanical devices were tried with results which were always unsatisfactory and frequently fatal to the papyri. All sorts of cranks offered themselves and made proposals. Hayter describes the attempt of one of these,

recommended as an excellent chymist both in theory and in experiment. This gentleman wrote his Proposal together with his data. Broken pieces of several of the more impaired manuscripts, classed according to their respective defects, were set apart by my order for his inspection. After considering during some time and in detail their defects, after having been permitted by me to make other various unsuccessful attempts, at last, without convincing me by any single argument which he adduced, he was permitted to try vegetable gas. The greatest part of each mass flew, under his trial, to useless atoms; besides not a character was to be found upon any single piece. The dreadful odour drove us all from the Museum. That in fact is a part of the royal palace, which, if the court had been there, must also have been precipitately abandoned.[1]

In 1806 the French invaded Naples and Hayter had to retire to Sicily, leaving all the papyri behind. The process of unrolling the papyri more amenable to treatment had proceeded with a fair amount of dispatch. During the four years 1802-6 about 200 rolls had been opened, and nearly 100 had been copied in facsimile. A number of the rolls were sent to England as a gift to the Prince of Wales from the Court of Naples. These seem to have been very resistant to treatment and to have been

[1] Rev. John Hayter, *Report upon the Herculanean Manuscripts* (London, 1811), p. 50.

under experiment by qualified men in the Royal Society and in the British Museum without any satisfactory result. After some time two of the manuscripts were placed

in the hands of a medical gentleman who was known to have formerly employed himself in minute anatomy, and to be familiar with the processes of mechanics and the operations of chemistry, in hopes that he would be able to discover some means of detaching the conglutinated surfaces from each other. At first, as it often happens in such cases, he appeared to be very confident of ultimate success; but difficulties afterwards occurred, and he did not continue his experiments long enough to overcome them, or even very materially to lessen them.

In this frank confession of failure Young sums up his abortive attempts to deal with the papyrus rolls. Chemical agents of all kinds he tried, and even maceration in water, but without result.

The next person to offer was a German of the name of Sickler, and as the Government had now assumed financial responsibility a committee was set up by Parliament, consisting among others of Sir Humphry Davy, Dr Burney and Sir William Hamilton. Mr Sickler's efforts were no more successful. A final test of his 'method' was made in Black Rod's apartment at the House of Commons on 27 June 1817, and with a tribute to his zeal and assiduity Mr Sickler's engagement was terminated, and a report, submitted to Parliament by the Committee, was ordered to be printed in March 1818 and appears in vol. xv at p. 23 in the Reports published in 1819.

The final effort was made by Sir Humphry Davy himself. Sponsored by the Prince Regent and commended by letter to the King of Naples, Davy set off for Italy in May 1818. He satisfied himself that the state of the rolls was not due to heat, but that the leaves were 'generally cemented into one mass by a peculiar substance which had formed during the fermentation and chemical change of the vegetable matter comprising them in a long course of ages'.[1]

This view was not accepted by Young and neither he nor Davy seems ever to have convinced the other. Certainly Davy

[1] *Journal of the Royal Institution* (April, 1819).

was the more successful and achieved the partial unrolling of some twenty-three manuscripts. At this point, however, the general plan broke down—partly owing to the injured state of the manuscripts and partly owing to the jealous obstruction of the Curators of the Museum where the manuscripts were lodged. Even Davy reported that 1265 of the papyri offered little hope of success and not more than 120 seemed worth attempting. It is a disappointing record and shows how the high hopes which had at one time been cherished gradually faded.

But if Young was only one link in a chain of failures so far as the unrolling process was concerned, he made a substantial contribution to the restoration of the text of one of the more important papyri. The first to become available was translated by Mazziochi and turned out to be a rather dull and unimportant fragment of a tract on Music by Philodemus. The achievements of the Rev. John Hayter, under the auspices of the Prince of Wales, were published in 1810 under the title *Herculanensia*, edited by Sir William Drummond and Robert Walpole. The book contains a series of dissertations on Herculaneum and a facsimile of one of the papyri showing the gaps, together with a reproduction of the text as restored by the Academicians of Portici. The reproductions were accompanied by copious notes.

It was this publication that brought Young into the field. He contributed an article to *The Quarterly Review* in which he gave an account of the work. He is critical of the scholarship of the writers and joins issue with them and with the Academicians in the matter of many of their attempts at the restoration of the text. He makes his own suggestions and adds:

We do not mean to insist on every one of these corrections as certainly preferable to the text which has been printed, much less as affording us decidedly the genuine words of the author; but we imagine that the greater number will be admitted as indisputable.

He then gives a full translation and follows it with a protest at the slow pace at which the manuscripts are being given to the public:

Almost forty years were spent in preparing for the press one work of Philodemus, which had been completely unrolled in 1755 and was only published in 1793; when we consider this and reflect on the shortness of human life, and on our own grey hairs, we tremble to think how little chance there is of our being benefited by any great proportion of the eighty manuscripts still unpublished; especially if some of the most learned of our commentators are to hang whole pages of notes, on words which have even been erroneously inserted, or are to copy whole poems, for the sake of repeating remarks, which are to be found almost in our school books. . . . We should therefore earnestly recommend that the simple text of the manuscripts should appear at once, in all the pristine dignity of an editio princeps, unsullied by the addition of any extraneous matter.

Young's very critical article drew a quite ineffective reply from Hayter,[1] who was no match for him as a classical scholar, and his contentions have, in the main, been upheld. On the value of the article my colleague L. H. G. Greenwood has kindly given me the following notes:

(1) The critical comments on the work of Drummond and Hayter are in general justified and show both sound learning and excellent sense.

(2) Subsequent scholars (including Theodor Gomperz, 1866 and W. Scott, 1885) believed the article to have been written by the well-known scholar Peter Elmsley: which is a strong testimony to its merit as a piece of scholarship.

(3) Gomperz's edition of the text of the papyrus (Leipzig, 1866) adopts a large number of the article's emendations and conjectural readings, though by no means all. His text as a whole differs considerably from that proposed by Young (other scholars had worked at the papyrus between 1810 and 1866): but the number of footnotes quoting Elmsley(?) (pp. 77–89) shows the high value he set on the article: there are hardly any references to the *Edinburgh Review* article by C. J. Blomfield.

(4) The general conclusion is that Young's article was of some real value as a link in the chain of studies that have gradually produced a more trustworthy text than he (or anyone else) could have produced at so early a date.

[1] Rev. John Hayter, *Observations upon a Review of the 'Herculanensia'* (London, 1810).

It was this article in *The Quarterly Review* which suggested Young as a contributor on the subject to the *Encyclopaedia*. His contribution follows the lines of the earlier article and gives Davy full credit for his successful work, although still dissenting from his theory:

And in the course of the last few months one of the most illustrious ornaments of British science, supported by a similar liberality on the part of our Government, has been engaged in far more rapidly bursting the fetters of the imprisoned authors by the masterly touch of his magic wand. . . . Whatever differences of opinion there may be respecting the reasoning on which Sir Humphry Davy appears to have grounded his processes, there can be little doubt that they have been actually employed with considerable advantage.

Like all his other articles up to this point, 'Herculaneum' was anonymous, and Napier, who was always on the look-out for an opportunity to persuade Young to come out into the open, wrote to tell him that Davy had at once guessed the author. Young replies:[1]

Davy knows what I had done respecting the papyri of Herculaneum and could therefore be at no loss to know the author of the article; I trust also that he was pleased with it, at least as far as he is personally concerned, for he is treated with rather more respect than his mere success would have demanded.

Before we consider Young's work on Languages and Philology, we must pause to view the evidence available before he came into the field. From earliest times mankind has shown interest in the birth and growth of languages. Several different theories have been advanced to explain their origin, but not one is completely satisfactory, even today.

Ancient nations considered that ready-made speech was a gift from their gods. In Genesis ii, verses 19 and 20, God caused Adam to give names to all living things. Later on, in chapter xi, an explanation of the diversity of languages is advanced in the story of the building of the tower of Babel. God caused the confusion of tongues, to prevent man from building 'a city and

[1] Brit. Mus. Add. MSS. 34612, f. 387.

a tower, whose top may reach unto heaven'.[1] This particular theory of the origin of language lasted till the latter half of the eighteenth century, when the researches of Sir William Jones (1746-94) revealed Sanskrit and led to a wealth of knowledge of the relationship of ancient and modern languages. Young was a contemporary of Johann Gottfried Herder (1744–1803), whose essay on 'The Origin of Language' (1772) marks the beginning of the scientific explanation of language. Herder refutes the divine-origin theory of language, making it quite clear that man invented language, although the evidence available at this time was not conclusive. Young's knowledge of the ancient languages and his mastery of several modern languages reminds us of the similar attainments of his contemporary Sir William Jones, Judge of the Supreme Court of Calcutta, who knew ten foreign languages including Hebrew, Arabic and Persian. He also had made a special study of Sanskrit and advanced theories of the common origin it afforded for the later Greek, Latin, Gothic and Celtic languages.

In 1806 appeared volume I of Professor J. C. Adelung's *Mithridates, oder Allgemeine Sprachkunde*. Through the efforts of Professor Vater, as editor, there was published, three years afterwards, volume II, and in 1812 volume III. Part I of this book was reviewed by Young in *The Quarterly Review* for October 1813, under the title 'Adelung's General History of Languages'. Johann Christoph Adelung (1732-1806), a distinguished German philologist and grammarian, was the principal librarian to the Elector of Saxony, having been appointed in 1787. His complete account of German grammar, vocabulary and idiom is produced in his *Grammatico: A critical dictionary of the Higher German Tongue*, and so recalls Dr Johnson's similar efforts in our own language. Adelung followed this work by an account of Saxon history and comparative language, which is to be found in volume I of his *Mithridates*, referred to above. Young had attempted to give 'an abstract of all that was either known with certainty, or supposed with probability, respecting the relations of different languages to one another, and the steps

[1] Gen. xi, 1–9.

by which the more modern have been derived from the more ancient, and become current in the respective countries'.[1]

Young next produced, in *The Quarterly Review* for October 1815, two articles on the same general subject by reviewing two works of Jamieson and Townsend respectively. These were 'Hermes Scythicus: or the Radical Affinities of the Greek and Latin Languages to the Gothic: to which is prefixed a Dissertation on the Historical Proofs of the Scythian Origin of the Greeks' by John Jamieson; and 'The character of Moses established for veracity as a historian recording events subsequent to the Deluge' by the Rev. Joseph Townsend.

John Jamieson, D.D. (1759–1838) graduated in the University of Glasgow and was an eminent theologian and philologist. Sir Walter Scott, referring to Jamieson, describes him as 'an excellent good man and full of auld Scottish cracks'.[2] His best and chief work is considered to be the *Etymological Dictionary of the Scottish Language*, which appeared in 1808. The two works supported some of Young's conclusions expressed in his review of Adelung's *Mithridates*.

The article on 'Languages' published in the Supplement of the *Encyclopaedia Britannica*, volume v (1824), gave Young the opportunity to resume the subject of Language and Philology from a more strictly historical angle, with an attempt to classify all the known languages of the ancient world, with special reference to Europe, Asia and Africa. The essay was designed to treat languages as they are distinct from each other, and he immediately found difficulty in defining what should constitute a separate language. He called those languages distinct which required an interpreter for communication between persons of the respective nations, and adds:[3]

Still, however, it remains doubtful whether the Danes and the Swedes could not, in general, understand each other tolerably well, and whether the Scottish Highlanders and the Irish would be able to drink their whisky together without an interpreter; nor is it possible to say if the twenty ways of pronouncing the sounds

[1] *Quarterly Review* (1815), p. 96.
[2] Lockhart, *Life of Scott*, vol. VI, p. 331.   [3] *Works*, vol. III, p. 480.

belonging to the Chinese characters ought, or ought not to be, considered as so many languages or dialects, though they would render all oral intercourse between the persons so speaking the language actually impracticable. But whether we call such variations different languages, or different dialects, or merely different pronunciations of the same dialect, it is obvious that they all ought to be noticed in a complete history of languages; and, at the same time, that the languages so nearly allied must stand next to each other in a systematical order; the perfection of which would be to place the nearest together those languages in which the number of coincidences in the signification of words, throughout the language, are the most numerous.

It has sometimes been imagined that all languages in existence present something like a trace of having been deduced from a common origin; and it would be difficult to confute this opinion by any positive evidence, unless every separate language had been completely analysed and examined by a person well acquainted with a variety of the languages with which it might be compared.

Thus Young's work on languages includes an account of their origin and structure as well as their affinities. He also maintains that a study of languages can be applied in testing the truth of historical evidence. Travellers have been impressed with the similarity in the architecture of temples in India and Egypt, from which it might be concluded that the two races were of common origin; but their languages are so dissimilar that any such conclusion would be false. Young tackles the problem of the coincidence of words in two or more languages from a mathematical angle, in order to show how far wide of the truth is the conclusion that these languages are of common origin. In an essay published in the *Philosophical Transactions*, 1819,[1] on 'Probabilities' he states:

Nothing whatever could be inferred, with respect to the relation of two languages, from the coincidence of the sense of any single word in both of them; that is supposing the same simple and limited combination of sounds to occur in both, but to be applied accidentally to the same number of objects, without any common links of connection; and that the odds would only be three to one against

---

[1] *Ibid.* vol. II, p. 8.

the agreement of two words; but if three words appeared to be identical, it would be more than ten to one that they must be derived, in both cases from some parent language, or introduced in some other manner from a common source; six words would give near 1700 chances to one, and eight near 100,000 to one; so that in these last cases the evidence would be little short of certainty.

Young contended that the high probabilities mentioned above prove the existence of a connection, possibly through some common primitive language, or through emigration, conquest or trade. Townsend's book supported the former view, although the languages he examined belonged to the Indo-European class with the exception of the Mongol language.

In order to classify languages, members of a family must show coincidences, although where a language was imperfectly known a geographical distinction would be resorted to in defining the class to which it belonged. Young divided existing languages into five families: Monosyllabic, Indo-European, Tartaric, African and American. He made use of Adelung's work to arrive at this classification by taking the words 'heaven' or 'sky', and 'earth'—likely to be found in all languages—in the 400 languages to which reference would be made. Later in the article he describes, briefly, each member.

Of the Chinese language he states:[1]

The strongest proof of the great antiquity of the Chinese language appears to be the great simplicity of its structure, and the want of those abbreviations and conventional implications which have some-times been called the wings of language. It is natural that in attempting to express ideas at once by characters the rude pictures of material objects should first have been principally, if not exclusively, traced; thus the Egyptians had $\odot$, $\mathbb{D}$ for the *sun* and *moon*, and $\oplus$ for a *country* or *field*, and the Chinese have still 日, 月, 田 for these objects respectively.

After a brief reference to Sanskrit in the second family, in which he shows how many variations and degenerations occur in the diversity of modern dialects in India, he comments on the excellent work done by missionary organizations as reported

[1] *Works*, vol. III, p. 509.

in *A Brief View of the Baptist Missions and Translations* (London, 1815). The Scriptures were translated into the languages of India as well as those of Armenia and Persia. Of the modern European languages the treatment Young adopts may be gathered from the following quotation regarding our own language:[1]

The Saxons are mentioned by Ptolemy as a small nation in Holstein; whence in conjunction with the Frislanders and the Angles of South Jutland, they came over to England about 450 A.D. The Saxons settled principally south of the Thames, the Angles north. At the Union of the Heptarchy the Saxon dialect prevailed, and the Anglish, which nearly resembled the Danish of that time, was less in use; but new swarms of Danes having inundated the north of England in 787, the Danish dialect was introduced by Canute and his followers; and it is about this period that our earliest specimens of the Anglo-Saxon are dated. The Saxon dialect again obtained ascendancy under Edward the Confessor, and although some French was introduced by this Prince, and still more by William the Conqueror, into the higher circles of society, the courts of law and the schools, yet the use of the French language never became general among the lower classes, and the Saxon recovered much of its currency in the thirteenth century, when the cities and corporate towns rose into importance under Edward I; in the fourteenth century it was permanently established, with the modifications it received from the French. . . . It is still more German than French; in the Lord's Prayer, the only words of Latin origin are Trespass, Temptation and Deliver.

Young then quotes Adelung on the simplicity of English:[2]

It is the most simple of all European languages, the termination of its substantives being only changed in the genitive and in the plural, and the alterations of the roots of the verbs not exceeding six or seven. This simplicity depends in some measure on a philosophical accuracy which is carried systematically through the whole language, so that the adjectives, particles and article are indeclinable, being in their nature destitute of any idea of gender, case or number; and the form of generic distinction is (almost entirely) confined to objects which are entitled to it. The pronunciation, on the other

[1] *Ibid.* p. 529.   [2] *Quarterly Review* (October 1813), pp. 272–3.

hand, is extremely intricate and foreign proper names, in particular, are much mutilated whenever they are adopted by the English.

The whole article, comprising some 33,000 words, is important as showing the great interest Young maintained in Philology in addition to his original researches in the hieroglyphics. At the end of the Supplement he gives a list of twenty-three authorities, comprising the period 1555 to 1816, from a variety of European countries, which indicates the thoroughness with which he consulted the sources of information. Much new material has been added to this interesting subject by von Humboldt, Franz Bopp, Max Muller, Coeurdoux, Grimm, von Schlegel, Burnouf, Lassen, Princep, Jespersen, and W. D. Witney.

XIII

STANDARDS OF LENGTH; YOUNG AND
THE ADMIRALTY; LIFE ASSURANCE

*'I have been employed in methodizing a report on the provincial
weights and measures of the different parts of Great Britain and its
dependencies.'*

YOUNG—From letter to HUDSON GURNEY, 1819

*'Though science is much respected by their Lordships and your paper
is much esteemed, it is too learned.'*—The Admiralty to YOUNG

STANDARDS OF LENGTH

THE use of standards of length and weight goes back a very
long way in history. A standard of length marked off on the
statue of a Sumerian king of about 2300 B.C. still survives. In
our own country the yard and its subdivision the foot came to
be adopted as units of length; it is said that in A.D. 1101 King
Henry I adopted the length of his own arm as the standard
yard. As an appeal to the king to allow a yard measure to be
compared with his arm must have been a very awkward matter,
it is not surprising that later the standard foot was inscribed at
the base of a column in the Old Cathedral of St Paul's.

In Scotland during the same period the inch was defined as
the breadth of three barleycorns, although in A.D. 1150 King
David I, less susceptible to the temptation of self-aggrandize-
ment and more aware of individual differences, defined the
Scottish inch as the mean measure of the thumbs of three men.
The men were to be 'an muckle man, an man of measurable
stature and a lytell man', and the thumbs were to be measured
at the root of the nail.

At first local measures varied from place to place and it was
difficult to secure uniformity. During the reign of Queen
Elizabeth a brass bar representing the 'Imperial Standard Yard'
was constructed, as were also brass weights, both Troy and

Avoirdupois, and so well was this done that no further action was felt to be necessary for about a century and a half. Indeed it was the progress of science rather than considerations of trade which led to a review of the situation. Advances in science are closely linked with increased accuracy of measurement, and this, in turn, requires that units be exactly defined and standards constructed and reproduced with precision. Nor can science, being an international activity, confine its attention to the units and standards of any one country.

In his *Encyclopaedia* article Young indicates how the next steps were made on the initiative of the Royal Society. The work resulted in 1742 in a new standard yard, of which two copies were made in 1758 under the authority of a Committee of the House of Commons. One of these copies was presented to the House with the intention that it should be given legal status, but nothing effective was done until 1824.

Meantime, as Young points out in his article, a new point had arisen. The French Revolutionary government had made two innovations—(*a*) the adoption of the decimal system, and (*b*) the adoption of a 'natural' instead of an 'arbitrary' unit. The idea of the latter proposal was that the unit should be defined with reference to some length fixed in nature and so recoverable from nature. The length chosen by the French was the forty-millionth part of the meridian through Paris, and this was called a metre. It was afterwards found that it was easier to copy a metre bar than to remeasure the appropriate meridian and the 'natural' unit was quietly abandoned.

Meantime the British—not to be outdone—had thought of another 'natural' unit of length. The time of swing of a simple pendulum depends on its length measured from the point of suspension to the centre of the bob, and the time is the same for all pendulums of the same length. The length of a simple pendulum which beats seconds is therefore a 'natural' standard of length which can be constructed anywhere.

In his article Young summarizes the report of a Parliamentary Committee of 1814 which gave the length of the seconds pendulum as 39.13047 in., the length of the metre as 39.3828 in., and recommended that the gallon should be defined as the volume occupied by 10 lb. of pure water, so that on appeal to a magistrate the correctness of a measure could be checked by filling it with rain water and weighing the contents!

So far as the length of the metre was concerned the measurement was challenged by Young. The length of a bar depends of course upon its temperature. Young pointed out that the metre bar was correct at 32°F. while the British yard was correct at 62°F. and no allowance had been made for this discrepancy. His calculation corrected the figure to 39.3710 in. instead of 39.3828 in. This difference may seem small, but lengths could be very accurately measured even then and this small difference was very material.

In 1816 a new initiative was taken by Davies Gilbert in the House of Commons, as a result of which the good offices of the Astronomer Royal and the Royal Society were invoked and a new Committee was set up. This included the President and Secretaries of the Royal Society, together with Blagden, Gilbert, Wollaston, Young, Kater, Mudge, Brown, Rennie and Troughton. On this Committee Young was very active. The various possible methods of experimenting were discussed, especially for the determination of the length of the seconds pendulum. 'Dr Young proposed a method derived from that of Whitehouse and very perfect in theory, but somewhat complicated, and which has never yet been practically executed.'

A very important contribution came from Kater, who designed a pendulum consisting of a loaded metal bar with two knife edges, one near each end. The two masses which loaded the bar could slide along it and were adjusted so that the time of vibration of the bar was one second, whichever knife edge the bar swung on. It was known that when this condition was satisfied the distance between the knife edges was the

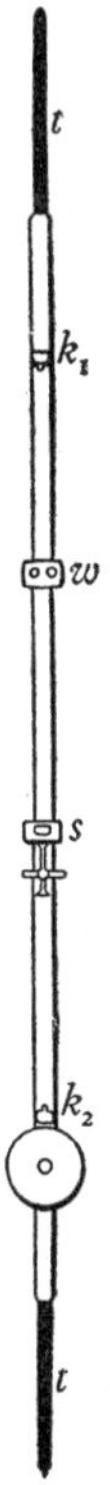

Fig. 24. Kater's Convertible Pendulum

length of the seconds pendulum, and this measurement was of course much easier to make than the distance from the point of suspension of a simple pendulum to the centre of its bob.

In order that this work should be embodied in an Act of Parliament a Commission was appointed in 1818 under writ of the Privy Seal and consisted of Sir Joseph Banks, Sir George Clerk, Mr Davies Gilbert, Dr W. Hyde Wollaston, Dr Thomas Young and Captain Henry Kater. Young was appointed to act as Secretary, with the assistance of a 'clerk who had studied the law'; Kater was charged with further necessary experiments; Sir George Clerk and Davies Gilbert were to put the proposals into legislative form.

Young, with the assistance of the clerk, made a thorough study of all the relevant statutes and regulations, and also collected as far as possible all the terms employed in any part of Great Britain for indicating weights or measures in local use not conforming to the national standards. In 1818 Kater published a paper on his pendulum with a note by Young, and in 1819 Young published a paper in which he dealt with three considerations relevant to Kater's experiments:

(1) a discussion of the method of obtaining the best value of an observation from a series of independent readings; (2) the increase of density of the central parts of the earth due to the pressure of the surface layers; and (3) the correction to be applied to the results of the pendulum experiments to allow for the height above sea-level at which they were conducted.

The Commissioners embodied their findings in a series of reports in 1819, 1820 and 1821. Their main findings in the reports, for which Young was responsible, were:

(1) The introduction of radical changes would cause great confusion.

(2) There is no practical advantage in adopting a 'natural' standard and no sufficient reason for a change.

(3) The decimal scale offers no advantages (a decision no doubt influenced by reaction against the French Revolutionary Government's adoption of it).

(4) Bird's Standard[1] of 1760 to be adopted.

(5) Seconds pendulum = 39.13929 in.
   Metre   = 39.37079 in.

The standard yard, if lost, to be recovered from the measured length of the seconds pendulum. (This provision was intended to make the best of both worlds, by avoiding a change of unit but using the natural length for replacement.)

The Bill based on these recommendations was piloted through Parliament by Sir George Clerk and after some vicissitudes became law in 1824. The Preamble sets out the irregularities which still prevailed:

Whereas notwithstanding it is provided by the Great Charter that there shall be but one Measure and one Weight throughout the realm, and by the Treaty of Union between England and Scotland that the same weights and measures should be used throughout Great Britain as were then established in England, yet different weights and measures, some larger and some less, are still in use in various places throughout the United Kingdom of Great Britain and Ireland, and the true measure of the present standards is not verily known, which is the cause of great confusion and of manifest frauds, etc.

The definition of the unit may interest those unfamiliar with our ordinary transactions involving length:

Be it therefore enacted, that from and after the 1st January, 1824, the straight line or distance between the centres of the two points in the gold studs in the straight brass rod, now in the custody of the Clerk of the House of Commons, whereon the words and figures 'Standard Yard, 1760' are engraved, shall be, and the same is hereby declared to be, the original and genuine standard of that measure of length or linear extension called a yard.

The Act goes on to declare that, if the standard is defaced or destroyed, it be restored by making a new standard yard

---

[1] Bird's two standard bars were made in 1758 and 1760, respectively, for a committee appointed by the House of Commons under the chairmanship of Lord Carysfort. These were to be copies of the Royal Society standard as laid down by Graham, 1742–3. One marked 'Standard Yard 1758' was presented to the House as the legal standard of length. (Sir R. Glazebrook, *Proceedings of the Physical Society*, 'Standards of Measurement, their History and Development'.)

bearing the same proportion to the seconds pendulum as the original standard.

It is curious that, although they had decided against a 'natural' standard, the Commissioners should have proposed to make a new standard bar by reference to the seconds pendulum. Measurements with the seconds pendulum were open to far greater uncertainties than those made by comparing two bars. When in 1835 the House of Commons was burned down and the standard yard seriously damaged, the Commissioners appointed to deal with the situation constructed the new standard by comparison with an accurate copy of the old, and although they made no change in the subdivision of the units, they expressed approval of the decimal system.

YOUNG AND THE ADMIRALTY

About the same time that Dr Young was engaged upon inquiries into weights and measures he was called on to furnish a report to the Admiralty on methods of shipbuilding. A controversy grew up round proposals for changes in the method of construction suggested by a master shipwright of Chatham named Robert Seppings. In 1800 he had discovered a new method for examining the keels and lower timbers of vessels while in dock. For this the Admiralty gave him £1000 and the Society of Arts the Copley Medal. Seppings next turned his attention to the phenomenon of 'Logging', viz. the arching of the length of a ship which took place at launching. This was sometimes so great that the ship's back was actually broken. Seppings's suggestion was the very simple one of bracing rectangular frame timbers by diagonal trusses so as to resist the tendency of the rectangle to collapse under load.

He was allowed to try his ideas with H.M.S. *Kent*, when docked for repairs in 1805, and later in 1810 with H.M.S. *Tremendous*, and the results spurred the Admiralty to action. They wrote a letter, copies of which were dispatched to Young, Banks, Wollaston and Rennie, asking for their help. It was signed by Sir John Barrow, Secretary to the Admiralty, and dated 19 November 1811:[1]

[1] Public Records Adm. 2/903/101.

Sir, Mr Seppings the Master Shipwright of Chatham Dockyard having submitted to My Lords Commissioners of the Admiralty a model for the construction of ships of war on a new principle by which it would appear that an advantage is obtained in point of strength and durability while at the same time a very considerable saving of timber is effected and My Lords having caused a ship of 74 guns to be fastened according to this new mode of construction which after a trial of many months in the North Sea has been found to answer every expectation that the projector himself could have formed and being desirous of submitting this new principle to the consideration of such men of science and practical experience as may have turned their attention to mechanics in general and more particularly to the construction and fastening of ships.

I am therefore directed by their Lordships to acquaint you that on Wednesday the 24th inst. at one o'clock Mr Seppings will be ordered to attend at this Office for the purpose of exhibiting his model and explaining the principle on which it is constructed and to request the favour of your attendance on this occasion.

To this Young replied on 22 November, with characteristic self-confidence:[1]

I ought perhaps to have returned an earlier answer to your official letter but I have made so many resolutions to forbear all further concern with the mathematical sciences that I could not at once determine to deviate from them by accepting their Lordships' invitation. Recollecting, however, that as far as I know, I am the only person in the country that has communicated to the public any attempt to improve the *theory* of carpentry and that it would be scarcely decent to draw back on an occasion where I was called to assist in a case of *practical* importance, I have overruled my hesitations; and I shall attend on Wednesday with so much the more pleasure as I cannot help fancying from the little that I know of the question in agitation, I should be able, if I had leisure to discuss it thoroughly, to reconcile the discordant opinions which now prevail respecting it.

The question was highly controversial. The older shipwrights were against the innovation; and because Seppings was against rounded stems, which made possible the very commodious and luxurious quarters used by Admirals, there was considerable

[1] Public Records Adm. 1/1509.

opposition at high levels. Sir John Barrow was solidly behind the Seppings proposals.

Young prepared a characteristically thorough, careful and cautious report. It was submitted to the Admiralty on 30 December, having taken just over a month to complete, and in a somewhat modified form was read to the Royal Society and published in 1814.[1] He made an examination of some of the older ships to find out where the weakness lay and to determine exactly what happened when 'logging' took place. Next he proceeded to examine the theory of the forces acting on a ship, due to the distribution of its weight and to the pressure of the water on the keel, and endeavoured to show how these forces conspired to produce 'logging'. Considering Seppings's proposals in the light of this examination, he gave them unqualified approval in respect of some applications but was more critical in the matter of others. He considered every objection which he could think of and finally expressed his approval in somewhat cautious and qualified terms:[2]

It is by no means impossible that experience may suggest some better substantiated objections to these innovations than have hitherto occurred: but none of these objections which have yet been advanced appear to be sufficiently valid to warrant a discontinuance of the cautious and experimental introduction of Mr Seppings' arrangements which have been commenced by orders of the Board of Admiralty.

The report appears to have satisfied no one. It dealt with the theory in a way which was quite beyond the reach of the very able but severely practical Seppings. Nor was the latter the only one who found it too heavy-going. An Admiralty official wrote: 'Though science is much respected by their Lordships and your paper is much esteemed, it is too learned.'[3]

The report was also too non-committal for Sir John Barrow and the other pro-Seppings enthusiasts. Sir John Barrow had given high praise to the proposals, particularly in *The Quarterly*

[1] *Phil. Trans.* for 1814.   [2] *Works*, vol. I, p. 561.
[3] *Ibid.* p. 536.

Review.[1] Of Young's report he says:[2]

We have perused Dr Young's remarks with care and, we may add, with pain; for if we understand them rightly, which we are by no means sure that we always do, the tendency is, if not to deprive the author of the merit of the invention, at least to diminish the value of it. He cannot, we think, disapprove of the principle; yet so many conditionals, hypotheticals and potentials are employed, that if approbation be meant, either of the principle or its application, it is at any rate 'damned with faint praise'. Dr Young will not infer from this that we under-value science, or that we do not cordially agree with him that no assistance which can be afforded by the abstract sciences should be withheld from the service of the public. Far be it from us to think otherwise: our regret arises from seeing 'abstract science' misapplied, in raising doubts on points of practice which common sense and experience are best able to determine, and which no calculus can reach.

Young's report was in point of fact a very sound piece of work. The principle was not entirely new, but some of the applications which Seppings gave it in naval architecture marked a valuable advance and became incorporated in shipbuilding practice.

LIFE ASSURANCE

In the third decade of the nineteenth century there was considerable speculation, in the financial world particularly, in regard to Life Assurance. Peacock states[3] that in the years 1824–5 'Of 624 schemes projected in the first outburst of this fever of speculation, not more than one in five survived the cold stage of reaction which succeeded it, and of these not a few were seriously, if not irreparably, crippled by the ruined or damaged fortunes of many of their founders.'

The Palladium Insurance Company was founded at this time, the Directors appointing Dr Thomas Young, F.R.S., as Inspector of Calculations at a salary of £500 p.a., to commence from the establishment of the Society; and also to hold the appointment of Physician at the same time: dated 30 March 1824. In 1856 the Palladium amalgamated with the Eagle, which has become

[1] Vol. XII (1815), p. 460.   [2] *Ibid.* p. 456.   [3] Peacock, *op. cit.* p. 404.

the present Eagle Star Assurance Co. Ltd. Very liberal terms
were offered to Young, for, in addition to his salary, a considerable number of reserved shares were placed at his disposal, but

with characteristic forbearance, however, he refused to reap where
he had not sown, and declined to accept the offer. In the same spirit,
he afterwards voluntarily proposed, and accepted, a reduced salary
of £400 p.a. as soon as he had ascertained that the duties of his
office occupied a smaller portion of his time than he first anticipated;
a rare example of conscientiousness in administration of such
institutions.[1]

Young had ventured into the field of actuarial science when
he published a paper entitled 'An Algebraical Expression for
the Value of Lives' in the *Philosophical Magazine* for 1816.[2] I[3] am
indebted to Mr M. E. Ogborn, F.I.A., Joint Actuary of the
Equitable Life Assurance Society, London, for the following
comments on this paper of Young's:

It is of interest as giving a simple formula reproducing the bills of
mortality, apparently for London in 1815. A table is given comparing the proportion of the whole deaths falling before a certain
age according to the formula, with the actual proportion recorded in
the bills of mortality for 1815. If this expression is to have any
practical use the deaths at each age must be related to the same
number of births. During the early eighteenth century, in default of
population statistics, it was customary to assume that the population
remained constant and although this assumption may have been
sufficient in the early eighteenth century, it certainly was not
appropriate at the close of the century when the upward swing of
population was well on the way. Dr Young proceeds to integrate
his expression in order to show the average duration of life, but
this is only appropriate if the population has remained constant so
that the deaths can be assumed to be derived from the same number
of births throughout the table. Dr Young nowhere mentions this
assumption, though it is possible that he may have applied some
correction, but he does not refer in any way to this question.

Naturally, Young's new appointment made him return to
the study of actuarial science, with the result that five more

---

[1] Peacock, *op. cit.* p. 404.   [2] Vol. XLVII, p. 1.   [3] F.O.

articles appeared under his name. The work can be divided into three groups:

(1) An endeavour to obtain formulae applicable to life assurance in any part of the country.

(2) An attempt to fit these formulae to certain existing tables.

(3) A criticism of certain actuaries and societies.

His paper, read before the Royal Society and published in the *Philosophical Transactions* for 1826, is a complicated formula to express in mathematical form what would now be called the 'curve of deaths'. Of this paper Mr Ogborn states:

It represents the number of deaths at each age of life as shown by a mortality table to occur among 100,000 births. The formula has some twenty constants and with such a formula it is not surprising that Dr Young obtained close agreement. In this paper also Dr Young was unlucky that only the year before Gompertz had published the paper containing his famous hypothesis which has had a very large influence on all subsequent actuarial practice. It was *Gompertz* who noticed that many of the functions depending on human life had a geometrical character and his hypothesis was effectively that the force of mortality constituted a geometrical progression.[1]

The latter part of Young's paper deals with half-yearly and quarterly annuities, in which he states that the value of a life annuity of 1 has to be increased by $\frac{1}{4}$ to allow for half-yearly payments, and correspondingly for other periods, a practice which has continued to the present day.

Dr Richard Price (1723–91), F.R.S., who was a pioneer and in a real sense a founder of both the theory and practice of Life Assurance, published in 1771 'Observations on Reversionary Payments', in which he singled out the Equitable

---

[1] I (F.O.) am indebted to Mr E. C. Witcombe for the following information:

There is evidence of the geometric law in human activity (as stated by Gompertz) in the athletic records of the present day. Re-stated in terms of distance (s) and time (t), it can be expressed as follows: if the distances are in geometric progression, then the times for these distances are also in geometric progression. Hence the law can be expressed as $\log t = k \log s$ (k being a constant).

For the world's athletic and Olympic records, k has the values 1.116 and 1.12 respectively. For the world and British walking records $k = 1.10$; for cycling $k = 1.08$; for skating (records rather too limited in number) $k = 1.06$; for amateur track events $k = 1.05$, and for horse racing $k = 1.08$.

Society as the only one established on a proper foundation. He observed that the expectation of life varied from city to city and again for different classes of the population, but he was able to draw up his celebrated Northampton Table from observations of the years 1735–80, assuming a stationary population. This table he considered more accurate and more likely to give the mean rates for the country as a whole than the London table. Price's nephew, William Morgan (1750–1833), joined the Equitable as Assistant Actuary in 1774 and became the Actuary the following year. He was successful in every way, expressing his commonsense views vigorously. He published a large number of papers on actuarial practice and gave evidence before the Committee of the House of Commons on Friendly Societies in 1825 and 1827. The following year, Dr Young wrote a letter, which was printed in the *Annals of Philosophy*, November 1828, on the experience of the Equitable Society, which he stated confirmed Gompertz's hypothesis over a considerable period. He criticized William Morgan about the continued use of the Northampton Table by the Equitable. Morgan maintained that Equitable experience confirmed the accuracy of the Northampton Table, which clearly it did not. Probably Morgan meant that mortality experience confirmed the Society in its use of the Northampton Table. Young's concluding paragraph only served to irritate Morgan, who by now was becoming an old man averse to change:[1]

I sincerely hope that these considerations may help to undeceive the too credulous public, who have of late not only received some hints that tend to insinuate the probability of an occasional recurrence of patriarchal longevity, but who have been required to believe, upon the authority of a most respectable mathematician, that the true and unerring value of life is not to be obtained by taking an average of various decrements, but by adopting the extreme of all conceivable estimates, founded only on a hasty assertion of Mr Morgan, and unsupported by any detailed report; an estimate which makes the great climacteric of mankind (i.e. the

[1] *Works*, vol. II, p. 377.

years in which the greatest number of adults die), in this country, not a paltry 54, or the too much dreaded 63 but no less than 82! An age to which nearly one sixth of the survivors at 10 are supposed to attain.

No doubt the use of the Northampton Table by the Equitable Society was fully justified, for by it Morgan ensured a good flow of profits which were distributed to the members (there were no shareholders), and this was necessary for the credit and security of the Society. The large profits were distributed from time to time by way of bonus to the members. In his reply to Young's criticism, Morgan lost no time in vindicating himself whilst retaliating on his opponent, as follows:

The public he says have lately been overwhelmed with tables of the decrements of human life, framed either by amalgamating all the old tables into one heterogeneous mass and thus giving the true probabilities of life in no place whatever, or by interpolating some of the decrements in one table into those of another; for which purpose a vast variety has been given of complicated and useless formulae. But little or no advance has been made in determining more correctly the probabilities and duration of human life. The tables published in the Report of the Committee of the House of Commons are in general so incorrect and some of them even so absurd, as to be unfit for use, and serve only to encourage the popular delusion of the improved healthiness and greater longevity of the people of this kingdom.

In Brande's *Quarterly Journal* for 1828 Young published an article on practical comparison of the different tables of mortality. A number of approximations are made which might be helpful in making calculations, but, with the accurate tables available today, they are not of great interest apart from the link they form with modern statistical work. Two years previously he had also sent an article to Brande's *Quarterly Journal* dealing with the application of chances to the subdivision of risks. Apparently the subject has been studied in greater detail in Sweden than in this country. Young was particularly interested in the case of a new society building up its portfolio rather than in an established one, attention being given to deposits, a feature which was much to the fore in the Life Assurance Companies Act 1870 and the Assurance Companies Act 1909, but was abolished by the Assurance Companies Act of 1946.

XIV

NAUTICAL ALMANAC AND BOARD OF LONGITUDE

'To a nation, also, whose present and future lay on the water, the famous Nautical Almanac of 1767 was worth many ships and men. How much of "useless" astronomy and "academic" mathematics was not squeezed into the tables and helped Jervis to win at St Vincent and Nelson at Trafalgar?'

SIR CHARLES GRANT ROBERTSON
(*England under the Hanoverians*)

IN the reign of Queen Anne an Act of Parliament was passed 'for providing a public reward for such person or persons as shall discover the longitude at sea'. An impressive Commission of Longitude was formed, including the Lord High Admiral of Great Britain (or the First Lord of the Admiralty), the Speaker of the House of Commons, the First Commissioner of the Navy, the President of the Board of Trade, the Admirals of the Red, White and Blue Squadrons, the Master of Trinity House, the Astronomer Royal of Greenwich, and the Savilian, Lucasian and Plumian Professors of Mathematics and Astronomy at Oxford and Cambridge, to carry out the work. The representation was slightly modified in the reign of George II and again in George III's reign, by which time most of the original Commission were dead. The previous 'Acts' were repealed in 1818 and a new Commission formed, with a much stronger representation of men of science, including three additional members of the Royal Society and three 'resident' commissioners who were expected to be permanently in London to carry on the work of the Board. This led to the nomination of Thomas Young, Hyde Wollaston and Captain Henry Kater. Approximately £5000 was allotted as an annual charge, made up as follows:

For Experiments & Calculations useful to Navigation £1000
    „   „   Ascertaining Latitude & Longitude £1000

For Various Proposals & Inventions   £2000
    „   Salaries   £ 500
    „   Computers   £ 500

In a letter to Napier dated 3 February 1819, Young writes:

I ought to thank you for your friendly congratulations on the appointment to the Secretaryship of the Board of Longitude, which however I undertook very unwillingly, having expected to have the superintendence of the Nautical Almanac without it.

It was Young's appointment in 1818 as Superintendent of the *Nautical Almanac* and Secretary of the Board of Longitude which made him decide to add his name to his various scientific publications. Previously, it will be remembered, he thought the public were entitled to know of him solely through his professional work as a doctor. His new appointment, by virtue of a warrant of the Admiralty,[1] carried a salary of £300 p.a. as Superintendent and £100 p.a. for the office of Secretary.

Maskelyne, who was Astronomer Royal from 1765 to 1811, began the publication of the *Nautical Almanac* for 1767, to promote the interests of navigation as well as to record the positions of the planets with respect to the fixed stars. In 1761, three years after his election to a Fellowship of the Royal Society, he had sailed to St Helena to observe a transit of Venus. Although the prime object of the voyage was not attained owing to bad weather, he was able to introduce lunar observations for ascertaining longitude. As Astronomer Royal he became a member of the Board of Longitude and was mainly responsible for the increased accuracy of astronomical observations in this country. After Maskelyne's death in 1811 and before Young took over the work, errors had been allowed to appear in the *Almanac* which tended to compromise the character of the publication. Criticisms of the *Nautical Almanac* by Davies Gilbert were noted by the new Secretary and reserved for a future occasion. They were:

1. Calculations to be made for mean time only.
2. Places of all new planets to be inserted.
3. Right Ascension to be calculated and inserted in seconds.

[1] Board of Longitude Papers, vol. VIII (Greenwich Royal Observatory).

4. Distance of the moon from Jupiter to be inserted.
5. Occultations of a greater number of fixed stars to be included.
6. A fifth computer to be appointed.

Young soon corrected the errors, but followed strictly the line of his predecessors in designing the *Almanac* primarily for nautical rather than astronomical purposes. The first publication of the *Nautical Almanac* by the new Secretary again received much criticism, especially from astronomers, of whom the most vehement was F. Baily (1774–1844), formerly an authority on Life Annuities, who had turned his attention to astronomy. Young had retained some material of mainly astronomical interest, e.g. types of telescope to be used for observing the satellites of Jupiter. The omission of other data he considered justified for historical reasons, since they were made by Maskelyne, but he allowed concessions in the matter of tables of the moon's distance from the principal planets. This brought the *Almanac* more into line with the similar publications on the Continent. An additional cause for complaint was Young's method of publishing his lists of occultations and various astronomical investigations, entitled 'Nautical Collections', in the *Journal of the Royal Institution*, instead of including them in a supplement or appendix to the *Nautical Almanac*.

A year later, by Orders in Council, the remuneration of the members of the Board was reconsidered and a scale of rewards arranged to supplement the full reward of £20,000 offered by the Longitude Act of 1818 for the captain and crew of the first ship to complete the North-West Passage from the Atlantic to the Pacific Oceans. In the same way a scale of lesser awards was established to supplement the same Act for penetration of 89° North. If the object was only partly completed, the awards were:

By sailing within the Arctic Circle:

110°W from Greenwich		£5000
130°W ,, ,,		£10,000
150°W ,, ,,		£15,000

With latitude 83°N, 85°, 87° or 88° an award of £1000, £2000, £3000, or £4000.

With regard to the *Nautical Almanac*, some improvements were suggested and agreed upon immediately, viz: the Astronomer Royal was to pay particular attention to observations of the distance of Jupiter from the moon.

On 22 July 1820 Young wrote to Barrow the following recommendation from the Board of Longitude:[1]

It would be highly conducive to the improvement of Practical Astronomy and Navigation that a permanent Observatory should be established at the Cape of Good Hope; and that in their opinion nothing could more essentially promote the glory of the British name than that this Nation should be the foremost in such an undertaking.

This received favourable comments from Barrow, and was recommended to the Treasury. In a further letter, dated 5 February 1821, Young states that the instructions for the Astronomer at the Cape will comprise:

1. Conditions to be sought for the location of the Observatory.
2. A preliminary survey of the Southern Stars.
3. Observations on the same stars by the same methods and recorded in the same manner as at Greenwich.
4. Particular attention to be paid to the rediscovery of Encke's Comet.
5. No opportunity to be neglected of making any observations capable of improving the theory of refraction.
6. A half-yearly report to be sent to the Secretary of the Board.

In the same year Thomas Colby and J. F. W. Herschel joined the Board as resident Commissioners.

One of the most important duties of the new Board was to verify the claim of the discovery of a North-West Passage via the straits bordering the North Canadian Territories. On 27 November 1820 a reward of £5000 was made to Lieutenants Wm. Edward Parry and Matthew Loddon, in command of H.M. Ships *Hecla* and *Griper*, who, during the summer of 1819, reached and passed the longitude of 110° West from Greenwich by sailing within the Arctic Circle. The expedition was un-

1 Adm. 1/3461.

successful in finding a complete passage, but the value of the work done can be judged from Young's reference in a letter to Gurney, dated 6 November 1820:

And here is the *polar expedition* arrived, whom I am to examine on their oaths to get them the £5000, which it seems will be spent in lowering the price of oil, by the information they have given the whalers. I imagine also they have set the practical question of the passage at rest, as it is obvious that there would be no reasonable chance of getting to Behrings' Straits in the short arctic summer of six weeks, even if there is a passage, which seems by no means improbable—though Barrow's 'Polar Bason' is certainly nothing but a lock of ice—for they found that it was only near land that there was anything like a possibility of navigating, the mean annual temperature of the year being 0° on the islands, which is 30° lower than would be inferred from the analogy of the inhabited world. I should not, however, be surprised if the curiosity of the Admiralty prompted them to continue the research, and I have no objection to curiosity in others, though it is a great many years since I was scolded for that quality myself.

In 1821 the Board of Longitude and the Admiralty decided to assist Captain Edward Sabine, R.A., to proceed to the neighbourhood of the equator to make experiments with the pendulum, observations on refraction and the measurement of magnetic dip. The magnetic attraction of ships was another important problem requiring solution, and Young wrote to Barrow recommending the award of £500 to Professor Barlow, of the Royal Military Academy, Woolwich 'in consideration of the practical utility of his invention of a plate of iron to be so placed as to compensate for the magnetic attraction of the ship'.[1]

Shortly after Young's appointment as Superintendent of the *Nautical Almanac* the first moves were made to form an independent astronomical society. The first meeting took place on 12 January 1820, when a committee was formed with F. Baily as secretary. In the early days it was feared that its objects might overlap and compete with the work undertaken by members of the Royal Society, whose President (Sir Joseph

[1] *History of the Royal Astronomical Society*, p. 1.

Banks) was in opposition from the first. The Duke of Somerset, after accepting nomination as President of the new society, withdrew his name in a letter dated 9 March because Sir Joseph 'apprehended the ruin of the Royal Society'. J. F. W. Herschel was a very active member of the council of the new society, one of whose first aims was to reform the *Nautical Almanac*.

'On Thursday, November 30th, 1820, the Council met at Baily's house to consider a request for accurate tables of the 45 Greenwich stars for 1822, 1823 and 1824. . . . The actual request was not pressed when the Council promised to do its best. According to a report made a week later the main obstacle was the 'indolent' Board of Longitude. In the Nautical Almanac for 1822 there is, indeed, a list of 45 stars but ephemerides are only given for 24 of them, so that there are such gaps as 2 hours 28 minutes (α Arietis to Aldebaran) and 3 hours 18 minutes (Regulus to Spica) during which an observer could not conveniently find his clock error. The Nautical Almanac for 1826 showed no improvement. In 1822 the Board of Longitude consisted of:

J. W. Croker	S. P. Rigaud
Joseph Banks, P.R.S.	Isaac Milner
Davies Gilbert	Samuel Vince
Rob. Woodhouse	W. Lax
John Pond (Astronomer Royal)	W. H. Wollaston
A. Robertson	W. Mudge
and Thomas Young, Secretary.[1]	

H. H. Turner, late Professor of Astronomy of Oxford, says:[2] 'From their laxity we should expect to find them officials innocent of astronomy, but they include some very respectable names, especially the Secretary.' He adds, 'A Board or Committee is apt to combine not the wisdom but the folly of its members'.

I[3] am indebted to Dr J. G. Porter of H.M. *Nautical Almanac* Office for the following notes on Turner's comments on the Members of the Board of Longitude:

I have never been happy about this phase of Royal Astronomical Society history. Turner's comment on the 'laxity' of these officials

---

[1] *History of the Royal Astronomical Society*, p. 14. [2] *Ibid.* p. 15. [3] F.O.

seems to me to be unjustified. Of the twelve names given here, five are those of eminent astronomers, men of the type that had fought their way up to the top by sheer hard work and ability:

Rigaud was Savilian Professor at Oxford, and particularly well known for his literary and historical work.

Pond was the Astronomer Royal of the time, interested in star positions.

Samuel Vince was easily the outstanding theoretical astronomer of his day. Plumian Professor of Astronomy at Cambridge, his books and tables were the ultimate authority in those days.

Wollaston was a Vice-President of the Royal Society and had a distinguished record as a scientist and as an astronomer.

Davies Gilbert was Vice-President of the Royal Society (later President at the time of the 1830 Report). He was a friend of Malachy Hitchins, and familiar with *Nautical Almanac* work. An M.P., he could handle matters in the House of Commons as well.

I should mention that Vince died in 1821. However, it is significant to note that from 1814 to 1820 the whole of the *Nautical Almanac* was computed from Vince's Tables (*Astronomy*, vol. III) and from 1821 to 1832 the only changes made were to substitute new tables of the Moon and of Jupiter's satellites.

I have little doubt in my own mind that Vince's work carried a great deal of weight. Young, who was merely Secretary, could do little to influence this Board, which was, in any case, clearly dominated by the character of Banks. Did Turner honestly regard Banks as the type of man guilty of laxity?

Laxity is the wrong word—conservatism, perhaps?

In an appendix to the translation of Cagnoli's Memoir on determining the figure of the earth (1819), Baily stated that the new Board of Longitude had the power and the means (£4000 p.a.) to enlarge the original plan of the *Nautical Almanac* and undertake other astronomical work. Baily published astronomical data in the *Philosophical Magazine*, 1820, and he printed for private circulation 'Astronomical Tables & Remarks for the year 1822'. Two years later he published 'Remarks on the present defective state of the "Nautical Almanac",'[1] in which he referred to his recently published

[1] London (1822), 72 pages, dated 7 May.

'Tables' differing in parts from those of a similar kind in the *Nautical Almanac*. He included a point-by-point reply to an anonymous article in the *Journal of the Royal Institution* which had been written by Young answering the alleged deficiencies in the *Nautical Almanac*, Baily having mentioned these in the introduction to his published Tables. His most serious complaint was that the *Nautical Almanac* compared unfavourably with the Coimbra and Milan ephemerides. Baily also pointed out that the French Bureau des Longitudes, established in 1796, more than eighty years after the British one, did not contain any useless members, or 'learned professors, who lived upwards of fifty miles from the place of meeting and consequently seldom attend the Board'. Sir James South (1785-1867), a pioneer of the Royal Astronomical Society, added his support to Baily's criticisms in a pamphlet, 'Practical Observations on the Nautical Almanac', 64 pages, dated 1822, by asserting that the *Nautical Almanac* had always contained information which was only of use to astronomers and that there was good reason for extending it. He also drew attention to the more up-to-date French *Connaissance des Temps*, regarding observations of the eclipse of Jupiter's satellites, and concluded that the positions of the planets ought to be given more frequently and more accurately.

Schumacher, of the Danish Hydrographic Office, also published in 1822 the first of a series of year books, entitled 'Distances of the four planets, Venus, Mars, Jupiter and Saturn, from the Moon, together with their places for every day in the year'. Young made arrangements with Schumacher in 1822 to have a large number of copies for subsequent years imported into England; only fifty were sold annually, and he accordingly concluded that *practical* seamen did not want information of that kind.

The demand for reform was becoming stronger when J. F. W. Herschel, in 1827 at a meeting of the Board of Longitude, produced a paper regarding improvements in the *Nautical Almanac*. As a result an enlargement was made by publishing separately a Supplement beginning with the year 1828; but it was published after the beginning of the year.

Towards the end of 1828 it was decided to abolish the Board of Longitude, whereupon the Admiralty appointed Young, Sabine and Faraday to carry on its duties. By an Order in Council dated 27 October it was resolved that:

A resident committee be appointed to advise with us on all questions of discoveries, inventions, calculations and other scientific subjects, such Committee to be composed of three persons to be chosen from among the Council of the Royal Society, and whereas we think fit that you the aforesaid shall compose the said Committee for one year from the present we do constitute and appoint you. . . .

A salary of £100 per annum was authorized as well as the outstanding salaries of the officials of the Board of Longitude up to its dissolution.

Young's work is seen to be closely connected with the Admiralty, to whom he wrote[1] on 10 January 1829, mentioning the expenses involved in Faraday's optical glass experiments and securing their approval of meeting the cost. Later in the letter he states:

With respect to the Nautical Almanac I conclude that it is the intention of the Board of Admiralty that the computers hitherto employed should proceed with their labour as heretofore and that I should make no essential changes in the work or the workmen without their express direction. Note—It is their Lordships' intention that the Nautical Almanac should be proceeded with as heretofore. Mr Baily it seems is about to print a pamphlet containing *Further* remarks on the defective state of the Nautical Almanac intended chiefly for circulation among those Members of Parliament who may be likely to take an interest in the subject when *brought before the House of Commons*. Mr Baily will never rest satisfied until the Astronomical Society not content with the humiliation of the the Royal Society shall succeed in dictating to the *Admiralty* and the *British Parliament*, and the warfare begun in the Morning Chronicle is no doubt to be continued in the House of Commons, that is if the attack of 'banditti', unresisted because contemptible, can be called a *warfare*. Innocent, indeed, they are not, because they injure the ignorant seamen; and if I knew how to repel them effectually in this point of view, I should be most ready to attempt it.

[1] Adm. 1/3469.

Again, in a letter to Gurney the next day (11 January 1829), he writes:

Our new Committee of Longitude is settled at last for the present, though the 'Radical' abuse of the Nautical Almanac is likely to continue: but fortunately for my security they have put the Admiralty and Nautical Almanac together, so that they may do their worst. Croker[1] has appointed Sabine, Faraday and me to constitute a Scientific Committee to advise the Admiralty which was all the Board of Longitude could do, and it is better that things should be called by their right names. Faraday is wanted, they say, as a chemist: and I recommended him as the best in the Council: Sabine will be useful in examining instruments. . . . There are certainly some excuses for the affair of the Board of Longitude in the encouragement which it held out to the ravings of madmen: and the Admiralty prefers the intention of putting down £1000 a year in the estimates of miscellaneous rewards to useful inventing.

Baily's pamphlets on the shortcomings of the *Nautical Almanac* were answered in a report[2] to the Admiralty containing the objection and Young's reply.

Objection (1): The *Nautical Almanac* always intended for the use of astronomers as well as navigators.

Reply: Navigation primarily—Young adds: 'the cultivation of abstract science being obviously of far less importance than the preservation of the lives and property of seafaring persons.'

Objection (2): The *Nautical Almanac* of 1818 had 58 errors; that of 1830 has also 58.

Reply: 48 of these errors arise from *one*, and this was detected before more than one-fiftieth of the issue was sold. The computer's error was not detected by the comparer because of a coincidence, but was ultimately found by a detailed check with the *Connaissance des Temps*. The latter for 1822 lists 73 errata for the preceding volume, and the editor acknowledges these corrections as being mainly due to Young and the comparison. With the reverse comparison the number of errors in the *Nautical Almanac* in the last few years was always under 20— those in the French work regularly over 40. A similar acknow-

---

[1] Admiralty Secretary.   [2] Adm. 1/3469.

ledgment to Young was made in 1827 in the French work, with regard to the assertion of the superiority of Schumacher's almanacs made by Baily:

In a paper published some years ago, Professor Schumacher took occasion in the 6th number of his Astronomical Newspaper to express his formal dissent from Mr Baily's decision, but the candid opinion of *an* impartial foreigner appears to have no weight with the antagonists of the Nautical Almanac.

Objection (3): The distances of the planets from the moon ought to be inserted as well as their daily places.
Reply: Planets rarely visible if the stars are invisible and Schumacher's tables of planetary distances introduced into the country met with very small circulation. This indicated no great demand and therefore no justification for the increased bulk of the *Nautical Almanac*.

Objection (4): No list of occultations.
Reply: Occultations to the 4th magnitude were included. The extension to the 6th magnitude would give large increase in bulk with little corresponding advantage. The occultations inserted in the *Nautical Almanac* from 1816 to 1821 were deduced from erroneous data supplied by Dr Maskelyne. 'The mistake was never discovered by practical astronomers till it was corrected by the present Superintendent.'

Later, on 28 January 1829, a Memorandum was presented to the Chancellor of the Exchequer asking for the reform of the *Nautical Almanac* to be expedited. Then in the following month a motion was made in the House of Commons for the production of papers connected with the late Board of Longitude and the *Nautical Almanac*, and on 17 March they were ordered to be printed.[1] They are: The Memorandum of 28 January with a copy of Herschel's paper read to the Board of Longitude on 5 April 1827, Young's reply to the Memorandum, and an account of the expenses of the late Board of Longitude. The Memorandum states that the *Almanac* fell into disrepute after Maskelyne's death; that there were fifty-eight errors in the

[1] Parliamentary Papers, 1829, v. 21, pp. 219-31.

volume for 1818 and the same number in the volume for 1830; that it does not contain the lunar distances of the principal planets, nor any occultations; that the tables of the sun used by the computers are known to be inaccurate; that the accurate places of all the planets should be given every day. Finally, the request is made to form a new Board of Longitude. Young presented his report in answer to the various charges, but another attack from Sir James South (1785–1867), published on 25 April under the title 'Refutation of the numerous mis-statements and fallacies contained in a paper to the Admiralty by Dr Thomas Young', tended to hinder rather than help the cause of reform. South was one of the founder-members of the Astronomical Society and a keen supporter of Baily, but he was not an easy man to get on with, and never forgot an injury. Added to this, he formed hasty conclusions, was easily roused, of uncertain temper, and very careless of giving offence by his writings. He was therefore less convincing than Baily in his criticism of the *Nautical Almanac*. Dreyer writes 'The volume of South was no doubt disapproved by many'; and Airy writes in his *Autobiography*:[1]

In February and March I had letters from Young about the Nautical Almanac; he was unwilling to make any great change but glad to receive any small assistance. South, who had been keeping up a series of attacks on Young, wrote to me to enquire how I stood in engagements of assistance to Young, I replied that I should assist Young whenever he asked me, and that I disapproved of South's course. The date of the first visitation of the Cambridge Observatory must have been near May 11th. I invited South and Baily to my house; South and I were very nearly quarrelling about the treatment of Young. In a few days after Dr Young died (May 10th) I applied to Lord Melville for the superintendence of the Nautical Almanac: Mr Croker replied that it devolved legally upon the Astronomer Royal and on May 10th, Pond wrote to ask my assistance when I could give any.

South's style is illustrated by the following specimen:

Smyth when surveying the Mediterranean was obliged to use the ephemerides of Paris, Milan, Bologna and Florence on account of

[1] Sir George B. Airy (1801–91), *Autobiography*, p. 87.

omissions and errors in the Nautical Almanac (this, Smyth in a letter certified to be true). But wishing to show civility to a Spanish Captain, he presented him with his copies of the Nautical Almanac for the current and subsequent years. Captain Smyth with his foreign ephemerides found his way to England, but there is an awkward story afloat that the Spanish Captain has not since been heard of.[1]

The only other references we find are from the excerpts from the diary of Hudson Gurney for 1829. He visited Young very frequently during his last illness. On 4 May, under the heading 'Nautical Almanac', Gurney states: 'Young's wish was to have the English and the French as nearly as might be on the same plan—in order that by comparing they might correct mutually any error which might slip into either.'

On 28 July 1830 the Admiralty addressed a letter to the Council of the Astronomical Society, stating that directions had been given to Pond, who was now in charge of the *Nautical Almanac*, to insert certain additions. A request was made of the Society to state whether these improvements were sufficient. A large committee of forty members was appointed and a full report submitted to the Council in November of the same year. This was approved and forwarded to the Admiralty. Practically all the suggestions were accepted, and so began a fruitful co-operation to the benefit of sailors and astronomers.

Peacock, reviewing the controversy, states:[2]

It is difficult for the warmest admirers of Dr Young altogether to justify the line of conduct he pursued. Of the two grounds upon which he chiefly rested his defence—expense to the Government, and the interests of navigation—the first was absolutely unworthy of notice, and the second could hardly be compromised by the embarrassment produced by placing in the hands of seamen more than they required, when the most simple instructions would direct them what to look for.

Weighing the available evidence, it seems that Young's whole attitude was one of supporting independent science and advancing the interests of the Royal Society. He appears to have

---

[1] *History of the Royal Astronomical Society*, p. 60.   [2] Peacock, *op. cit.* p. 365.

ignored the Astronomical Society, and one is left with the feeling that his loyalty to the senior Society gave him a prejudiced view of British astronomy and its claims.

Dr D. H. Sadler, the present Superintendent of the *Nautical Almanac*, has kindly given me his views on the controversy. Young, he considers, was unjustly criticized for not introducing into the *Nautical Almanac* alterations that were solely of use to astronomers and not to navigators. In *Occasional Notes*,[1] Dr Sadler writes critically of the part that astronomers played in the development of navigation during the nineteenth century and states that the 1834 revision of the *Almanac* was, in fact, an improvement from the navigator's point of view. But the *Nautical Almanac* could have been made a much more useful navigational publication if the astronomers had devoted their attention towards that one object only.

[1] Royal Astronomical Society, *Occasional Notes*, vol. II, no. 13 (Sept. 1949).

XV

EVENTS IN LATER LIFE

'It is well for me that I have not to live over again; I doubt if I should make so good a use of my time as mere accident has compelled me to do. Many things I could certainly mend, and spare myself both time and trouble: but on the whole, if I had done very differently from what I have, I dare say I should have repented more than I now do of anything—and this is a tolerable retrospect of 40 years of one's life.' Letter from YOUNG to HUDSON GURNEY

IN spite of the variety of his pursuits Young's course of life was remarkably uniform. He lived in London from November to June and at Worthing for the rest of the year. Occasionally he paid visits to his friends at Sunninghill or to the house of his old friend Hudson Gurney in Norfolk, but his own opinion was that London was the place which suited him best. There he was able to pursue his interests and meet the people whose company he enjoyed. He usually found the best relaxation from a difficult investigation in one subject by occupying himself in some other field of study. This is clearly brought out in the following letter to Gurney, dated 18 December 1820:

What a pity it is that you are a rich banker and a member of parliament! Had you been called a lawyer or a doctor, you might have had a chance of being made a bookseller's drudge and becoming useful in your generation, without complaining of want of resolution to employ yourself. About this time last year I was giving myself a holiday of a few weeks, and I fell into a sort of fidgetty languor and fancied I was growing old; it went off very soon however, and I am convinced that there is no remedy so effectual for this and other intellectual diseases as plenty of employment, without over-fatigue or anxiety. This autumn I have been in fact going on with the work which I was then almost frightened at having undertaken, and am already printing the first part of it— being only a translation with a commentary, it will do better with-

out my name than with it. I am also writing over again my article
on languages in the Quarterly Review with many additions for the
next supplement of the Encyclopaedia Britannica—and a biographical memoir on Lagrange will be almost as long, requiring a
list of 100 different papers on the most abstruse parts of the mathematics. I have then the business of the Board of Longitude to
manage, and some of the Royal Society. The Arctic expedition is
now settled; but we are fitting out our astronomer for the Cape
with all his books and instruments, then there is a committee of
elegant extracts to consider of the tonnage of ships, appointed by
the Royal Society, the Admiralty, the Board of Trade, and the
Treasury—which will not take long, but I shall have the onus—then
there is my hospital—to speak modestly of my private patients—
who are very discreet at this time of the year. By the way, such a
day as this would make one glad to be anywhere rather than in
London. I was forced to read by the fire and write in the dark at
1 o'clock: for I thought if I had candles I should scarcely have resolution to take my ride. Then I must not forget that I must very shortly
fulfil my promise to do a little more to the Hieroglyphics, and after
one number more I shall be able to judge if the thing is worth
continuing or not. . . .

I hope the general mildness with which the winter has set in will
be favourable to valetudinarians: we had two bitter days—Friday
and Saturday: but now it is again warm. I do not wonder that you
croak a little as a landed proprietor, but what comforts me is to see
the income of the last quarter so much improved. I hope you will
be able pro forma to offer some civilities to Augustus Ellis, though
I believe there is little chance of his being able to accept them, as he
is going about on different shooting expeditions, for some weeks,
I believe.

If you wish to acquire immortal fame and fifty guineas, as a poet,
you have only to write upon *Dartmoor*! There is a 'Royal Society of
Literature' established, which sent round proposals for a prize of
100 guineas for the best essay on Homer: 50 for the best poem on
Dartmoor—and something else for an essay on the history of the
Greek Language. I find the Bishop of St Asaph's, Burgess, is the
busy man. There are six *judges*, the Masters of Westminster, Charter-
house, and St Paul's, for the Classics, Prince Hoare for the arts,
Taylor Combe for antiquities, and I fancy Payne Knight for literary
history, or some such description—but of the last I am not sure.

Davy has been giving dinners as P.R.S.—not better certainly nor pleasanter than he used to give before—and *Wednesday* evening parties; hitherto much inferior to the old Sundays, but time will show how they are attended—to me the distance will be rather more convenient of a cold night than Soho Square. I think he will be obliged to go back to Sunday.

I do not believe that you are much the older for anything that occurred when you were a boy: nor do I think that I should have been the worse *in health* if I had been less rigid in my regimen. It is well for me that I have not to live over again; I doubt if I should make so good a use of my time as mere accident has compelled me to do. Many things I could certainly mend, and spare myself both time and trouble: but on the whole, if I had done *very differently* from what I have, I dare say I should have repented *more* than I now do of *anything*—and this is a tolerable retrospect of 40 years of one's life. The youngest man that I know, I think is W. Spencer, whom I met the other day, looking about 40, and he is 56 at least—and recollecting perfectly the particulars of a conversation that he had with me 25 years ago at the old Duke of Richmond's, though we had never once met since, notwithstanding that we have both been living partly in the same society in London. Now if you were to compare notes with W. Spencer on the subject of my prophecy, I doubt whether he would allow my reasoning to be much better than that of other prophets. I have learned more or less perfectly a tolerable variety of things in this world: but there are two things that I have never yet learned, and I suppose I never shall—to get up and to go to bed. It is past 12, and literally Monday morning as I have dated my letter, but I must write for an hour longer.

In connection with the article 'Egypt' which Young prepared for the *Encyclopaedia Britannica*, he drew on material supplied from Belzoni's excavations at Thebes, and was much disappointed in Barrow's review, which implied that the book owed its existence to his diligence rather than his sagacity. Hence we find in a further letter to Gurney[1] Young's reactions to current opinion:

I am greatly dissatisfied with my own share in Barrow's panegyric, as well as with the omission of the abstract which was promised me of my own discoveries: you know how little I undervalue the

[1] 28 Dec. 1820.

praise of diligence, believing, as you are aware I do, that there is *little* else that distinguishes man from man: but surely something might have been said of *sagacity*, if not of *talent*, where the subject was such as to render mere *diligence* almost a negative merit, in a person who is pledged to the public to bestow his *labour* on other objects, whatever latitude he may claim for his *amusements*: besides the term *indefatigable* which he employs is exactly what a man may say of himself—and I dare say many people will believe that I wrote the whole or the greatest part of the article. But no matter, I know myself what he ought to have said, and that is the true satisfaction after all: I have derived more pleasure within these few days from a contemptuous hint of a great mathematician, which I can at once show to be unjust, and from an elaborate attempt to substitute a new theory for one of mine, which I can easily prove to be far less accurate, than I should probably have received from the most fulsome compliments—and literally, mihi plaudo Ipse domi, on the occurrence.

Young was always most concerned that full credit should go to the pioneer of original work, though he was equally ready to withdraw his own claims to priority if any doubt whatever existed. Thus in his paper on the survivorship of the younger of two given lives,[1] in his researches in Life Assurance, where later he found his ideas anticipated by Francis Baily, he withdrew most graciously.

From the autumn of 1820 to the end of his life he made his home in London and gave up his medical practice in Worthing. His many duties with the Royal Society, the Admiralty and the Board of Longitude made this move inevitable. He was a member of the Council of the Royal Society for twenty-five years and for the greater part of this time he was its foreign secretary. The duty of writing to those distinguished men of science of other lands who were honoured by the Royal Society electing them 'Foreign Members' devolved upon Young, and we gather from the correspondence how much pleasure he derived from it. In 1804, letters were sent to Gauss, Olbers, Piazzi and Baron Zach. Two years later the names of Prévost and Cuvier, among others, are to be found, but the

[1] *Works*, vol. II, p. 397.

occasion of March 1811 when Malus received the Royal Society Medal for distinguished work in Young's own field of double refraction gave him the greatest satisfaction. Similarly, in writing to Arago on 16 April 1818, he observes:

You will readily believe I feel a sincere pleasure in transmitting to you the diploma which certifies your election as Foreign Member of the Royal Society of London; for you well know that if there were any station more elevated to which distinguished merit in physical science would lead its professor, there is no one whom it could make me happier to see raised to it than yourself.

After referring to a note on the 'Dip' needle, then to his own appointment as a Commissioner of Longitude and to the work on the pendulum by Captain Kater, he continues:

Congratulate M. Dupin on his discovery of the steam engine and the hydraulic pressure inventions of the French. No doubt he will tell us in continuation of his remarks that we are indebted to the French for the progress that has been made in deciphering the Egyptian Hieroglyphics since the French certainly *first* discovered the Rosetta Stone.

In the next ten years the names of the following distinguished physicists appear among those elected as Foreign Members of the Royal Society: M. Poisson (1818), Fourier (1823), Fresnel (1825), Dulong and Ampère (1827) and Encke (1828). To all of them Young sent a letter of greetings and congratulations, pointing out those researches they had made which the Council of the Royal Society considered to be of greatest merit.

His first visit to France was during the uneasy Peace of Amiens in 1802, when he attended the Institute of France for the first time and it was on his return to England he was made foreign secretary of the Royal Society. After the close of the Napoleonic Wars he made two visits to Paris in 1817 and was delighted with his reception by the foremost scientists of France. It was not until 1821 that he found the leisure to carry out an ambitious tour of Europe and on this occasion he was accompanied by Mrs Young. Details of the journey are given in three letters dated 8 July, 8 September and 21 October from Novi, Florence and Brussels respectively. At a meeting of the Institute of Paris he met everybody he wanted to see, particularly von Humboldt, Laplace and Arago. Most of his time on tour was devoted to visiting the historic cities of Italy, ample reference in the correspondence being made to Rome (where the guide was an old Cambridge friend, Dodwell), Genoa, Naples, Pisa, Florence, Venice and Milan. He was not only able to revive his interest in the glories of Greece and Rome but he also found it possible to examine many of the Egyptian monuments preserved in Italy. He writes:

Pisa amply repaid us for taking this circuitous route; Leghorn, if possible, still more. But what you will be pleased to hear, is the discovery that I made of a bilingual stone among Drovetti's things, which promises to be an invaluable supplement to the Rosetta inscription as I dare say Drovetti is well aware. There are very few distinct hieroglyphic characters about the tablet, and the rings for the names of the king are left blank: but there are one or two well known personages of the Egyptian Pantheon whom I shall be glad to find named in Greek, and the blank names can be of little consequence as they must have been some of the dynasty of the Ptolemies, and I think there are some emblems of Ptolemy Philopator. Under the tablet are about 15 lines of the enchorial character, and about 32 in Greek, not at all distinctly legible, but nowhere totally effaced, so that I believe that with care every part of the inscription may be recovered.

I could not get leave to take a copy, the merchant having no authority to do anything beyond the safe custody of the collection. But he has consented that I should send an experienced artist from Florence to take two casts, or rather impressions of the stone, one or both of which I hope Drovetti will let me have for myself or for the Museum on fair terms: but if he does not, I have only stipulated that whenever the collection is embarked, the copies shall remain safe at Leghorn until it has arrived at the place of its destination without injury from shipwreck or other accidents; and I shall have the satisfaction of thinking that I have at least done something for the preservation of the second great treasure of Egyptian literature, which is so far of infinitely more consequence than the first, as I suppose there are no good copies of it yet in existence: and if the original were lost without a copy, we should lose the means of confirming or correcting and perhaps of greatly extending what the Rosetta Stone has already enabled us to establish.

At Florence I did hope to have felt myself completely at home and at ease, the most laborious part of our expedition having been performed, and the remainder leaving us an easy task in a temperate season and a frequented and interesting route. But unhappily we have found here such accounts of poor Mrs Maxwell's health as make it indispensable that we should hasten home to take our share in the attentions which she is entitled to receive from her family; and unless we get rather more favourable letters at Milan we shall certainly be in London this day six weeks, provided no unforeseen accident should detain us. I mean to adhere to my original route as far as Geneva, and then to give up Switzerland and the Rhine if it should be necessary, and to return by Dijon, Troyes and Lille. You have not forgotten your usual laziness, or I think you would have sent me a few lines to Rome or elsewhere, as I believe I humbly suggested in a letter from Novi. On the whole our expedition has been extremely prosperous and like most other things I have done in life I am very glad that I have done it, though I am by no means certain that I should have resolution to do it again: it seems like the last act of my boyhood and the first of my old age: on the one hand a sort of finish to my Latin and Greek, and on the other, a setting at defiance all professional conveniences in a way which may be deemed somewhat imprudent in a servant of the public. But I do not owe the public much, and I suppose I shall never be paid much of what the public owes me.

In the note asking for a cast of the Drovetti stone Young gave his reason that *he was the only living person who could fully appreciate its value*. Since Champollion did not make known his discoveries till the following year no charge can be advanced that Young was exceeding his claims. The application was without success till seven years later, when Young had almost decided to withdraw from further research on the hieroglyphics. By that time, too, many more inscriptions had been found, largely supplanting the Drovetti record.

The tour was brought to an end by the news from England that Mrs Young's mother was seriously ill, and she died before they returned. In the meantime Gurney had approached Sir Thomas Lawrence, one of the foremost painters of the day, to

w*

paint a portrait of Young. The introduction was made by the sculptor, Chantrey, and Young comments on the negotiations:[1]

I am told that Lawrence will certainly undertake it (the portrait), and even his beginning will be the greatest—or rather the only— personal honour that I have ever received; for which, as for sundry particulars, I shall not forget my obligations to you. I hope for the sake of *my friends and the public* that I shall not be blown up in the steam boat before this important affair is completed, and still more before I have made another attempt at Paris to aim another blow at Drovetti and his stone of Menouf.

The photograph which forms the frontispiece to this book is taken from an engraving by G. R. Ward of Lawrence's portrait. A second engraving is to be found as frontispiece to Young's *Egyptian Dictionary*, published in 1831. This was made by G. Adcock and shows a half-length portrait with Young seated and holding in his right hand a pair of spectacles.[2] Lawrence's portraits generally brought out the essential characteristics of those he painted, and Young's case is no exception. His fine open countenance displays his kindly disposition, while the depth of his forehead and the wide spacing of his eyes indicate his great intellectual gifts. Culture and refinement are to be seen in his thin nose and well-shaped mouth. His chin is of good proportions, suggesting strength of purpose and tenacity.

About this time he indicated to his friend Gurney, in a letter written on St Andrew's Day, that he would publish an octavo volume, under the title '*An Account of some recent discoveries in Egyptian Literature and Antiquities*, by Thomas Young, etc.'. His fame as an original worker in deciphering the hieroglyphics was known to all his friends both in Britain and on the Continent of Europe, and his persistence in publishing anonymously no longer served its original purpose. It was well known, too, that as long ago as 1817 he had been the inspiration behind the move to establish an Egyptian Society for the purpose of getting the public interested in the material available and the success so far achieved in interpreting it.[3] Peacock's

[1] Peacock, *op. cit.* p. 459.
[2] The original portrait is now in the possession of Mr Q. E. Gurney, T.D., Bawdeswell Hall, Norfolk.   [3] P. 224.

comments here are illuminating in showing how much the movement depended on Young's enthusiasm, and what eventually happened:[1]

A year or two afterwards (1819) this scheme was carried into effect. Dr Young became the Egyptian Society, without colleagues or assistant. The principal subscribers to it were Mr Gurney, Lord Mountmorris, Lord Aberdeen, Sir Joseph Banks, Sir William Rouse Boughton, Mr William Hamilton, Mr Marsden, Mr Taylor Combe, Mr George Ellis, Dr Butler, Mr Lloyd and Mr Drury of Harrow. Two fasciculi were published, containing about thirty plates, the last fasciculus of the two being devoted entirely to the Rosetta inscription, with a comparative index. The costs of the engravings, however, were found to exceed considerably the amount of the subscriptions—notwithstanding a large contribution from one of his friends—and the publication was on the point of being abandoned when it was proposed by some members of the Royal Society of Literature, which had recently been established and munificently endowed by the Prince Regent, that the Society should adopt it as their own. After some negotiations, Dr Young agreed to the proposal, and continued, as before, to edit the work, being allowed to exercise his own discretion with respect to documents which should be engraved.

He was again able to pay a brief visit to Belgium and Holland in 1824, where the distressing conditions of the poorer classes in the towns reminded him of the similar conditions in industrial England: 'The poor are wretchedly poor—not, as it seems from want of civilisation, but from the excess of it at the moment, the introduction of machinery having thrown thousands out of employment.'

Probably his removal from the house in Welbeck Street to a more roomy one in Park Square gave him the greatest pleasure of his declining years:

Here he led the life of a philosopher, surrounded by every domestic comfort, and enjoying the pleasures of an extensive and cultivated society, who knew how to appreciate him. He expressed himself as having now attained all the main objects which he had looked forward to in life, as the subject either of his hopes or his wishes.

[1] Peacock, *op. cit.* p. 451.

This end being, to use his own words, 'the pursuit of such fame as he valued, or of such acquirements as he might think to deserve it.'[1]

Equally pleasurable was his election, on 6 August 1827, as Foreign Member of the Academy of Science, at Paris. There were eight foreign associates of this distinguished body of scientists, and Young was elected in the place of Volta (1745–1827). According to Peacock, the other competitors were the great astronomers Bessel and Olbers, Robert Brown the botanist, Semmering the anatomist, Blumenbach the naturalist, Leopold von Buck the geologist, Dalton the chemist and Plana the mathematician. His contemporaries, Wollaston and Davy, had already been elected; both were members of the Council of the Royal Society, Davy being its President. But already Davy's health was poor and, in an endeavour to restore it, he was advised to live in Italy. The move necessitated his resignation from the Presidency of the Royal Society. It was customary for the President to entertain members to dinners at regular intervals, so that the office involved considerable expense. Various names of wealthy men were considered, but naturally there was some criticism from those who wished to change the system by electing the best man, irrespective of his income. In this connection Young received support, for in writing to his sister-in-law, Mrs Earle, who was on holiday in Italy, he says: 'I find there has been pretty general conversation about making *ME* President of the Royal Society, and I really think if I were foolish enough to wish for the office, I am at this *moment* popular enough to obtain it; but you well know that nothing is farther from my wishes.'

On St Andrew's Day, 1827, the choice of Davies Gilbert was made; he had held the office of Treasurer, and from the time of Davy's resignation had been temporary President. A year later Wollaston made a gift to the Royal Society to encourage experimental research. His action stimulated others, including the President himself. Young's comments on the meeting bring out two points—first, his reticence, and secondly, his estimation of his own achievements. He is writing to his old friend Gurney

[1] Hudson Gurney, Memoir, pp. 37–8.

on 7 December 1828 and later on 17 December, and says:

When Gilbert had announced his benefaction, Amyot said he had never heard me make a speech, and I summoned up courage to take the first opportunity of muttering out, 'Mr President! A gentleman on my right observes that he never heard me make a speech. Now, Sir, I cannot help remarking of you and your magnificent donation, 'Tu mutis quoque piscibus Donatura cygni, si libeat, sonum.' And as I am accidentally the senior officer of the Society, though by no means in the highest rank, I take the liberty of thanking you and Dr Wollaston in the name of the Society for your princely liberality, and for the example you have set of the way in which Science ought to be encouraged in this country, not by tormenting the Government to do this, that and the other for us, but by doing what is wanted for ourselves, which is the truly dignified character of an independent English Gentleman.' If I had wished to be applauded the plot was well laid, as I was unavoidably a sharer in the 'tremendous' noise that was made for Wollaston and Gilbert. Wollaston is said to be sinking almost daily. I was in his house this morning, but I did not see him.

Young then refers to the progress he has made with his Egyptian Dictionary, stating that such a volume will ensure a permanent record of his original work in this field of study. (p. 248). He continues the letter:

On recollection you must mean that my friend South does not overrate *me* when he proposes that the Society at large should supersede me in the appointment of Foreign Secretary which has hitherto been a '*job*' of the President and Council and should make Mr Ivory my successor, whose qualifications are a total ignorance of all foreign languages, and a disposition to quarrel with all persons of merit, almost as great as that of Mr South himself.

I thought you must have seen in the papers that Wollaston had made over £2,000 stock to Trustees for the Royal Society after his death, as the beginning of a *donation fund* for paying the expenses of experiments to be made from time to time by direction of the Royal Society and that Gilbert had added another £1,000. Warburton gave 100 guineas—and it seems a begging letter is to go round I suppose to stand in stead of the Board of Longitude: and this I think spoils all the comparative magnificence of the present as far as related to Wollaston: but I said I thought in such a case his wish should be over law.

For myself it is my pride and pleasure as far as I am able to supersede the necessity of experiments and especially of expensive ones. I have just been inventing a mode of determining the figure of the earth from two points in sight of each other, without going either to Lapland or to Peru,[1] and this must stand instead of my contribution to the Donation Fund: for if I save expense I do more than if I paid it.

Young was anxious to preserve that freedom for science which he considered essential for its true development. He wanted it to be independent of private or Government patronage. This explains his unequivocal attitude in refusing to extend the *Nautical Almanac*. If the Government 'paid the bill' he knew it would 'have to call the tune', and he preferred a *laissez-faire* policy, trusting to leave things as they were. The benefits from science due to the progress of arts and natural philosophy would automatically raise the standard of living, but he was sufficiently well schooled in liberal principles to oppose any direction from above. Later in the century, and above all in our day, we have seen a complete reversal of such a policy, to the great material benefit of the nation. No individuals, however wealthy and public-spirited, could give that incentive to research which we have seen given by Governments during the last twenty years, although a great curtailment in freedom has been inevitable, a result which is unfortunate and to be deplored.

Early in January 1829 Young's health began to fail, the first symptoms being repeated attacks of asthma and general weakness. Nevertheless he continued his attendance at the Council Meetings of the Royal Society up to 26 March; he also persevered with his *Rudiments of an Egyptian Dictionary*, and, as will be recalled, bore the brunt of the attacks of Baily and South on the reform of the *Nautical Almanac*.

He lingered on through April and died on 10 May. The post-mortem examination carried out by his doctors revealed

---

[1] The paper, entitled 'Determination of the Figure of the Earth from a single tangent', was never published by Young. It was found among his papers after his death, and now forms Appendix B in Peacock's *Life of Young*.

an ossification of the aorta extending to the heart, the appearance being that of a completely worn-out man. This disease, which must have been caused by his incessant labour, usually assails a subject at a much later age than 56. Gurney observes in his diary that this probably 'accounted for the position in which he had the habit of walking, when unobserved, with his hands behind him'. He was buried at Farnborough in Kent on 16 May, in the family vault of the Maxwells.

It was during Young's last illness that much of his sound character was shown. He was mindful to a degree of the feelings of others, and in spite of severe provocation from South and Baily his last wish was that nothing should be published from his notes that might prove hurtful to the feelings of others. In spite of such great weakness that he could not hold a pen he continued with a pencil the last few notes on his *Egyptian Dictionary*, which effort he said was a great amusement to him— that 'he had set his mind on completing it—that if he got round, it was a work he should have great pleasure in having finished, and if this disease cut short his days, it was satisfaction to him never to have been idle through life'.

Young had prepared a short autobiography, which was given to Gurney and formed the material of the Memoir preceding the *Egyptian Dictionary*. Gurney visited Mrs Young on 23 May to discuss the project. He brought with him an accohnt of Young's life up to the time of his first residence in London. She then took the opportunity of recalling Young's attitude towards religion, indicating how his Quaker upbringing had strongly influenced his religious practices (p. 56).

It is from such references by those near and dear to him that we get a true glimpse of his character. He enjoyed to the full the good things of life, being fond of dancing, riding and those pleasures obtained by moving in cultured society. He was quite a good conversationalist and could take his part as an accompanist or singer. Considering his breadth of knowledge and his originality, he showed no signs of the eccentricities sometimes accompanying genius, but he always had a great belief in his own powers. A decisive factor in preserving the normal temperament he displayed was the happiness of his marriage. We do not find many references to Mrs Young apart from Young's correspondence with Gurney. She came of a cultivated and aristocratic family, a branch of the Maxwells of Caldrewood Castle, Lanarkshire. A woman of sound common sense, she esteemed and understood her husband and shared his interests. She was also very friendly with the Gurneys and relied on them in tidying up Young's affairs after his death.

Davies Gilbert in his valedictory address on Young to the Royal Society states:

Young came into the world with a confidence in his own talents growing out of an expectation of excellence entertained in common by all his friends, which expectation was more than realised in the progress of his future life. The multiplied objects which he pursued were carried to such an extent that each might have been supposed to have exclusively occupied the full powers of his mind; knowledge in the abstract, the most enlarged generalisations, and the most minute and intricate details were equally affected by him, but he had most pleasure in that which appeared to be most difficult of investigation. . . . The example is only to be followed by those of equal capacity and equal perseverance; and rather recommends the concentration of research within the limits of some defined portion of science, than the endeavour to embrace the whole.

Young's own opinion was:[1]

That it was probably not advantageous to mankind that researches of some inquirers should be concentrated within a given compass, but that others should pass more rapidly through a wider range— that the faculties of the mind were more exercised and probably rendered stronger by going beyond the rudiments, and overcoming the great elementary difficulties, of a variety of studies, than by employing the same number of hours in one pursuit—that the doctrine of the division of labour, however applicable to the material product was not so to intellect, and that it went to reduce the dignity of man in the scale of rational existences. He thought it so impossible to foresee the capabilities of the improvement in any science, so much of accident having led to the most important discoveries, that no man could say what might be the comparative

[1] Peacock, *op. cit.* pp. 482–3.

advantage of any one study over another; and though he would scarcely have recommended the plan of his own as a model of those of others, he was still satisfied in the course which he had pursued.

Young aimed at the truth, the whole truth, and nothing but the truth. No exaggeration or high colouring in conversation or writing could he tolerate. Undoubtedly his methods of publishing his discoveries in a wide variety of journals, often anonymously, prevented his contemporaries from obtaining a correct appraisement of his qualities and abilities.

It was Mrs Young's wish to place an appropriate monument to her husband in Westminster Abbey, and eventually a profile medallion was placed there, with an inscription on a slab beneath it. The inscription, which was written by Gurney, reads thus:

SACRED TO THE MEMORY OF

THOMAS YOUNG, M.D.,

FELLOW AND FOREIGN SECRETARY OF THE ROYAL SOCIETY,
MEMBER OF THE NATIONAL INSTITUTE OF FRANCE;
A MAN ALIKE EMINENT
IN ALMOST EVERY DEPARTMENT OF HUMAN LEARNING
PATIENT OF UNINTERMITTED LABOUR,
ENDOWED WITH THE FACULTY OF INTUITIVE PERCEPTION,
WHO, BRINGING AN EQUAL MASTERY
TO THE MOST ABSTRUSE INVESTIGATIONS
OF LETTERS AND SCIENCE,
FIRST ESTABLISHED THE UNDULATORY THEORY OF LIGHT,
AND FIRST PENETRATED THE OBSCURITY
WHICH HAD VEILED FOR AGES
THE HIEROGLYPHICS OF EGYPT.

ENDEARED TO HIS FRIENDS BY HIS DOMESTIC VIRTUES,
HONOURED BY THE WORLD FOR HIS UNRIVALLED
ACQUIREMENTS, HE DIED IN THE HOPES OF THE
RESURRECTION OF THE JUST,

———

BORN AT MILVERTON, IN SOMERSETSHIRE, JUNE 13th, 1773,
DIED IN PARK SQUARE, LONDON, MAY 10th, 1829,
IN THE 56th YEAR OF HIS AGE.

APPENDIX I

ARTICLE FOR THE 'ENCYCLOPAEDIA BRITANNICA' ON
'DOUBLE REFRACTION'

THE good offices of Arago as a contributor to the *Encyclopaedia Britannica* had been enlisted by Leslie, acting on behalf of Napier, before Young came into the picture at all. The summary of subsequent correspondence about the article on Double Refraction is as follows:

2 Sept. 22: Napier to Young, asking him to see Arago while he is in Paris and to get him to expedite his promised article.

28 Sept. 22:[1] Arago to Young. Regrets missing Young while he was in Paris and explains that he had been asked for an article on Light and that the volume containing it had appeared while he was actually at work. He had considered himself discharged but was asked for an article on Polarization within a month. He had replied that this was impossible but that he would do an article on Refraction (Double), otherwise he would cancel the arrangement. To this he had no reply.

30 Sept. 22:[2] Young to Napier. Passes on information about Arago and says that he resents the limits of space imposed on him. 'With regard to the limit I shall probably be able to persuade him that three sheets will be amply sufficient; and if he is too much engaged to undertake it willingly there is a young friend of his and mine, Mr Fresnel, who is as well acquainted with the phenomena of polarization as either of us and who has just published a very candid and luminous article to the theory of light in a supplement to Thomson's Chemistry which has appeared here. I shall take the liberty of making an arrangement between Arago, him and myself in such a manner as to accommodate you according to your wishes but Fresnel, as well as Arago, is particularly engaged for a few weeks.'

8 Oct. 22:[3] Napier to Young. Says that Refraction will be reached almost at once and invites Young to do the article himself.

[1] MS. Correspondence of Thomas Young, Royal Society Library.
[2] Brit. Mus. Add. MSS. 34613, f. 104.
[3] *Ibid.* f. 108.

18 Nov. 22:[1] Young to Fresnel. Has written to Arago a month ago but Arago has not deigned to reply. He suggests that in view of the urgency of the matter Fresnel should get a definite reply from Arago about the article, and if he should refuse should at once begin himself a summary of the facts similar to that given by him in Thomson's *Chemistry*, but not showing too much the partiality which he and Young both entertain for the wave theory. 'I will translate the article and will acknowledge it jointly with you unless Arago is prepared to co-operate.'

11 Dec. 22:[2] Napier to Young. All the MSS for the half-volume are now in hand except that of Arago. Begs Young to begin the article at once unless sure of Arago.

12 Dec. 22:[3] Arago to Young. 'It is said (in your letter) that I did not *deign* to reply to your last letter. This word deign appears to me, I confess, singular from your pen, above all when it is remembered that it is addressed to one who has publicly, without reserve and in all circumstances professed the frankest admiration for your work and for your character. I might have flattered myself that the translation was an inexact one of an English word not fully understood; but even this escape is denied me: the letter in which the word occurs is written in French. I must therefore resign myself and try to explain that I am less to blame than has been supposed.'

He continues with a display of irritation against Napier, who never gives him time enough for anything, and wishes he had never heard of the article. Finally he makes an offer to go ahead without promising a date, to work to the space allotted by Napier, to leave Young to prune the article to the exact length and to finish it with tables of figures to make this easier. Napier can then go on printing subsequent articles. If this proposal is accepted he will start at once— if not he will wash his hands of the whole thing. It is a big job and Fresnel, having no languages, cannot help.

27 March 23:[4] Fresnel to Young. 'When you wrote to me (18 Nov. 1822) about the article on the polarization of light which M. Arago had undertaken to write, I informed him at once of what you asked of me, and, having learned that he had already written to you, I thought it useless to inform you that I had carried out your

[1] J. A. Fresnel, *Oeuvres Complètes*, vol. II, p. 759.
[2] Brit. Mus. Add. MSS. 34613, f. 119.
[3] MS. Correspondence of Thomas Young.
[4] Fresnel, *op. cit.* vol. II, p. 762.

commission. On his return from Metz, he told me that he would be glad to take advantage of the offer I had made him to assist in this work. I again assured him that I would start work immediately he suggested it, while at the same time I should be glad if he could dispense with my help. Up till now he has not put my willingness to the test and I hope that he will have no need to do so.'

27 April 23:[1] Napier to Young. Presses again for news of Arago's article.

30 April 23:[2] Young to Napier. Believes that Arago is working on it.

6 May 23:[3] Napier to Young. Distressed about Arago.

26 Oct. 23:[4] Napier to Young. Complains bitterly at Arago's behaviour. He has conceded all that Arago has asked but has had no word from him. He hopes that Young will himself fill the gap if necessary.

28 Nov. 23:[5] Napier to Young. Bitter attack on Arago. 'In one word, I neither will, nor can, nor ought tho' I could, wait one day for him, and indeed, having long seen that he is either utterly ignorant of business or utterly indifferent to what he promises in literary contracts, I have admitted some articles which I had intended to exclude to make room for the three sheets allotted to him. I would have been in a fine scrape if, trusting to Arago, I had made the half volume three sheets short of its complement. Now my dear Sir, I trust you will not desert me in this situation in which I placed myself indeed in the confidence that you would do something if your friend failed. You must forthwith set about a short article for which you have partly prepared the way in your valuable one on Chromatics. It would never do, after so many references, to omit the subject, independently of its being necessary to have something about it from its utter novelty. I give you my word of honour that I shall be printed off about the end of January, and that it is wholly out of my power to defer the publication longer than will be necessary to print such article as you can send me. . . . I shall say no more, but trust to hear that you have begun. It will be one of the greatest services you have done in the work in near nine years of most valuable service.'

---

[1] Brit. Mus. Add. MSS. 34613, f. 137.   [2] *Ibid.* f. 139.   [3] *Ibid.* f. 144.
[4] *Ibid.* f. 200.   [5] *Ibid.* f. 215.

24 Dec. 23:[1] Arago to Young (reply to letter not preserved). Young's letter has been translated by Mme Arago and she has assured her husband that his seeming misdeeds have almost cost him Young's friendship. He is full of excuses—Government business, etc. Finally he asks for a paper just published by Brewster on the subject.

This letter was at once dispatched to Napier and on the back of it Young has written: 'I regret that I could not possibly do anything original for you at present on polarization. I have not sufficiently studied crystallography and mineralogy to make it easy for me to recollect all the necessary distinctions so that I could much more readily have given you an Essay on Scotch Law, which I have never studied, or on the game of Whist, which I do not play, than on Polarization of which I should be expected to know at least everything that has been published. But there would have been the greater difficulty. I could not have done it without giving Arago, after all his faults, some cause of offence. I have therefore nothing left but to urge him to hasten and to shorten his article and even to send me his rough memorandums if he has not time to copy them. I shall take care to send him the books mentioned if they are to be had.'

17 Jan. 24:[2] Arago to Young (presumably in reply to a letter not preserved). Sends further apologies. Has been awaiting Brewster's article and two days after receiving this will send his MS.

10 Feb. 24:[3] Arago to Young. Sends first section of article without apologies or explanation. Young sent this on to Napier and on it wrote: 'I shall probably send you the translation by Monday's post, or Tuesday's at furthest, and if I get the rest in the course of the week your three weeks will not be expired before you receive it.'

8 March 24 (postmark):[4] Arago to Young. Replies to a letter from Young in a distinctly frivolous strain, by no means justifying Young's assurances to Napier. He expresses pleasure at seeing Young's handwriting and quotes from an English paper (not named) as follows:

'Hieroglyphics appear destined to bring misfortune to the learned men who study them. Mr Spohn has only just died in Germany when a short illness has carried off our celebrated Dr Young.' He continues: 'We had only just received this desolating news when

---

[1] *Ibid.* f. 211.   [2] MS. Correspondence of Thomas Young.
[3] Brit. Mus. Add. MSS. 34613, f. 229.
[4] MS. Correspondence of Thomas Young.

M. de Humboldt and I searched the city to discover among your compatriots what foundation it could have. It seemed to me impossible that you could have left this world incognito; that all the best accredited journals should not be filled with lamentations on a disaster so great and so unexpected. These considerations reassured me sufficiently to refrain from a reference at the Academy, of which I am now President, to the sad announcement which your detestable journal had inserted. I admit, however, that I was not insensible to the *material* proof of its falsity supplied by your letter.'

He goes on to promise the final sheets in three or four days.

23 March 24:[1] Young to Napier (evidently in reply to a letter in which the difficulties of the publishers were mentioned). 'You have rightly construed my silence. I have heard once from Arago since I wrote to you. His letter contained some very insufficient reasons for delay, with a promise that he would send me the continuation in three or four days. A week has now elapsed without anything. I cannot help believing that he will send me more matter by Monday or Tuesday.

'The publishers must do as they please. My advice would be to wait, even if it were a month. I will write by the next post to tell Arago the contents of your letter and will beg him to send me, without a moment's delay, whatever memorandums he may have made. . . . In the meantime I have no doubt at all, with all my knowledge of Arago, that he will have sent off *something* before he gets my letters.'

23 March 24:[2] Napier to Young. Young must *promise* to complete the article forthwith. If so, the publishers will wait till April 5 or 6. The answer must be 'in course and decisive.'

30 March 24:[3] Young to Napier. 'I have acted to the best of my judgment and ability between the proprietors and Mr Arago and I am still willing to do all that can be expected from me or from any man so circumstanced, but I cannot and *will not* undertake that you shall have the article finished in any way by next Monday. The proprietors must publish the work when and as they please. I shall not condemn them and they cannot with justice complain of me, nor, I apprehend, of you.' He cannot do the article as well as Arago can and has written to Arago telling him that he 'cannot wait a moment.'

[1] Brit. Mus. Add. MSS. 34613, f. 213.
[2] *Ibid.* f. 233.
[3] *Ibid.* f. 235.

2 April 24: Arago to Young. An indignant protest. He had just finished the article and now it seems the volume is being published without waiting for the completion. He complains that he was given no *final* date and suspects that the whole incident is due to Brewster. If so, Brewster may congratulate himself as Arago in the historical part 'divests him of a great number of the plumes with which he had decked himself in the eyes of his compatriots.' He sends no MS. and asks that no part of his article should be published.

3 April 24:[1] Napier to Young. Describes his 'disagreeable negotiations' with the publishers. This has been the 'most disagreeable job of the whole work'. Copies are now being printed off without the article and with a notice that it will be distributed separately when ready. If it arrives in time it will be bound up with the later copies. April 10 is set as the target date.

3 May 24:[2] Young to Napier. Has written a *scolding* letter to Arago.

12 May 24:[3] Napier to Young. A very strong, but on the whole restrained, letter. He reports that all sales have stopped with the discovery that the volume is incomplete, and that there is a general demand either to furnish the article or take back the books. Further delay of two or three weeks will have consequences of the most distressing description. 'There is no other course to save the book but your writing the article.'

22 May 24:[4] Arago to Young. Promises to return to the 'accursed article', to copy what is written, and to finish the rest and send it to Young without delay.

28 May 24:[5] Napier to Young. The want of the article on Polarization is every day felt in the most distressing manner. He hopes Young will forthwith set about completing the article himself.

3 July 24:[6] Napier to Young. He makes a really firm attempt to place responsibility on Young and denounces Arago. 'I deceive myself much if the earlier letters which I had the pleasure of receiving from you in regard to this unfortunate article, did not authorize me to conclude not only that you *could* yourself write on Polarization, but that you *would* do so if Arago failed.'

---

[1] Brit. Mus. Add. MSS. 34613, f. 237.   [2] *Ibid.* f. 243.
[3] *Ibid.* f. 249.   [4] MS. Correspondence of Thomas Young.
[5] Brit. Mus. Add. MSS. 34613, f. 254.   [6] *Ibid.* f. 269.

6 Aug. 24:[1] Napier to Young. He reproaches Young for his continued silence and again holds him responsible. 'Though you have not condescended to favour me with a single line in answer to a very pressing letter written a month ago, I am very willing to believe that you may have had, what you conceived, good reasons for your silence. Be they however what they may, I trust you will write me on receipt of this. I know well that you became involved in the trouble connected with M. Arago's article from a desire to serve the book and to serve me, and it is very painful to me to be obliged to write to you at all upon this subject. At the same time, as you are aware, I never would have engaged with him in any shape, but under a sort of guarantee that if he failed you would supply his place. I do conceive that I am not at any rate guilty of any impertinent intrusion, in applying to you under the painful circumstances in which his conduct has placed me. You do not know and do not, I think, readily apprehend the nature of these circumstances, otherwise you could not possibly have left me exposed to them, without a word from you, for a month. Not a set of the book will sell—every post brings bitter complaints from every quarter—and I am threatened with being made responsible, by legal measures, for large pecuniary loss owing to the want of this accursed article. When I have said this I surely need say not more to induce you at least to inform me what you are to do.'

Presumably Young replied to this letter, but if so the letter has not survived. The next link in the correspondence is a letter in which Young unburdens himself to Fresnel.

14 Oct. 24:[2] Young to Fresnel. 'It is with the greatest possible pain that I find myself abandoned, in the most painful circumstances, by our confrère M. Arago whom I have always regarded as one of my best friends, and on whose friendship I have always prided myself both publicly and privately. You know my strong desire that the article in the Supplement of the Encyclopaedia Britannica might be the joint work of M. Arago, yourself and me. M. Arago has expected to be able to complete it without troubling you:—at present it would be both useless and unjust to ask you to take any responsibility. I expect that the article will appear anonymously and will attempt to develop the precious fragment already received from M. Arago; the facts will be drawn for the most part from the article Optics in the Encyclopaedia written by M. Brewster, and

[1] Brit. Mus. Add. MSS. f. 276.   [2] Fresnel, *Oeuvres Complètes*, vol. II, p. 765.

I know well that M. Arago wishes to challenge some of the dates claimed by M. Brewster in favour of his compatriots.

'But if you could send me, in a week or ten days, some notes on the history of this subject to which you have contributed so much, or some notes on your experiments or your theories which have some bearing on the subject, you would infinitely oblige me and I would take care that the author of the continuation of the article would do you justice as well as M. Arago and all those who would have reason to complain of M. Brewster's article.'

16 Oct. 24:[1] Fresnel to Young. Regrets he cannot do anything at present. Could do something about the Optical phenomena after a fortnight, but could not complete it in less than a month. He cannot help with the history as he cannot read English and has no time even to read the French.

9 Nov. 24: Young to Napier. 'You recollect that no news was to be good news of Arago's proceedings and that his promise to be ready by the 15th is still in force, though I have not heard from him since the lettter I sent you. I have been prepared these ten days for writing the copy of my continuation: but expecting as I still do to hear from Arago every day, I cannot have the heart to finish up till the last moment what I am confident will never be required. . . . I have, however, written this day also to Arago to mention the circumstances to him, and to remind him that the time will be expired if he has not his packet ready to send me by return of post. The moment that I hear anything good or bad I will let you know.'

17 Nov. 24:[2] Young to Fresnel. Gladly accepts his offer. The abstract of his theoretical ideas will come in as part of the mosaic which Young will have to substitute for a better-constructed piece of work. 'Arago has given me the beginning and the fundamental facts in considerable detail. I still hope that he will provide me with a history of the discoveries; and I shall add what I have already tried to do to provide a theoretical illustration of the phenomena with some new ideas which I have recently thought of and in combining this with the contribution I am entitled to expect from your ideas I do not doubt that I shall meet passably the exigency of the occasion. Do your best for me then; perhaps it will be better not to inform M. Arago in case he considers himself discharged from pursuing what he has undertaken.'

[1] *Ibid.* p. 766. [2] *Ibid.* p. 767.

26 Nov. 24:[1] Arago to Young. Hopes to send the end of this 'everlasting' article before November 29 but is much pressed by other business.

26 Nov. 24:[2] Fresnel to Young. Delay in reply due to serious illness making impossible even the slightest effort. Realizes that his health necessitates immediate and complete rest. 'It is with regret that I see the impossibility of writing the note asked for. Yet why should I regret not being able to write for an English Publication?'
Then follows the protest about British neglect of French scientists given on p. 199. The letter concludes: 'I shall not speak to M. Arago of your second letter. I mentioned the first, he was surprised that you had asked me for my *theoretical* ideas as you had asked *him* to exclude all that savoured of hypothesis. He goes to Metz in a few days (on government business) and hopes to do the article in his evenings.'

24 Dec. 24:[3] Arago to Young. On his arrival home from Metz he found letter from Young. Hastens to assure him that short of illness he will receive the last lines of the article in seven or eight days.

19 Jan. 25:[4] Fresnel to Young. Has had a severe illness and still must avoid all strain. Arrears of essential work must take precedence. Has begun work on his contribution. Had delayed reply until he could say this.

24 Jan. 25 (postmark):[5] Arago to Young. Encloses the historical note which concludes his article.

13 April 25:[6] Napier to Young. Encloses £68 fee for article on Polarization—to be divided between author and translator. Loss to proprietors so great that they are in no humour to be liberal.

4 Sept. 25:[7] Fresnel to Young. Encloses his contribution, but of course, too late.

[1] MS. Correspondence of Thomas Young.
[2] Fresnel, *op. cit.* p. 768.
[3] MS. Correspondence of Thomas Young.
[4] Fresnel, *op. cit.* p. 772.
[5] MS. Correspondence of Thomas Young.
[6] Brit. Mus. Add. MSS. 34613, f. 293.
[7] Fresnel, *op. cit.* p. 776.

APPENDIX II

THOMAS YOUNG AS A CIVIL SERVANT

I am indebted to Mr Edmund Dews, of Jesus College, Oxford, for the following notes on Thomas Young as a Civil Servant.
—F.O.

A study of the Longitude Papers in the library of the Royal Greenwich Observatory makes it clear that Thomas Young's achievements as a civil servant have never been fairly assessed, because overshadowed by the *Nautical Almanac* controversy. To place this controversy in proper perspective it is necessary to understand the nature of Young's relations with the Board of Longitude, of which he was Secretary.

The Board was a minor department of state, informally presided over by the First Lord or one of the Secretaries of the Admiralty, or in their absence usually by the President of the Royal Society. In addition to the Astronomer Royal, it had, before 1818, consisted mainly of lay members—who seldom attended—and five university professors, who received an allowance for coming to London to the three or four meetings each year. For a third of a century the leading members had been Sir Joseph Banks, the President of the Royal Society, and Nevil Maskelyne, the Astronomer Royal. Under these men the Board had progressed far toward becoming, almost in a modern sense, a general-purpose research department for the Admiralty, although it was still mainly concerned with the support of research in the physical sciences related to navigation. For a time the Board enjoyed a high reputation among men of science, on the continent as well as in Britain; but after the partial withdrawal of Sir Joseph Banks in 1806 and the death of Maskelyne in 1811, the leadership of the Board failed, and it fell into inefficiency and decay. John Pond, Maskelyne's successor as Astronomer Royal, was an excellent practical observer, but he lacked Maskelyne's administrative talents, and was inadequate to perform Maskelyne's duties as treasurer of the Board and editor of the *Nautical Almanac*. When members of Maskelyne's team of *Almanac* computers and comparers retired, Pond failed to establish a competent new team working to a proper system. Mistakes in the *Almanac* became too frequent, and Pond's accounts for the Board were hopelessly muddled. The situation eventually became known to the House of Commons, which reformed the Board by the Longitude Act of 1818.[1]

The plan of this legislation was to strengthen the Board by professionalizing it. The non-scientific membership was reduced, the representation of the Royal Society was increased, and provision was made for three scientific civil servants—members of the Board—to be resident in London and paid an annual salary. In addition three scientific-administrative posts were created, intended if possible to be held by the same person: these were the posts of Secretary of the Board, Superintendent of the *Nautical Almanac*, and Keeper of Chronometers. The most important of these was the Secretary of the Board.[2]

Young is not known to have had any connection with the Board before 1818, and his first formal association with it was his nomination by the Longitude Act to be one of the resident commissioners. He was never to serve in this capacity, however, for just before the first meeting of the reformed Board, he was appointed Secretary and Superintendent.[3] Young was therefore in a key position to achieve the desired reforms in the operation of the Board, and the success which was achieved must be credited to him. As Secretary he provided direction and method which the Board needed, brought order into its accounts and correspondence, and transacted its business in a way which has never received the praise it deserves.

As Superintendent of the *Nautical Almanac*, however, Young was in a more subordinate position. The statute provided that the Superintendent should do his work 'under the direction of the Board in general, and the Astronomer Royal in particular'. Criticisms of Young's policy for the *Nautical Almanac* mainly, and it may be intentionally, ignored the implications of this provision.

---

[1] 58 George III, c. 20.

[2] There had been a Secretary since 1762, but the responsibilities of the office were increased by the Act of 1818 and subsequent Orders in Council.

[3] The combined salaries of the two posts amounted to £400 a year, while the salary of a resident commissioner was £100 a year. It is not clear whether Young was offered the care of chronometers, but he never held the post, and it was later assigned to the Astronomer Royal (who still has it today), by Admiralty letter of 23 July, 1821.

Nowadays the point is likely to be better understood, and a civil servant should not often be exposed to such attacks as Young suffered for carrying out a policy approved by those to whom he was responsible. In fact the support and authority of the Board probably did sustain Young, and may explain why he troubled little in his own defence until the Board itself was in danger.

Since doubts have sometimes been raised about the competence of the Board, it will be useful to examine the following table of scientific members for the years 1818-28. The positions held by the members are shown, followed by the dates of their service with the Board.

SCIENTIFIC MEMBERS OF THE BOARD OF LONGITUDE 1818-28[1]

(Secretary: Thomas Young)

George Biddell Airy (Lucasian Professor of Mathematics, Cambridge), 1827-8.

Sir Joseph Banks (President of the Royal Society), 1818-20.

Thomas Colby (Resident Commissioner), 1821-8.

Sir Humphry Davy (President of the Royal Society), 1821-6.

Davies Gilbert (Royal Society Commissioner, later President of the Royal Society), 1818-28.

J. F. W. Herschel (Resident Commissioner), 1821-8.

Henry Kater (Resident Commissioner), 1818-28.

William Lax (Lowndean Professor of Mathematics, Cambridge), 1818-28.

Isaac Milner (Lucasian Professor of Mathematics, Cambridge), 1818-20.

William Mudge (Resident Commissioner), 1818-20.

John Pond (Astronomer Royal), 1818-28.

Baden Powell (Savilian Professor of Geometry, later of Astronomy, Oxford), 1818-28.

Abraham Robertson (Savilian Professor of Astronomy, Oxford), 1818-26.

Thomas Turton (Lucasian Professor of Mathematics, Cambridge), 1822-6.

[1] This list is based on the minute books of the Board. It may be compared with the rather misleading list for 1822 given in the *History of the Royal Astronomical Society* and reproduced above, p. 308. No attempt has been made to list here the non-scientific members, since these were always few, and only the two Secretaries of the Admiralty, Sir John Barrow and J. W. Croker, regularly attended.

Samuel Vince (Plumian Professor of Astronomy, Cambridge), 1818-20.

William Hyde Wollaston (Resident Commissioner, later Royal Society Commissioner), 1818-28.

Robert Woodhouse (Royal Society Commissioner, later Lucasian Professor of Mathematics, and afterwards Plumian Professor of Astronomy, Cambridge), 1819-27.

These were the men who were ultimately responsible for the form and contents of the *Nautical Almanac*. It would have been difficult in these years to select another group equally eminent in their field. It has been suggested, however, that whatever were the qualifications of individuals, the Board itself was lax and indolent, and the professional members seldom at its meetings. The records of the Board easily refute these charges. There was in fact so little ground for such assertions that it is difficult to understand how well-informed men of science such as South and Baily could really believe them. The professors were well paid for attendance and were faithful in attending the regular quarterly meetings of the Board. In the four years 1822-5, for example, Lax, Rigaud, Woodhouse and Turton were not once absent. As for the Board's general responsibility for the *Nautical Almanac*, so far from ignoring it, the Board exercised a frequent and sometimes minute supervision over Young's work as Superintendent. The reforms proposed for the *Almanac* (for the benefit of astronomers) were repeatedly brought to the Board's attention, particularly by several of its members who belonged to the Royal Astronomical Society. The arguments for changes were fully discussed, and Young's conservative position (based on the needs of seamen) consistently received the support of the Board, although a large number of minor improvements were made, many of them with Young's approval or on his own initiative. It is interesting to note that when the American *Ephemeris* was first published in 1852, it followed the distinction insisted upon by Young, and appeared in two editions, one for the use of seamen, the other for astronomers.[1]

The charges of inaccuracy are on a different footing. The actual work of computing the *Almanac* was largely a routine business,

[1] Prof. F. B. Potter, Chairman of the Naval History Committee of the United States Naval Academy, informs me that this course was decided upon at the time because American seamen preferred to use *abridged* versions of the British *Nautical Almanac*.

depending upon careful organization and good judgment rather than profound astronomical knowledge. It required a man of first-rate ability, but there was no question that the organization of the calculations was within Young's capacity. The measures he took to restore accuracy were well suited to the purpose, and in a few years produced good results. Young could not, of course, bring a new system into full operation immediately; still less could he undo all the imperfections in the work of Pond, which, performed several years in advance of publication, continued to blight the Almanacs to 1822 or 1823. Although provided with so good an excuse, Young could not gracefully plead it in personal defence, for Pond was still Astronomer Royal.

In any case it must be doubted if the charge of inaccuracy was ever seriously put forward by Young's critics after 1824; it was an effective tactical weapon in a campaign for reform which sometimes did not stop short of unscrupulous methods. The use of such methods by men of science was not likely to do the cause of science any good. The price finally paid for the 'reform' of the *Almanac* was the abolition of the Board of Longitude and the stopping for twenty years of regular provision for Government support of research in the physical sciences.

APPENDIX III

BIBLIOGRAPHY OF THE WRITINGS OF THOMAS YOUNG

I. WORKS

1. *A Course of Lectures on Natural Philosophy and the Mechanical Arts.* 1807, 2 vols. 4to; new ed., edited by Professor Kelland, 1845, 2 vols. 8vo.

2. *An Introduction to Medical Literature, including a System of Practical Nosology.* 1813, 8vo; new ed., with essay on 'Palpitations' added, 1823.

3. *A Practical and Historical Treatise on Consumptive Diseases.* 1815, 8vo.

4. *Letter of Canova and Memoirs of Visconti on the Elgin Marbles.* Translated (anonymous) 1816, 8vo.

5. *Elementary Illustrations of the Celestial Mechanics of Laplace.* 1821, 8vo.

6. *An Account of the Recent Discoveries in Hieroglyphical Literature and Egyptian Antiquities.* 1823, 8vo.

7. *Enchorial Egyptian Dictionary*, appended to the *Egyptian Grammar* by Henry Tattam. 1830.

A collection of translations, *Oeuvres Ophtalmologiques de Thomas Young*, was published in 1894.

II. PUBLISHED PAPERS

1. Description of a new species of Opercularia. [1794] *Linn. Soc. Trans.* III (1797), 30-2. Also in *Römer's Archiv. Botan.* II (1799-1801), 32-4.

2. Outlines of experiments and enquiries respecting Sound and Light. *Phil. Trans.* (1800), 106-50.

3. Sur les découvertes faites par Aristote sur le son; et sur une formule pour les réfractions. *Bibl. Britannique* XVIII (1801), 354-61.

4. The mechanism of the eye. [Bakerian Lecture, 1800] *Phil. Trans.* (1801), 23-88.

5. A letter respecting Sound and Light in reply to some observations of Prof. Robison. *Nicholson's Journal* V (1809), 161-7.

6. An answer to Mr Gough's essay on the Theory of Compound Sounds. *Nicholson's Journal* II (1802), 264-8.

7. On the phenomena of Sound. *Nicholson's Journal* III (1802), 145-6.

8. The Theory of Light and Colour. [Bakerian Lecture, 1801] *Phil. Trans.* (1802), 12-48. Also in Gilbert, *Annal.* XXXIX (1811), 156-205.

9. An account of some cases of the production of colour, not hitherto described. *Phil. Trans.* (1802), 387-97. Also in Gilbert, *Annal.* XXXIX (1811), 206-20.

10. On the velocity of Sound. *Roy. Inst. J.* I (1802), 214-16.

11. An account of an experiment on the velocity of water through a vertical pipe. *Roy. Inst. J.* I (1802), 231-3. Also in *Nicholson's Journal* VI (1803), 59-61.

12. Description of an apparatus for exhibiting the colours of thin plates by means of the solar microscope. *Roy. Inst. J.* (1802), 241-5. Also in Gilbert, *Annal.* XXXIX (1811), 255-61.

13. Harmonic sliders. *Roy. Inst. J.* (1802), 261-4.

14. Observations in reply to Mr Gough's letter on the Grave Harmonics. *Nicholson's Journal* IV (1803), 72-4.

15. A theory of haloes and parhelia. *Nicholson's Journal* VI (1803), 56-8. Also in *Roy. Inst. J.* II (1803), 4-7, 78-80.

16. Remarks on resistance of fluids. *Roy. Inst. J.* II (1803), 14-16.

17. Calculation of motion of a body projected from the moon. *Roy. Inst. J.* II (1803), 16-17.

18. Further consideration on the resistance of fluids. *Roy. Inst. J.* II (1803), 78-80.

19. Experiments and calculations relative to Physical Optics. [Bakerian Lecture, 1803] *Phil. Trans.* (1804), 1-16. Also in Gilbert, *Annal.* XXXIX (1811), 260-90.

20. An essay on the cohesion of fluids. [1804] *Phil. Trans.* (1805), 74-87.

21. Remarks on looming or horizontal refraction. [Signed Emeritus] *Nicholson's Journal* XVII (1807), 153-5.

22. Example of a calculation in the doctrine of chances; a Tide Table, remarks on the breaking of waves. [Signed Hydrophilus] *Nicholson's Journal* XVIII (1807), 116-19.

23. Remarks on the structure of covered ways, independent of the principle of the arch in equilibrium; and on the best form for arches in buildings. [Signed Apsophus] *Nicholson's Journal* XVIII (1807), 241-8.

24. Transformation of Mr Dubuat's hydraulic theorem. *Nicholson's Journal* XVIII (1807), 309-10.

25. Remarks on a pamphlet, lately published by the Rev. S. Vince respecting the cause of gravitation; Comments. [Signed Dytiscus] *Nicholson's Journal* XIX (1808), 304-7; XX (1808), 276-7.

26. Calculation on rate of expansion of a supposed lunar atmosphere. [Signed Hemerobius] *Nicholson's Journal* XX (1808), 117-21.

27. A concise method of determining the figure of a gravitating body revolving round another. *Nicholson's Journal* XX (1808), 208-14.

28. Calculation of the direct attraction of a spheroid and demonstration of Clairaut's Theorem. [Signed ABCD] *Nicholson's Journal* XX (1808), 273-5.

29. Hydraulic investigations subservient to an intended Croonian Lecture on the motion of the blood. *Phil. Trans.* (1808), 164-86. Also in *Nicholson's Journal* XXII (1809), p. 104-24.

30. An example of the utility of a series in finding a fluent. [Signed EFGH] *Nicholson's Journal* XXII (1809), 213-15.

31. Further application of a series to the correction of the heights of the barometer. [Signed EFGH] *Nicholson's Journal* XXIV (1809) 81-91.

32. A Memoria Technica for double elective attractions. *Nicholson's Journal* XXII (1809), 304-5.

33. On the function of the heart and arteries. [Croonian Lecture] *Phil. Trans.* (1809), 1-31.

34. A numerical table of elective attractions with remarks on the sequences of double decomposition. *Phil. Trans.* (1809), 148-60.

35. A theory of the tides, including the consideration of resistance. [Signed EFGH] *Nicholson's Journal* XXXV (1813), 145-9, 217-27.

36. Remarks on the measurement of minute particles, especially those of the blood and pus. Thomson, *Annal. Phil.* II (1813), 115-18, 190-5.

37. Essay on the medical effects of climates. *Phil. Mag.* XLI (1813), 210-14, 255-63.

38. On changeable colours and glories. *Phil. Mag.* XLII (1813), 292-6.

39. Remarks on the employment of oblique riders, and on other alterations in the construction of ships. *Phil. Trans.* (1814), 303-36.

40. An investigation of the pressure sustained by fixed supports of flexible substances. [Signed A B C D] *Phil. Mag.* XLVI (1815), 139-45.

41. An algebraic expression for the values of lives with a mode of finding the correct value of a number of joint lives. [Signed A B C D] *Phil. Mag.* XLVII (1816), 3-8.

42. Observations d'un météore lumineux. *Ann. de Chemie* IX (1818), 88-90.

43. Remarks on the probabilities of error in physical observations and on the density of the earth considered especially with regard to the reduction of experiments on the pendulum. *Phil. Trans.* (1819), 70-95.

44. Investigations of the correction of places of stars for aberration and mutation. [Signed S.B.L.] *Quart. J. Sci.* VIII (1820), 21-7.

45. Remarks on Laplace's latest computation of the density of the earth. [Signed S.B.L.] *Quart. J. Sci.* IX (1820), 32-5.

46. Computations for clearing the compass of the regular effect of a ship's permanent attraction. *Quart. J. Sci.* IX (1820), 372-80.

47. Remarks on the depression of mercury in glass tubes. [Signed S.B.L., 1820] *Quart. J. Sci.* XI (1821), 83-5.

48. Computation of the effect of terrestrial refraction in the actual condition of the atmosphere. [Anonymous] *Quart. J. Sci.* XI (1821), 174-6.

49. Postscript on atmospherical refraction. [1819] *Quart. J. Sci.* XI (1821), 353-64.

50. Reply to Mr Ivory's remarks on the series of the article 'Cohesion'. [Signed S.B.L.] *Phil. Mag.* LVII (1821), 376-8.

51. Apology for 'Postscript on Refraction' in answer to Ivory's. *Quart. J. Sci.* XII (1822), 390-6.

52. Variation in temperature of the atmosphere deduced from mean refraction. [Anonymous] *Quart. J. Sci* XII (1822), 396-8.

53. Remarks on the astronomical measurements of the Ancients. [Anonymous] *Quart. J. Sci.* XIV (1822), 190-1.

54. The resistance of the air, determined from Captain Kater's experiments on the pendulum. [Anonymous] *Quart. J. Sci.* XV (1823), 351-6.

55. Extension of inverse series for computation of refraction together with direct solution of the problem. [Anonymous] *Quart. J. Sci.* XVI (1823), 139-48.

56. Description of an improved sliding rule for gauging casks. *Quart. J. Sci.* XVI (1823), 357-64.

57. A finite and exact expression for the refraction of an atmosphere nearly resembling that of the earth. *Phil. Trans.* (1824), 159-61.

58. Extracts relating to the theory of the tides. [Anonymous] *Quart. J. Sci.* XVII (1824), 295-315.

59. Historical sketch of the various solutions of the problem of atmospherical refraction, from the time of Dr Brook Taylor to that of the latest computations. [Anonymous] *Quart. J. Sci.* XVIII (1825), 347-57.

60. A formula for expressing the decrement of human life. *Phil. Trans.* (1826, Part 3), 281-303.

61. Remarks on the principles of algebraic calculation and fluxional notation. [Signed T.Y.] *Quart. J. Sci.* XX (1826), 321-5.

62. A brief investigation of the properties of Geodetic Curves. [Signed T.Y.] *Quart. J. Sci.* XXI (1826), 136-7.

63. A simple rectification of the Geodetic Curve. [Signed T.Y.] *Quart. J. Sci.* XXI (1826), 153-5.

64. Considerations on the reduction of the length of the pendulum corrected to sea level. *Quart. J. Sci.* XXI (1826), 167-8.

65. A table of coefficients subservient to Geodetical Calculations. [Signed T.Y.] *Quart. J. Sci.* XXI (1826), 337-45.

66. Estimate of the effect on the terms involving the square of the disturbing force on the determination of the figure of the earth. *Quart. J. Sci.* XXI (1826), 346-7.

67. Remarks on the principle of Compound Interest. [Signed F.R.S.L.] *Phil. Mag.* II (1827), 332-3.

68. Practical application of the doctrine of chances as it regards the subdivision of risks. [Signed A.B.C.D.] *Quart. J. Sci* XXII (1827), 84-94.

69. Note on Professor Svanberg's reduction of the length of the pendulum. *Quart. J. Sci.* XXII (1827), 365-7.

70. On experience of the Equitable Society. [Signed X X X X] *Phil. Mag.* IV (1828), 339-43.

71. Simple determination of the most ancient epoch of astronomical chronology. *Quart. J. Sci.* I (1828), 195-8.

72. Practical composition of different tables of mortality. [Signed X X X X] *Quart. J. Sci.* I (1828), 342-57.

73. Computation of longitudes on a spheroid. *Quart. J. Sci.* II (1828), 418-20.

74. Theory of colours observed in the experiments of Fraunhofer. *Edin. J. Sci.* I (1829), 112-16. Also in *Ann. de Chimie* XL (1829), 178-83.

INDEX OF NAMES

58